690 UND
Underwood
Build:
contr

APR

MW00580993

BUILDING CODE COMPLIANCE
FOR CONTRACTORS
& INSPECTORS
Based on the 2009
International Residential Code

by Lynn Underwood

- Turn your estimate into a bid.
- Turn your bid into a contract.
- ConstructionContractWriter.com

Presented By:

KILGORE MEMORIAL LIBRARY FOUNDATION
6058 (CHARLOTTE BROOKE TRUST

Acknowledgments

Although it appears that an author is solely responsible for a book, that is almost never the case, especially a technical work.

My thanks go to the following:

Mark Johnson, Senior Vice President with the International Code Council, carefully guided this along in its infancy.

Many others willing to read drafts of this work made the work better with their comments.

Special appreciation to staff and members of the ICC for their support and assistance along the way!

Gary Moselle, Publisher (and part-time editor) is a consummate professional whose vision made this work possible. His guidance, editing and suggestions were always on target.

Looking for other construction reference manuals?

Craftsman has the books to fill your needs. **Call toll-free 1-800-829-8123** or write to Craftsman Book Company, P.O. Box 6500, Carlsbad, CA 92018 for a **FREE CATALOG** of over 100 books, including how-to manuals, annual cost books, and estimating software.

Visit our Web site: http://www.craftsman-book.com

Library of Congress Cataloging-in-Publication Data

Underwood, Lynn.
 Building code compliance for contractors & inspectors / by Lynn Underwood.
   p. cm.
 "Based on the 2009 *International Residential Code.*"
 Includes index.
 ISBN 978-1-57218-238-7
 1. Building inspection. 2. Building laws—United States. I. Title.
 TH439.U53 2010
 690´.21--dc22   2010025017

©2010 Craftsman Book Company

Illustrations by Devona Quindoy, dqartdesigns@gmail.com

Contents

Section I

Section II

Who Needs Building Codes?

Builders know how to build. So why bother with all these codes and inspections?

Great idea — if you're a contractor. But it hasn't worked, at least since 1792 B.C. That's when Hammurabi, king of the Babylonian Empire, authored what may have been the first building code:

Hammurabi's Building Code Section 229: *If a builder builds a house for someone, and does not construct it properly, and the house which he built falls in and kills its owner, then the builder shall be put to death.*

No doubt, more than a few Babylonian contractors considered that excessive regulation. But Hammurabi's Code earned respect that's lasted nearly 4,000 years. In retrospect, the code was probably a good idea, even if not popular with builders at the time.

Hammurabi's Code wouldn't work today. Materials have changed. Our understanding of what constitutes a construction defect has changed. Complexity has multiplied a hundredfold, but some things remain much the same. For example, you'll notice that Hammurabi's Code both sets standards for construction and penalties for infractions. Modern ICC codes do the same, though they're much more focused on standards than penalties. For example, you won't find a reference to capital punishment anywhere in the ICC, no matter how severe the infraction. But you'll find far more detail. To some, especially contractors, the complexity probably seems unnecessary — or even counterproductive.

If you've been in the construction industry a while, you know that complexity adds both expense and risk — the expense of trying to comply and the risk that work has to be torn out. You probably also know that contractors live by cutting costs. Most construction, whether residential, commercial or public works, is done at a price fixed before work begins. Surprises on a construction site are nearly always bad news for the contractor. When something goes wrong, the extra expense usually comes out of the contractor's profit margin. That hasn't changed in 4,000 years:

Hammurabi's Building Code Section 233: *If a builder builds a house for someone, even though he has not yet completed it, if then the walls seem toppling, the builder must make the walls solid from his own means.*

Few modern contractors face the extra expense of toppling walls. But nearly every contractor can tell a story about the extra cost of code compliance. The most common experience may be simply waiting for the inspector to arrive. Other stories weave a more expensive tale. Maybe a contractor didn't have exactly the right door or ridge beam on hand. But some other material is on hand and should work just as well. OK, almost as well. Or maybe a lesser-skilled carpenter didn't fit those studs under the stairs quite as accurately as he should have. Hey, once the drywall's up, what's the problem?

"Most construction, whether residential, commercial or public works, is done at a price fixed before work begins."

As an experienced contractor, you've probably done something like this more than once. And you still consider yourself a quality builder. And I agree. But what about the guy who isn't? He cuts every corner he can — to save himself a buck. He's the one who gives all contractors a bad name. He's part of the reason why most communities enforce building codes very strictly.

But there's another reason for building codes. They serve as standards or guides. They identify for architect, designers and builders what has to be done and where. Codes describe what size lumber to use, how walls and ceilings have to be weatherproofed and insulated, how windows and doors have to be installed, where guardrails and exits are needed, and a thousand other details intended to promote occupant safety and structural integrity. Essentially, codes identify what's considered good building practice and what isn't. And they give every property owner confidence that a new building will be both safe and habitable — for many years.

In a way, contractors should be comforted by an ICC code. Without modern codes, every property owner would have to follow a builder around the job to be sure the concrete is thick enough, sheathing has enough nails and the transit-mix company delivered the right mud. Both owners and lenders are protected by the building code and code inspection. When complete, the structure will be both safe and durable. In the manufacturing industry, this is usually called *quality control*. Today, as 4,000 years ago, it's still a good idea.

Code Enforcement

For the record, when I refer to the building code, I'm referring to the *International Residential Code (IRC) for One- and Two-Family Dwellings*, published by the International Code Council, Inc. (ICC). Where the *IRC* has been adopted, it's an inspector's responsibility to check compliance with the *IRC* as work is completed. Inspectors have to know precisely what standard applies to each phase of construction. Remember the framing under the stairs I mentioned earlier? An inspector needs to be there before drywall goes up. That's the only way to be sure it's done right. If those studs aren't straightened before the rock gets hung, no one will ever know — until the stairs start to creak and eventually collapse a few years later. Inspectors shouldn't (and can't) simply just take the builder's word for it.

A contractor's job isn't easy. But neither is building code enforcement. I don't expect to see many building inspectors on a contractor's Christmas card list. I prefer a friendly spirit of cooperation and mutual respect. Both the contractor and the inspector have an essential role to play in every construction project. Working together, a contractor and an inspector create something that will serve as a source of pride and comfort for many years. The people who'll live or work in that building can rely on both the inspector's vigilance and the contractor's expertise. That doesn't happen in every country. Read the international news about the loss of life due to earthquakes and building fires and you'll understand the advantage everyone enjoys where modern building codes are enforced.

Criticism of building inspectors is common among contractors. Some in the industry see inspectors as government bureaucrats with little common sense and the power to cause problems. Others suspect that most inspectors are incompetents who couldn't make it as contractors. I'm not going to take sides in that debate. But I know that practically all code inspectors are dedicated professionals with a reasonably good grasp of the codes they enforce. Most get no pleasure from rejecting work. Nearly all would rather see a job pass inspection the first time. When I was an inspector, it was a good day when I could approve every job on my dispatch list. I was truly disappointed when some job didn't pass final inspection.

I think most construction professionals understand, at least in the abstract, why we need codes and inspectors. But every builder I know has a lot of irons in the fire and too little time to stay current on code requirements. A contractor's focus on the bottom line can put building safety on the back burner. Inspectors can, or should, help contractors strike a balance that benefits us all.

What You'll Find in this Manual

First, I'll make a confession. I'm a building official, not a contractor. And this manual was conceived as a how-to manual for building inspectors. There aren't many guides on how to become a building inspector. I co-authored one now sold by the ICC. But the more I considered the subject, the more I realized: what constitutes good guidance for building inspectors also makes great advice for builders.

Most of this book will describe what an inspector should look for and what should happen when it's found. Essentially, this manual is a set of questions for building inspectors. But if this manual is a set of questions for inspectors, isn't this manual also a set of answers for construction contractors? Wouldn't you like to have a peek at the inspector's guide before calling in the inspector? That's a little like a football coach breezing through the opposing team's playbook before the start of the game.

I hope you agree. Knowing in advance what the inspector wants to see offers an (almost) unfair advantage to any contractor. Use this guide to do your own snap inspection before the inspector shows up. Better yet, use this manual as a guide to what constitutes good construction practice — and is almost certain to pass inspection the first time.

If you're an experienced construction contractor and already know what every inspector in the local building department wants to see, OK. Maybe you don't need the opposing team's playbook. Maybe you know the inspection process forward and backward. Maybe you pass every inspection the first time and don't need advice from anyone. If that's your category, you may want to return this manual for a refund. But I don't know many contractors who fit that description.

If your fingers are crossed every time an inspector walks on the job, this manual should be worth many times the cover price. I'm going to step you through the entire process item by item — permit processing, plan review, zoning and site development, all the codes (*IRC*, *IBC*, *IPC*, *IMC*, etc.), the rules of etiquette I recommend for both contractors and inspectors, and, of course, all the major inspections: concrete, framing, plumbing, electrical, etc.

I'll cover a lot of topics you may not have considered but that are part of code-compliance: Who should meet the inspector on the jobsite? How should a builder get electric power to an undeveloped site? Who should notify the power company to release a builder's request for temporary power? What inspections are required for each type of project? When an inspector fails a job, what happens next? What should happen if an inspector misses a code

> ### *Guidance for Building Inspectors (Only)*
>
> ■ *how to build a good relationship with the design professional, the engineer, and the architect for the project you'll be inspecting*
>
> ■ *how to avoid the appearance of impropriety between you and those you'll be inspecting*
>
> ■ *the importance of courtesy (including being on time)*
>
> ■ *how to get along with your peers*
>
> ■ *meet your boss (your supervisor or the general public?)*

> ### *Guidance for Contractors (Only)*
>
> ■ *tips for developing good relations with the building inspector*
>
> ■ *what to do and what to avoid when your job doesn't pass inspection*
>
> ■ *what to do if you feel you're being treated unfairly (appeals)*
>
> ■ *where the inspector has latitude in code enforcement and where it doesn't pay to argue the point*
>
> ■ *dozens of tips to ensure you pass the next inspection*

compliance issue on one inspection and catches the problem on a later inspection? What if the first inspector missed something and a different inspector catches it later? What's implied when a project passes final inspection?

Most experienced contractors have faced situations like these. Nearly every building inspector sees similar issues in the first year or two on the job. Your success as either a builder or an inspector can depend on your response to situations like these. No book can provide a solution to every code compliance problem. But I'm going to deliver a lifetime of code-compliance savvy between the covers of this manual.

One caution: Sometimes I'm going to be addressing contractors almost exclusively. You building inspectors may want to breeze through those sections — especially if you come from a contracting or construction trades background. And I know many inspectors who worked in construction before hanging up their tools.

Sometimes I'll be addressing code inspectors almost exclusively. If you're a contractor with years of experience as a building inspector, you need no special permission to breeze through these sections. But I don't know many contractors who started as building inspectors. So I recommend that you contractors stick your head in the huddle when I'm calling plays for building inspectors. You're sure to learn something valuable. If nothing else, you'll develop a good understanding of what motivates inspectors, why

they do what they do and the rules they have to play by. You probably won't believe it, but building inspectors have more rules to follow and limitations to observe than construction contractors. Knowing what a building inspector must do and can't do will give you a leg up when resolving nearly any code compliance issue. An appreciation of these "building inspector only" issues will help raise your standing to the "pro" level among building inspectors — almost as though you once worked as a building inspector.

The product of quality building inspections is human safety, comfort and well-being. Stay with me through the pages of this manual and you'll develop insights on why I feel building code enforcement is a noble profession.

Qualifications of a Good Building Inspector

Contractors: Don't skip this section. I'm going to explain when and why building inspectors should *not* demand compliance with every letter of the code.

To stay qualified, building inspectors have to keep up with code changes and the introduction of new building materials. Building inspectors need to know the construction trades and how work is done on construction sites. But maybe most important, inspectors need to understand the *intent* of the code. We'll come back to that issue many times in this manual.

While the code prescribes how building must be done, code provisions are the *minimum* — the *least* allowed under the law. If a builder wants to do more, like use heavier lumber or closer nail-spacing, that's fine. Nothing in the code restricts a builder from doing a better job than the minimum, and neither should an inspector. But, often, a builder wants to do something different that may or may not be better and may not comply with the letter of the code. This is where your experience and knowledge of building practice and plain old common sense come into play. Will what the builder wants to do meet the spirit (if not the letter) of the code?

An inexperienced inspector may feel safer saying "Here's how the *code* says you have to do it, so that's how you have to do it." But most provisions in the code include exceptions. There's almost always some way to do the job better than what the code requires without actually complying with the code. This is when your experience and judgment are required. Is this other way really as good? The intent of the code is to make the building sound. If the alternate method is sound construction, *allow it*.

By doing that, you encourage quality construction, initiative and creativity. You're showing respect for the contractor's skill and judgment. The next time you find an item that is clearly *not* done precisely to code, and it's truly not satisfactory, the contractor will be much more tolerant to your demand that work be redone. If you simply throw the code at a contractor, word for word, at every point, you can expect a battle at every turn. Instead of being on the contractor's team, you're creating an enemy. Lock horns with every contractor over every possible infraction and you'll hate showing up for work in the morning.

Here are some recommendations I've made to novice building inspectors in my office:

- Earn cooperation by developing trust built on mutual respect.

- Either explain code provisions simply and clearly or be willing to admit you don't know. In that case, you'll need to check on it and get back to the builder. Don't be afraid to say you don't know something. No one knows it all. Don't pretend otherwise.

- Be fair, no matter how you feel about the builder. It's the work you're inspecting, not the contractor. But don't cut any contractor a special deal. Treat every job and every builder by the same standard. Nobody respects an official who plays favorites.

- Stand firm when you know you're right. If you're indecisive, people will push you around. The pushiest, most argumentative contractor shouldn't get the most breaks. No one is above the law. Be prepared to stand your ground, no matter who is asking.

- Be flexible and considerate. Always try to see the contractor's side of an issue. My advice: If you can let something go, assuming it's not a code or safety violation, do it. There'll be times when you want something fixed that's not actually a code violation, something that's simply poor building practice. You may have missed it the first time, so you're on shaky ground to demand it now. You're more effective as an inspector if the contractor is on your side during times like these. Every contractor should consider you as part of his or her construction team.

- The best inspectors think fast on their feet. We're all better at figuring out how we should have handled a situation after it's over. But when you're on a jobsite and there's a problem, it's better to come up with the right response immediately.

- Keep your temper, even when a contractor throws a tantrum. You're a government official. You're expected to be civilized and professional. If you have a short fuse, look for another line of work.

Most code inspectors enter the field with some construction experience. While you don't need it to apply the code, it sure helps. But no one knows all the ins and outs of every phase of construction. So don't feel you're not qualified if you're not a construction expert. As you study and work with the code and as you spend more time on jobsites, you'll develop more experience with each part of the construction process.

Ask questions. Contractors and tradesmen interpret that as a sign of respect. Learn all you can about the construction trades. Master the industry vocabulary. If a builder asks you about a birdsmouth, a blank stare earns no respect. Ask tradesmen about their work. Much of what I know I picked up by being friendly, asking questions and listening carefully. Contractors appreciate your interest. Very few people have the right to come on a construction site and start asking questions. You have that right! Make the most of it.

Are You Ready for This Career Choice?

I feel some people aren't qualified by temperament to be building inspectors. If you're perceived as abrasive and hostile, you're going to be both ineffective and miserable in the job. Make an honest appraisal of your motivation and preparation for a career in code enforcement:

- Are you prepared for the inevitable changes in lifestyle? For example, many construction contractors make more than most building inspectors. Are you comfortable with that? Are you prepared to work fixed hours?

- Will your family support a new career choice?

- Do you enjoy watching and participating in construction work?

- Do you stop on the way to work to watch a house being built?

- Do you enjoy looking at construction plans?

- If you're not involved in construction, have you participated in any construction projects?

- Do you enjoy working with construction tools and equipment? Did you do well in shop classes in school?

- Can you anticipate at least some problems in a construction project before work begins?

- Are you highly organized and efficient in your daily life?

- Are you detail oriented — comfortable following rules and procedures exactly?

- Do you have a good memory?

- Are you comfortable discussing an issue with others before reaching a decision?

- Can you function effectively under stress?

- Are you persuasive? Can you convince others to follow your suggestions?

- How do you deal with your own mistakes? With mistakes made by others? Do you fix the problem, or affix the blame?

- How do you react to confrontations?

- Are you confident about your success in this career?

- Are you safety conscious?

- Do you understand that a career in code compliance and enforcement requires a major personal commitment?

- Do you know any building inspectors? Does their lifestyle appeal to you?

Now, let's look at the role you'll play if you get the job. You'll wear many hats as a code enforcement professional. Ideally, you'll be assigned responsibilities that match your background and level of knowledge. Most building inspectors wear two hats, one as the code police and a second as a teacher (or student). As a building safety expert, your decisions will normally be final. When wearing the enforcement hat, be careful about giving an opinion without careful thought. Avoid making commitments beyond your scope of authority. And since no building inspector knows everything about construction, you'll also be a student from time to time.

Know the Code

You'll never stop learning about the code because it's constantly changing. Every time someone dies or is injured in a building failure, whether from fire, wind or earthquake, there's a lesson to be learned. If a death or injury was avoidable, as a Building Official, you have the authority to propose changes to the code. Most of what you read in the ICC can be understood as an attempt to prevent repetition of mistakes made in an earlier time by others.

I recommend that you learn both what the code says and why it's that way. This book is loaded with the "why" of what's in the code — the history of code development. I think this is interesting. Even if you don't agree, knowing the "why" will help you respond to questions from builders. If you don't know the reason for some provision in the code requirement, your only answer to an objection will be, "Because it says so." An answer like that usually ends in a debate on government meddling in business. If you're more interested in compliance than debating points, understand the reason for the rule as well as you understand the rule. Most builders, once they understand the reason, will find a way to comply, with little or no objection.

Most of Chapter 2 of this book is devoted to the history of code development. I consider this information an essential part of your preparation for both the interview and the job. Every code expert needs to know how the code came to be — the whys and wherefores.

You'll encounter conflicts between different codes and even within the same code. Generally these inconsistencies will be a matter of interpretation. But when the contractor shows you a code section that seems to support his claim, and you've just shown him one that supports your position, you have a problem. In most all these cases, it comes down to *intent*. What was the goal of the code writers on this issue? You need to know. If the goal is still achieved by the contractor's interpretation, I recommend going along.

You'll also need to know about the more obscure parts of the code, like *Special Inspection* and *Structural Observation*. For example, some buildings will be subject to demolition if dangerous conditions are present. How do you know what to look for? What happens when the building code seems to conflict with industry standards? Which prevails?

Record Keeping

Another role for the building inspector: very careful record keeping. You'll be making decisions that affect public safety, including some life-or-death matters. Nearly every decision will affect a contractor's profit or loss on the job. Every dispute is a potential lawsuit. You need a written record of what you observed and what you decided. You're not going to remember what happened on a job several years ago. But if you're called into court, every judge will permit a witness to "refresh" his or her recollection by referring to notes made just after the event occurred. You don't want to be on the witness stand trying to remember what you found on a jobsite one morning two years ago and what you told the contractor. You visit dozens of jobs every week. Your memory isn't *that* good. And these records must be legible — clear enough to be read and understood by someone else should that need arise. A judge isn't going to be impressed with your halting guesses at what you might have meant by the scribbles you put in a ledger some time back — and neither will your supervisor.

People Skills

Your inspection standards should, as nearly as possible, match the inspection standards of every other inspector in your office. The results of any inspection shouldn't depend on who was assigned to the job. Uniform code enforcement is important. Since you'll most likely be just one of a team of inspectors, it's important that you and the other inspectors apply the same standards and issue the same messages to contractors. You'll have many opportunities to coordinate and harmonize standards with other inspectors.

Just as every thumbprint is different, every inspector is different. Each of us probably has our own special "thing" that bugs us when it's done wrong. We look for it and we clamp down when we see it. Maybe you get especially upset when carpenters forget the expansion joints in roof sheathing — you keep telling them and they keep forgetting it — and it *so* bugs you. The next inspector actually counts nails and will fail a job if a sheet is a nail short.

Pretty soon, the building community gets to know which inspector watches for expansion joints and which inspector will let expansion joints slide. Builders find a way to get the inspector they prefer. That's poor policy in any building department. All builders in your community should understand that inspectors in your office follow uniform standards. In the same vein, it's not fair to the builder if one inspector fails the job for lack of expansion joints and the second inspection is done by Mr. Nail Counter.

Learn the fine art of maintaining professional and yet personal relationships within the construction community. This requires walking a fine line. No matter how carefully you walk that line, there will be complaints about your inspections. You're in the code enforcement business. Those getting enforced can't be expected to like it. But avoid making adversaries out of the contractors you deal with. Keep in mind the expression, "Pick your battles." It's common among inspectors. Some confrontations simply aren't worth the effort and the bad feelings. Avoid nitpicking every little defect. Save your ammunition until something truly important needs to be fixed.

Occasionally you'll be asked to resolve a dispute between an owner and a builder. While this is a compliment — they believe in your expertise and trust your judgment and impartiality — it can also be a minefield. You don't know what was in the contract, you don't know what has already taken place, and you don't know contract law. In these cases, just state what you do know, which is what the code requires. If you know the code section, cite it by section number. If you have an opinion that goes beyond what's in the code or the reason for the rule, I recommend keeping that opinion to yourself. Resist the temptation to play Hammurabi.

Communication Skills

Suppose you're talking to a builder over the phone about a project. Try to visualize the work. Seeing it in person is, of course, far better. But most inspectors don't have the luxury of buzzing across town to have a look in person.

Sometimes the phone is your only option. Good communication skills come with practice and experience. But half of good communication involves listening carefully and asking the right questions. The contractor has a mental picture of what he or she is describing. You'll have a second picture. Ideally, those two mental pictures will coincide.

Occasionally you'll have a code question that can't be resolved — even after your explanation of the rule and the reason for the rule. If the builder still insists that you're off base, it's probably time to call in your supervisor, referred to as the "building official" in the code. I'll talk more about that in later chapters.

So, if you think you can handle all these things, and would enjoy being a code enforcement official, read on. If you've decided this is what you want to do, let's deal with getting you the job.

Getting the Job

Building inspectors, plans examiners, permit technicians and building officials are hired by public agencies such as a city, county, parish, state, or commonwealth. You get the job by demonstrating qualifications superior to other candidates. Hiring is, for the most part, similar to hiring in the private sector. One significant difference is that there are more rules.

Openings and Applications

Most openings must be advertised for a certain amount of time. Applications are usually screened by a Human Resources Department (HR) in the agency and then forwarded to the hiring authority.

To get past the initial screening, be sure your application is complete. If you meet the minimum qualifications for the position, you'll be certified and your name will be put on what's typically called the *Cert List*. The HR department head will usually ask the building official to help pick candidates to interview from this list. Generally, the list will be short enough that all candidates get an interview. But in larger municipalities, and when the competition is greater, only the best-qualified candidates will be granted an interview.

The Interview

When you're called for an interview, listen to the instructions carefully. To prepare, get a copy of the code being enforced. Study any sections that aren't familiar to you. Take notes. Study guides offered by the ICC cover subjects likely to be discussed in a placement interview.

Many publications offer suggestions for job interviews. My suggestion is to simply be yourself. Don't try to over-impress. HR people read those books too. And they'll know when you're repeating something you've been coached to say. If you're given any instructions to prepare for the interview, follow them closely. The interview panel that wrote instructions for the interview is sure to favor applicants who follow those instructions. Your preparation and cooperation assure the panel that you understand the importance of following instructions.

If you have the opportunity, try to get an early appointment. Interviewers are fresher in the morning. By afternoon, the panel will be tired of asking the same questions and hearing many of the same answers. Expect the questions to be similar for most applicants. This is a fair practice and gives each candidate the same opportunity to understand the nature of a question. Don't be surprised at how structured the interview is. For example, if you don't understand a question, the interviewer may only be permitted to repeat the question once, with no further explanation. If you don't get it, then that's part of the test. The interviewer wants to see if your understanding is on the same level as that of the other candidates. Study the glossary in the back of this book to brush up on construction terms.

Think carefully before you answer any question. Many questions will test your professional competence. For example, you'll probably be asked for a summary of your experience in construction. Have you supervised construction? Or did you just work as a carpenter?

Don't give in to the temptation to embellish on your experience. Construction is a trade. There's nothing subtle or theoretical about working on a jobsite. Either you worked as a foreman or you didn't. Don't exaggerate. You'll get caught right away. That's worse than admitting a lack of experience. But be thorough in describing your knowledge and your understanding of construction work. If you don't have practical experience in a particular area, talk about your general knowledge of construction. We've all helped neighbors or friends with a project that was above our skill level, and learned from it.

> *"If you have the opportunity, try to get an early appointment. Interviewers are fresher in the morning."*

Give detailed answers. Leave no doubt about your knowledge and understanding of the code. If you're asked to identify five places in a house where ground-fault circuit interrupters (GFCIs) are required, don't stop at five. Impress the panel with your thoroughness and knowledge. Offer other examples: Kitchen, bathrooms, laundry utility and bar, garages (unless on a dedicated circuit), outdoors at grade, crawl space, unfinished basement, boat houses and bar sinks. The interviewers don't expect a novice to know everything. But they will be impressed by a desire to learn. So show your interest.

Every interview will include an opportunity to describe qualifications. Use this time to describe why you want to become a building inspector. The interviewers probably are, or were, inspectors. Typically, they really like their jobs and are proud of the profession. Communicate how much you want to be part of that. Use anecdotes to explain your respect for building safety. Maybe your respect is based on your first building project when you received help from an inspector. You really appreciated that and want to return the favor by helping others. You could explain that you've worked in construction for several years and want a professional position. Expand on that by explaining that you want to give back to the community.

Your attraction to the profession will separate you from the crowd — and remind the interviewers why they chose code enforcement as a career. Discuss any prior relationships with other inspectors and tell how you got along with them. But avoid criticism. Don't mention "that idiot of an inspector" on your last construction job. "I'm sure not going to be like him." Remember, you're talking to *inspectors*. Use your head.

"If in doubt about what clothing is appropriate, visit the office a few days before the interview."

I'm amazed at what some applicants say during the interview. I had an applicant say that he wanted to get into government and that this job would be a good stepping-stone for him! Not the right thing to say to an interview panel, even if it's true.

Proper attire is essential. I suggest that candidates for any position dress at least slightly better than they would for the first day on the job. This shows respect for the interview panel and the position you're applying for. If in doubt about what clothing is appropriate, visit the office a few days before the interview. Check out what others in the office are wearing. Let that be your guide. If they're wearing shirts with no ties, wear a tie. If they're in shirts and ties, wear a jacket too. If you're a woman, I recommend wearing a smart business suit. Go easy on perfume or aftershave. Better yet, skip it entirely. Don't make the panel air out the interview room when you're done.

The interviewers are people who are where you want to be in a few years. Ask about their careers. How did they get there? Listen to their answers. Remember the panel members' names. Write them down on the notepad you bring with you. When you're asked questions, listen carefully. Then answer honestly. Most interview panels will try to evaluate your communication skills — how you deal with people. That's the essence of a building inspector's job. Be friendly and engaged, not formal and reserved. Show that you'll work well with both office personnel and the construction community.

For example, "If a customer arrived at your office at 4:50 p.m. to apply for a permit and you were headed out the door on a weekend fishing trip, what would you tell the customer?" The *correct* answer is that you would put the fishing rod in the truck, turn the lights on, and stay until business was done. Mention that it's a public official's responsibility to provide first-rate service to every taxpaying citizen. Begin your response by saying that you wouldn't leave before 5:00 p.m. in any case.

Bring a code book with you to the interview. Buy one from a technical or college bookstore if the code isn't sold by the building department. The ICC sells the *International Building Code (IBC)* and the *International Residential Code (IRC)* directly to the public at their Web site: http://www.iccsafe.org/Store.

You definitely don't want the interview panel to see you without a copy of the code. Place tabs at major sections. The more worn your copy of the code, the more credibility you'll carry with the interview panel.

Some on the interview panel probably have participated in code development. As preparation for the interview, find out if the local office had any role in recent code changes. If so, be sure to mention the section or sections involved. That distinguishes you as someone prepared to participate as a team member from day one. Google "home inspection blog" and you'll find a dozen or more sites that discuss code enforcement and code development. Spend a few hours reviewing the posts at these sites. Mention any of the issues you find on these sites to demonstrate your involvement and concern with code development.

Here's your summary of some good rules to follow during an interview:

- Be genuinely interested in the interviewers.

- Encourage the interviewers to talk about themselves.

- Make the interviewers feel important — and do it sincerely.

- Remember the interviewers' names.

- Be complimentary about code officials and the trade. Avoid anything negative.

- Have a code book, tabbed and ready for discussion.

- Be a good listener. Think before you answer.

- Give detailed and honest answers.

- Don't embellish on your experience.

- Dress appropriately for the job you're seeking.

- Smile.

How Much Can I Make?

Don't ask this question at the interview. The office will have a published salary range. Where you start on that scale will depend on your qualifications, not on your negotiating skills at the interview. Entry-level positions start on the lower half of the scale. But be sure to ask about opportunities for promotion. This shows initiative and motivation that's normally appreciated by supervisors. Ask about educational and training opportunities and membership in professional organizations such as building inspector chapters.

Leave salary negotiations until after you're offered the job. I've seen salaries range from $15 per hour for an entry-level inspector with no experience to well over $35 per hour for an experienced inspector. A plans examiner with an engineering or architectural background can draw as much as 50 percent more than an inspector with similar experience. Building officials' salaries are an oddity. In small jurisdictions, the building inspection department may be a one-person show. The starting salary may be about the same as an entry-level inspector. Medium or large jurisdictions may offer over $100,000 for a seasoned veteran with a high degree of skill and exceptional leadership abilities.

Public sector work is more stable than private sector work, though it may not pay quite as well. Jobs in the public sector are less subject to the business cycle than jobs in the construction industry. In slow economic times, building inspectors will be retained even when contractors are laying off work crews. That's important if you're responsible for the support of a family.

And public sector jobs usually offer better benefits than jobs in the private sector. Paid vacation and sick leave are far more common and more generous in government positions than on contractor payrolls. Other advantages can include retirement income, educational and training opportunities, potential for growth, a relaxed environment with less pressure, your own office and work vehicle, and the camaraderie of a staff with similar values.

From Permit to Final Inspection

Every construction project requires planning and organization. Construction on schedule and within budget doesn't happen by accident. Every professional builder understands that.

The permit issuing process and building inspection are part of every construction plan. Permit application, plan review and approval are significant steps. From initial soil analysis through final inspection, both the building inspector and the contractor need to understand the process. How do you apply for a building permit? How long will it take to get the permit? What's the cost? When a permit is issued, who's responsible for the project? Who may cancel a permit? If changes are made, how are they accepted by your jurisdiction? What changes can be made without the approval of a design professional? Who's responsible for making the corrections you request? We'll answer all of these questions and lots more in the following 11 chapters.

The Code Enforcement Staff — an Overview

A building department may have many functions and duties. But the primary objective is always the same: to ensure safe construction. The building official enforces the code and has the power of a law enforcement officer. For example, the building official has the right of entry, under prescribed conditions, to make an inspection.

Code enforcement staff usually consists of a plans examiner, plans technicians, various inspectors, a permit technician and clerical staff. Each has unique duties and responsibilities in code enforcement. Each coordinates work with other staff members. Whether you're a builder or a building inspector, you need to understand each position and its relationship to other positions.

The *building official* is the ultimate authority in every building department office and is responsible for code enforcement. The building official delegates duties to the building department staff. In the remainder of this chapter, I'll describe the responsibilities of principal staff members. In later chapters I'll expand on these descriptions.

Plans Examiner

A plans examiner reviews construction drawings to be sure they comply with the code. A building official or inspector may consult with a plans examiner for building code advice. Most of what a plans examiner does is completed in the department office. Occasionally a plans examiner may have to visit a construction site or consult with the designer, engineer, architect, general contractor, developer, or builder.

Building Inspector

Inspectors perform inspections on the jobsite, inspecting each stage of construction for compliance with building codes and approved plans. An inspector may also have to consult with the plans examiner or the building official. The plans examiner reviews only words and lines on paper. The inspector sees the finished product. The building official may call for an inspector's opinion to get a clear understanding of the job.

Permit Technician

A builder who walks up to the counter at the building department will be dealing with a permit technician. The permit technician is the "face" of the building department. At least initially, the public will judge the building department by the

personality and manner of the permit technician. A permit technician's tasks include answering questions, either over the counter or over the phone, and making limited plan reviews. The permit technician will also:

- process permit applications and proposed plans
- maintain records and do research for other staff members
- stock and maintain handouts and flyers on department policy
- work with engineers, architects and builders in the application and review process
- help resolve disputes and defuse angry customers

Hopefully (and usually), all of these staff positions work together and in harmony, contributing to completion of projects that comply with the code and can be certified as safe. If one inspector misses a violation, another inspector will probably catch the error. But at least some minor code violations remain in virtually every completed project. The goal is to discriminate between significant code violations that impact safety and technical violations that pose no risk of harm.

The Organization of This Book

That completes the preliminaries. The next nine chapters will cover operation of the building department. If you're a builder, don't dismiss the value of this information. True, most of what you find here doesn't relate to passing inspections. (We'll get to that in Chapter 10.) But any builder who has to deal with a building department will benefit from knowing how that department works. If your relations with building department staff leave something to be desired, or if your requests seem to rate low priority, if your appeals fall on deaf ears, I recommend studying the next nine chapters.

Chapter 2 takes a look at code background and development.

Chapter 3 discusses the organization of a typical building department.

Chapters 4, 5 and *6* cover details of different jobs in building code enforcement — plans examiner, building inspector, and permit technician.

Chapter 7 has advice from experienced inspectors.

Chapter 8 describes characteristics of an effective code enforcement official.

Chapter 9 has some rules for inspectors to follow.

Chapter 10 explains why builders should consider inspectors part of the construction team.

Chapter 11 is my summary of the most common code violations.

Chapter 12 covers code organization, intent and scope.

Chapters 13 through *25* have detailed checklists for each of the major building code inspections. For example, during the footing inspection (Chapter 13), the depth and width of the concrete must be checked. But what about an electrical ground connection to the footing steel? Or what about the required lap in sections of reinforcement steel? During framing, what does it mean to verify the center spacing of rafters? What's the difference between structural blocking and fire blocking? Where does the code require each to be installed? During a plumbing inspection, can a sanitary tee be used on its back? What support is required for floor decking? What nailing pattern is required for roof sheathing or wall siding? How do you check for a proper polarity installation of outlets during a final inspection?

I'll answer all these questions and hundreds more. I'll offer tips on what to look for and cite the code section that applies. With that information you can look it up and read the whole paragraph. Whether you're a builder or a building inspector, you'll have the information needed to make a persuasive argument.

If you're a building inspector, the last 13 chapters will provide valuable information. You won't have to page through a 600-page volume of fine print looking for the proof you need. If you're a contractor, conduct your own inspection while work is still going forward. Don't go on doing work that won't, or can't, be approved. Make corrections before calling for inspection. Preventing just one small error will save many times the cost of this manual.

Finally

Throughout this manual I'm going to assume that you have the *IRC* open to the section I'm discussing. Time and again, I'll guide you to the code section or table that has what you need to know. But I'm not going to quote long code sections or reproduce entire tables from the code. That's not my purpose. There's no substitute for the *IRC*. I won't suggest otherwise. In addition to this manual, you need access to a copy of the *IRC*.

I'll admit also that no single reference book can make you an authority on the building code. For that, you'll need to stir in a few years of experience. But I'll insist that this manual will help you make exceptionally rapid progress along the path of your chosen career, whether that career is in code enforcement (as an inspector) or code compliance (as a contractor).

Reasons for the Rules

Mr. Inspector, why do we have this rule? Why does it need to be done this way?

Whether your job is to follow the code (as a construction contractor) or to enforce the code (as an inspector), it helps to understand the reason for a rule. Contractors who know the reason for a rule can anticipate compliance problems. Inspectors who know why a rule exists can make good decisions about when a rule can be bent a little. That's the purpose of this chapter: to help you understand how and why the code came to be what it is today.

Most of this chapter will be for contractors who have to follow the rules. I'll cover subjects your inspector may not be eager to discuss in public: appeals, policy statements, interpretations, changing the code, and authority of your building inspector to make rules on the fly. Seasoned building inspectors probably know all

this already. Feel free to skip on to Chapter 3. To a contractor, the importance of what I describe in this chapter will be obvious.

First, understand that every inspector has authority to ignore the question at the top of this page. No inspector is required to answer the "why" question. And, I'll admit, some inspectors prefer the simplest possible response: "Because that's what it says in The Book."

But I feel the most effective inspectors arrive at a jobsite fully armed with answers to "Why" questions. It's a simple matter of mutual respect. As I mentioned in the last chapter, a builder who understands the reason for a rule will be far more cooperative when work has to be redone. Builders are reasonable people and reasonable people expect an explanation. An inspector with a good understanding of the code can explain the reason for nearly any code section. Once the reason is clear, most builders will cooperate. And believe me, voluntary cooperation makes an inspector's task much more pleasant. "Because it says so in the code" is a perfectly legitimate answer. But it's also the answer most likely to create resentment and marginal compliance.

It's normal for both builders and inspectors to take pride in their professional skill and knowledge. The most effective inspectors have a reputation for being both fair and knowledgeable. The best way to develop that reputation, in my opinion, is to respond to the "why" question with clear and convincing answers.

Of course, those who author and approve the code are obsessed with the "why" for every code section. But very little of that concern seeps into the code itself. If you want to understand how the code got to be what it is today, I recommend the remainder of this chapter.

Why We Need Building Codes

Human nature is to learn from mistakes. We close the barn door after the horse gets out. We install traffic lights and post speed limit signs after a major car wreck. In the same way, code sections are written after some calamity has drawn our attention to a problem. Tighter construction codes rarely spring from casual discussions between contractors and owners. Usually, the call for tighter control of construction work comes after a major structural collapse, a severe storm, a seismic event, or a devastating fire. Almost every modern code section is the result of something bad that happened somewhere. That's the most basic "why" behind every part of the code.

That's not to say we can't or shouldn't anticipate risk. Safety experts are good at that. For example, fire safety experts routinely urge communities to adopt rules designed to limit fire damage. Structural engineers know what's required to reduce damage from hurricanes and earthquakes. Water purity experts testify at state and local hearings about ways to improve sanitation standards and reduce the risk of waterborne disease and poisoning. Nearly without exception,

these experts are right. Also without exception, these proposals cost money, usually taxpayer money. Elected politicians avoid spending taxpayer money on proposals the voting public won't support.

But everything changes after a catastrophe — either severe damage and financial loss or personal injury and loss of life. Then blame falls on the experts, sometimes the same experts who recommended changes before the loss occurred. After a major loss from fire, flood or earthquake, you're sure to hear calls for reorganization and a crackdown on shoddy construction practice. Blame often lands on the desk of code enforcement officials. A city or county may dismiss the building official or clean out the entire building department after a catastrophic loss. That's a very persuasive "why" if you're a building official or inspector at the local building department.

So why do we need building codes? The short answer is, "To save lives and property." In fact, the purpose of the building code is among the first topics in the code. *IRC* Section 101.3 begins:

> *"The purpose of this code is to establish minimum requirements to safeguard the public safety, health and general welfare ..."*

Better than any other, these words from the *IRC* explain the "why" of the building code.

Building Failures

Anyone who watches the news on TV is well-acquainted with the risk of structural failures caused by fires, storms or earthquake. Some failures are inevitable (think volcanoes). But most loss of life that results from a building fire or collapse could be avoided by better building design and construction.

True, some losses result from poor judgment. For example, a landlord padlocked the exit doors on a large warehouse, leaving the workers trapped inside when a fire swept through the building. The code-required exits were there. But they didn't help when fire broke out. Nothing in the code prevents negligence by an owner.

The Most Common Reasons for Building Failures

Owner

■ *is unfamiliar with construction operations or has a false sense of competence*

■ *is interested in cutting costs in every way possible and doesn't see a lack of safety as a result*

■ *is careless, ignorant, or stingy regarding necessary maintenance*

Design professional (architect or engineer)

■ *accepts a project at a lower rate than needed to develop quality plans*

■ *hires an incompetent structural engineer*

■ *allows the owner to make changes to structural plans without consulting the structural engineer*

■ *doesn't supervise the project adequately during construction*

■ *expects the local building inspector to control the quality of the project and any changes to approved plans*

Contractor

■ *accepts the job at a price too low to allow use of quality materials and labor*

■ *makes unauthorized changes in approved plans without consulting the design professional or building department*

■ *disregards the building code or inspector*

■ *is careless during construction; takes too many chances*

■ *fails to supervise building trades and subcontractors*

Building department

■ *hasn't adopted an up-to-date building code*

■ *doesn't properly enforce the building code*

■ *hires insufficient or unqualified staff to enforce the building code*

■ *allows inadequate or inconsistent checking of plans, and no standardization of plan review*

■ *doesn't provide adequate field inspection during each construction phase*

■ *lacks political support for proper building code enforcement*

Another case of poor judgment, this time by a metal fabricator: Metal struts for a suspended truss system were made from dissimilar metals. Links joining the struts failed, causing the entire system to fail.

Still, most structural failures in the future can be prevented by studying failures in the past. Careful analysis shows several primary causes for structural failure in buildings. Many failures are caused by changes made to approved plans during construction. Another common cause is inadequate supervision by a superintendent or design professional during construction. Inexperienced public building inspectors who ignore these changes are equally culpable.

Most building failures aren't caused by a single mistake. Instead, they result from a series of acts or omission made by several people — owners, architects, engineers, contractors, or building inspectors.

Examples of tragic failures and the cause (or possible cause):

■ Two crowded walkways in the newly-built Hyatt Regency Hotel in Kansas City, Missouri collapsed in July, 1981, killing 114 and injuring almost 200. It remains the deadliest structural failure in U.S. history. Analysis found that the walkways weren't built as originally designed.

■ In 2000, a four lane concrete footbridge over Lowe's Motor Speedway in Charlotte, North Carolina collapsed under load from pedestrian traffic. A section of the bridge snapped in half and fell onto U.S. Highway 29. More than 100 people were injured, some seriously. The reason for the collapse hasn't been fully confirmed. But initial tests reveal that the grout had high concentrations of calcium chloride. This may have contributed to corrosion of steel cables that reinforced the concrete support beams.

■ A 91-year-old pier supporting a popular nightclub in Philadelphia, PA, collapsed in May 2000. Three people died and 31 were injured. An inspection *three days before* the accident revealed structural deficiencies suggesting that the pier could collapse.

Changes in design, construction, inspection or use would have prevented each of these failures. Every builder and every inspector has responsibility for preventing losses like these. Once you appreciate the risk, it's easy to understand the importance of building codes and code enforcement.

Building failures aren't as common in the U.S. today as they once were. A century of code development has given the United States the highest standard of building safety in the world. In the previous century, we had many more building failures. Today, there are more buildings and more people in those buildings. But loss of life due to building failures is not common. Building methods are better. Also, we're much more aware of liability for negligence. Builders and building departments get hauled into court when structures fail. Clearly, modern building codes, good code enforcement and better understanding among contractors have reduced loss of life and property damage due to building failure.

"A century of code development has given the United States the highest standard of building safety in the world."

For example, there was a significant earthquake near Olympia, Washington, in February 2001. Damage was minimal, at least partly due to modern building codes and better enforcement. Another example: the San Francisco earthquake of 1989 and the Port-au-Prince, Haiti, earthquake of 2010 were roughly equivalent in magnitude and about the same distance from populated areas. Loss of life in the San Francisco earthquake was 62. Without the advantage of an enforced building code, the Haitian earthquake killed over 150,000. True, Port-au-Prince isn't San Francisco. But I think you get the idea.

Building Codes — the Origins

In the 19th century, fire and disease devastated American cities. Planning, fire control and sanitation were primitive. The Chicago fire of 1871 destroyed 17,000 of Chicago's 60,000 buildings (half of which were built of wood), took approximately 300 lives and left 100,000 people homeless. The Chicago fire forced 60 fire insurance companies into bankruptcy. The need for change was obvious.

After the fire, the National Board of Fire Underwriters threatened to deny insurance coverage in Chicago if city government didn't adopt rules designed to prevent another such devastating fire. In response, Chicago enacted the *Building Code and Fire Prevention Ordinance* of 1875. This was among the first codes to require plan submission, review, and approval prior to construction. The code set standards for foundations, walls and roofs, and required fire escapes on dwellings exceeding four stories. If Hammurabi's code had covered all that, the Babylonians might still have an empire.

During the early part of the 20th century, building code enforcement was elective. Many jurisdictions didn't enforce any building code. Other jurisdictions adopted a code used in a neighboring city or county. There were many model building codes. Every city and county was free to adopt any of the model codes or even write their own code. Building code enforcement was a regional issue. Move from one community to another and you probably have to master a different building code. That makes good politics. Everyone gets the code they want. But it doesn't make much sense. What's good construction in Portland, Maine will be good construction in Portland, Oregon. There's truly no need for hundreds of different building codes.

National Electrical Code

A decade after Thomas Edison patented the first practical incandescent lamp in 1879, the National Electric Light Association developed rules for the safe use of electricity. In 1896, all U.S. and some European codes were incorporated into one code called the *National Code*. This code, renamed the *National Electrical Code (NEC)*, is sponsored by the National Fire Protection Association (NFPA). The Electrical section of the NFPA, called the NEC Committee, developed the text for the *NEC* and continues to publish it as an NFPA document *(NFPA 70)*.

The ICC and the I-Codes

The Building Officials and Code Administrators International (BOCA) was founded in Chicago in 1915. BOCA's first model code was published 35 years later. The Pacific Coast Building Officials Conference (later known as ICBO) published the first edition of the *Uniform Building Code (UBC)* in 1927. The Southern Building Code Congress International (SBCCI) was organized in 1940 and published the first *Southern Building Code (SBC)* in 1945.

Until the year 2000, most of the northern and eastern United States used the *BOCA* code. States west of the Mississippi used the *UBC*. Southeastern states followed the *SBC*. These code organizations were fiercely competitive. Each was eager to gain adoptions in as many cities, counties and states as possible. With adoptions came revenue from sale of their printed code books. The more books sold, the more money available to support staff and code development. But in truth, the codes weren't that different. The U.S. doesn't really need three separate and independent code-writing organizations.

Eventually, common sense prevailed. The International Code Council (ICC) was formed in 1994 to develop a single set of codes, including building, fire, plumbing, mechanical, fuel gas, zoning, and residential regulations. In 1996 the ICC recommended developing a comprehensive, stand-alone residential construction code for detached one- and two-family dwellings and multiple single-family dwellings (townhouses). The ICC first published this new code, called the *International Residential Code (IRC)*, in 2000. The *IRC* was designed as a companion to the *International Building Code (IBC)*, which was also published that year. These codes are members of the *International Code Family™*, and are called the I-Codes. This family also includes the following:

1. *International Fuel Gas Code (IFGC)*
2. *International Energy Conservation Code (IECC)*
3. *International Fire Code (IFC)*
4. *International Mechanical Code (IMC)*
5. *International Plumbing Code (IPC)*
6. *International Property Maintenance Code (IPMC)*
7. *International Private Sewage Disposal Code (IPSDC)*
8. *International Zoning Code (IZC)*
9. *International Performance Code (ICC PC)*
10. *International Existing Building Code*
11. *International Wildland-Urban Interface Code*
12. *International Green Construction Code*

These codes are designed to supplement one another. For example, the *IBC* may set the architectural fire prevention regulations for a fireworks factory. But the *IFC* will specify fire protection requirements for the factory. The *IBC* may require that a restaurant with a particular occupant load have two bathrooms. But the *IPC* will specify how the plumbing must be installed. The *IBC* may specify locations for HVAC equipment. But the *IMC* will specify how the equipment must be installed.

The *IRC* was published after a decade of debate among the ICBO, BOCA and SBCCI and is truly a state-of-the-art building code. It includes the parts of the *IBC*, *IMC*, *IFGC* and *IPC* that apply only to residential structures. It also includes parts of the *NEC* that apply to residential dwellings.

Most of the U.S. has now adopted the I-Codes. Typically the code is adopted at the state level. By law, in most states, cities, counties and towns are usually required to enforce all I-Codes adopted by the state. But local jurisdictions are free to adopt amendments, so long as they're not in conflict with the state I-Code. I'll explain these local amendments later in this chapter.

Every state is different. But Minnesota offers a good example of how codes published by the ICC work their way down to your jobsite. By statute, the Minnesota legislature gives authority to the Commissioner of the Department of Labor and Industry to adopt a building code. That's Minnesota Statute § 326B.106(1):

"[T]he commissioner shall by rule and in consultation with the Construction Codes Advisory Council establish a code of standards for the construction, reconstruction, alteration, and repair of

buildings, governing matters of structural materials, design and construction, fire protection, health, sanitation, and safety, including design and construction standards regarding heat loss control, illumination, and climate control."

With that authority from the legislature, the Department of Labor and Industry adopted a regulation identifying the codes to be enforced in Minnesota. That's Minnesota Administrative Code § 1305.0011(1).

"For purposes of this chapter, "IBC" means the 2006 edition of the International Building Code as promulgated by the International Code Council, Falls Church, Virginia. The IBC is incorporated by reference and made part of the Minnesota State Building Code except as qualified by the applicable provisions in chapter 1300, part 1305.0021, and as amended in this chapter. Portions of this chapter reproduce text and tables from the IBC. The IBC is not subject to frequent change and a copy of the IBC, with amendments for use in Minnesota, is available in the office of the commissioner of labor and industry. The IBC is copyright 2006 by the International Code Council, Inc. All rights reserved."

Three things you might want to note in § 1305.0011(1):

■ "Incorporated by reference" means that the entire *International Building Code* is made part of Minnesota law. And the name of the *IBC* is changed to the Minnesota State Building Code.

■ But the *IBC* is not adopted in whole. There are exceptions. The Commissioner is going to pick and choose what parts of the *IBC* become law in Minnesota.

■ To make it easy for Minnesota contractors to follow the law, the Commissioner is going to make a copy of the code (with Minnesota amendments) available for reference — at the St. Paul office.

Why, you may ask, doesn't the Commissioner put the building code on the Web so every contractor knows what has to be done? Look back at the copyright notice in the quoted paragraph above. The ICC owns the code and isn't going to allow Minnesota to give it away for free. The ICC depends on sale of code books to support code development. So what we have in Minnesota (and across the U.S.) is a long and complex law that's available to all, but at a price. The ICC sells the I-Codes, of course, as well as some state codes. And most states offer a read-only copy of their state amendments to the I-Codes at no cost.

Other Codes

BOCA, ICBO and SBCCI have merged into the ICC. But other organizations continue to publish codes. The International Association of Plumbing & Mechanical Officials (IAPMO) developed both the *Uniform Plumbing Code (UPC)* and the *Uniform Mechanical Code (UMC)*. The National Fire Protection Association (NFPA) still publishes the *National Electrical Code (NEC)*. Some cities and states even write their own code from scratch. For these and other publications, go to ICC's Web site: http://www.iccsafe.org/. While there, buy a copy of the *IRC*. My preference is the eCodes. You can buy a download of the entire *IRC* for less than $100.

Scope and Intent of the Code

IRC Section 101.2 states:

"The provisions of the International Residential Code for One- and Two-family Dwellings shall apply to the construction, alteration, movement, enlargement, replacement, repair, equipment, use and occupancy, location, removal and demolition of detached one- and two-family dwellings and townhouses not more than three stories above grade plane in height with a separate means of egress and their accessory structures."

The *intent* of the code is stated in *IRC* Section 101.3:

"The purpose of this code is to establish minimum requirements to safeguard the public safety, health and general welfare through affordability, structural strength, means of egress facilities, stability, sanitation, light and ventilation, energy conservation and safety to life and property from fire and other hazards attributed to the built environment and to provide safety to fire fighters and emergency responders during emergency operations."

In my opinion, these two paragraphs sum up the "what" and "why" of the building code. The essence of every I-Code is safety. Codes aren't intended to level the playing field for contractors. They aren't a source of revenue for government. They shouldn't encourage (or discourage) use of any particular construction material or method. The sole purpose of building codes is to make buildings safer for occupants.

Code Enforcement

The federal (U.S.) government doesn't enforce building codes on private property. That's left to state and local government. As you may have detected by now, cities, counties and states adopt and enforce building codes.

But there are exceptions, even in states that have adopted a statewide building code. For example, no building permit is required for construction on federal land. I-Codes aren't enforced by local jurisdictions on federal property. But several federal departments have adopted I-Codes for their own reference. Some state-owned property is exempt from inspection by the local building department, even if the state code applies. Some structures may be exempt due to conflicting authority. Some Native American reservations are exempt from permit requirements. Other reservations have agreements with local jurisdictions to have plan review and inspections done on a contract basis. Small building projects, such as a 200-square-foot detached storage building used as

an accessory to a home doesn't require a permit in most jurisdictions. In a few jurisdictions, code enforcement is still voluntary. A permit may be optional. Where there's no statewide code, a town, city or county may adopt its own code, or have no code at all.

But, as I mentioned, most states now have a statewide building code. Even where there is a statewide code, cities, counties and towns can adopt code amendments so long as they're not in conflict with the state code. A few states permit local governments to opt-out of portions of the statewide building code.

Local Amendments

Local changes to the model code are important where unique soil, climate or legacy conditions make following the statewide code impractical. For example, a community that has poor-quality soil may have special requirements for foundations. A community built on a ski slope will be more concerned with subsidence than a community in Kansas. Homes built in brushfire areas of Southern California face risks unique to that area. A lakeside community that has a severe erosion problem will be more concerned about foundation ventilation than a community in the Southwest desert. These differences are resolved as amendments to the model building code by the local jurisdictions.

Other local amendments to the code involve administrative issues, such as permit fees and fines for violation. Amendments like these are political and generally affect only the operation of the building department and the authority of the building official. For example, several states give the authority to interpret the code to a state official instead of local building officials.

Changing the Code

After 100 years of code development and refinement by experts, you would expect that the code would have reached perfection. Well, not exactly. The code is in constant flux.

Every year, proposed code changes are considered by committees of ICC members. Most of these members are from either code enforcement agencies, the construction industry, or represent design professionals. These committees review proposed code change and make recommendations for adoption. For example, one ICC committee reviews proposed changes to the residential mechanical and plumbing code. After public hearings and careful study, the committee will make a recommendation for approval or disapproval.

"For a larger, more complex problem that involves public safety, contact the state Consumer Affairs office."

Final approval of any change is left to a vote of ICC member jurisdictions — states, cities, counties and towns that use I-Codes. If a recommendation is approved, the change will appear in the next publication of the code (every three years).

Anyone can suggest a code change by submitting a proposal to the ICC. There are a few simple rules to follow. The ICC will publish the proposal and forward the idea to the appropriate committee for consideration. Anyone interested in the proposal can speak for or against the change, and many do. Any business affected by the code will want to be heard. If a public interest group wants to speak, they may. All comments are welcome.

Most code changes are proposed by building officials as a group or by the manufacturer or designer of the product or method of construction. Sometimes, users discover a flaw in an existing product. For example, problems with fire retardant in wood products were discovered only after approval, installation and use. Another example: Failures in polybutylene water pipe caused code officials to reexamine previous approvals.

Problems like these may make you wonder how the products were approved in the first place. Unfortunately, it can take many years to discover latent defects in a construction material. By that time, the product may have been installed in millions of homes.

Government product recalls and lawsuits can cause code officials to reconsider prior approvals. The Consumer Product Safety Commission is an independent government agency charged with monitoring the safety of materials and products used by the public. The CPSC has issued many recalls for construction materials. The CPSC works closely with the ICC on building material and product safety.

Building inspectors and contractors are usually among the first to learn of problems with building materials. An irate homeowner calls to report: "I've lived in this house less than two years and both hall light sconces have burnt out! Come look at them!" Even if your responsibility ended when the Certificate of Occupancy was issued or when the warranty expired, take the call seriously. Drop by to look at the problem!

Be careful what you say when checking the hall light sconce. Note the manufacturer's name and the model number. Promise to get back to the homeowner. Report the failure to the manufacturer. Ask that a factory representative make a more thorough investigation, if you think it's warranted. For a larger, more complex problem that involves public safety, contact the state Consumer Affairs office.

Remember, as far as the public is concerned, you're the expert.

More Changes: Discretion of Your Building Official

At the local level, every building official has authority to modify the code to meet special circumstances. For example, a previous code may have required that stairways be built with a certain rise and run. Now the stairs have to be replaced and the former rise and run no longer meet code requirements. Changing the slope of the stairway by extending stairs into room space would create a tripping hazard. *IRC* Section 104.10 permits the building official to make a case-by-case decision on modification of code requirements:

"Wherever there are practical difficulties involved in carrying out the provisions of this code, the building official shall have the authority to grant modifications for individual cases, provided the building official shall first find that special individual reason makes the strict letter of this code impractical and the modification is in compliance with the intent and purpose of this code and that such modification does not lessen health, life and fire safety requirements or structural. The details of action granting modifications shall be recorded and entered in the files of the department of building safety."

The code gives your building department permission to approve alternative materials and methods of construction. *IRC* Section 104.11 will be important if your home plan is for a rammed-earth yurt.

"The provisions of this code are not intended to prevent the installation of any material or to prohibit any design or method of construction not specifically prescribed by this code, provided that any such alternative has been approved. An alternative material, design or method of construction shall be approved where the building official finds that the proposed design is satisfactory and complies with the intent of the provisions of this code, and that the material, method or work offered is, for the purpose intended, at least the equivalent of that prescribed in this code ..."

Special cases will always require an exercise of judgment.

Policy Statements

A policy statement issued by a building official is another way to change a model code to fit the circumstances of a jurisdiction. *IRC* Section 104.1 states:

"The building official is hereby authorized and directed to enforce the provisions of this code. The building official

shall have the authority to render interpretations of this code and to adopt policies and procedures in order to clarify the application of its provisions. Such interpretations, policies and procedures shall be in conformance with the intent and purpose of this code. Such policies and procedures shall not have the effect of waiving requirements specifically provided for in this code."

This section allows the building official to interpret the meaning of every provision of the code. If there's a dispute, the opinion of the building official is the only one that counts.

I've found that disputes between builders and inspectors on interpretation of the code can nearly always be settled to mutual satisfaction. But there are exceptions. If a problem with interpretation of some particular code section keeps coming up, the building official has authority to issue a policy statement explaining the purpose and intent of that code section.

Preparing such a policy statement is no small thing for a building official. He or she will probably want to discuss the problem with inspectors, contractors and building officials in adjacent jurisdictions. In some cases, a formal interpretation from the ICC may be required.

Once a policy statement has been issued, it should be given the widest circulation possible. It's good practice to make policy statements available to both inspectors and contractors.

The Board of Appeals

There's another way to change interpretation of the code: the Board of Appeals. If a contractor doesn't agree with some interpretation of the building official, the contractor has a right of appeal. The Board of Appeals can either reverse or uphold the building official's decision. Once decided, that opinion becomes precedent and should be followed in all similar circumstances. A contractor who isn't satisfied with a decision of the Board of Appeals can always launch an appeal through the judicial system.

C H A P T E R   3

Building Code Enforcement Staff

Back in the first chapter I suggested that, at least for contractors, having this manual is a little like having a copy of the other team's play book. There won't be many surprises if you understand how the other team operates.

I believe reducing surprises is a legitimate goal for both contractors and building department staff. If you've been in construction for a while, you know perfectly well that there aren't many happy surprises on a jobsite. The unexpected (1) will nearly always increase cost to the contractor and (2) serves no useful purpose for a code enforcement official. As a contractor, you're eager to avoid surprises. The better you understand the inspector's play book, the less likely any surprises.

To reduce surprises, I'll use this chapter to describe the position of everyone you're likely to meet at a building department: titles, responsibilities, authority and where each fits in the organization. I'll also offer some generalizations about the people who hold each of these positions — experience level, educational background, likely motivation. The better you understand who you're talking to — or who you need to talk to — the more effective you'll be at resolving code enforcement issues.

You won't find any of this in the code. But I believe this is important information, whether you stand on the contractor's side or the inspector's side of the counter. And I guarantee that reading this chapter will help you develop a better understanding and more respect for what gets done at your local building department office.

Before we begin, let me explain something that may seem obvious. Building department personnel seldom wear uniforms and don't have numbers on their jerseys. Your inspector will probably be wearing a badge or a name tag or a hard hat with an

> ### *Job Titles in a Modern Building Code Enforcement Organization*
>
> chief building official
> assistant building official
> chief plumbing/mechanical official
> chief electrical official
> chief building inspector
> chief plans examiner
> building inspector
> combination dwelling inspector
> permit technician
> building plans examiner
> mechanical plans examiner
> plumbing plans examiner
> electrical plans examiner
> structural design examiner
> accessibility inspector
> property maintenance and housing inspector
> accessibility plans examiner
> zoning inspector
> electrical inspector
> commercial energy inspector
> plumbing inspector
> commercial energy plans examiner
> mechanical inspector
> residential energy inspector
> combination inspector
> residential energy plans examiner
> one- and two-family building inspector
> one- and two-family electrical inspector
> one- and two-family plumbing inspector
> one- and two-family mechanical inspector
> one- and two-family dwelling inspector
> uniform fire code inspector
> company officer fire code inspector
> underground storage tank inspector
> elevator inspector
> backflow prevention certification inspector

Once you've identified an inspector's title or position, use this chapter to convert that information into a job description. That's the quickest way I know to understand the authority and responsibility of any code enforcement official. It's also why I'm going to emphasize titles in this chapter.

Before we begin with titles, some cautions are in order. First, these titles can be a little confusing, at least at first. But most titles can be associated very easily with a task or function. So if you understand what has to be done, you can probably guess the title. Or, if you know the title, you can probably guess the function. I'll offer many examples on the following pages.

A second caution: Not every building department office uses the same titles, especially smaller offices where each official may wear several hats and perform many functions. So be forewarned. These titles aren't engraved in granite.

Finally, for the sake of simplicity, I'm going to refer to department personnel as though they were all of the masculine gender. That's wrong, of course. There's nothing in the code that limits or restricts a woman's role in code enforcement. More and more women are finding positions in building department offices. That's a trend I welcome. I've worked with female staff at every level of code enforcement. A woman was my mentor early in my career. I hope this manual encourages more women to enter the field. So please don't be offended if you see *he, his* and *him* throughout in this book. It could just as well be *she,* and *her.* In fact, that might be a welcome improvement for the next edition of this manual.

The Big Picture

Building code enforcement is the responsibility of the building official and building department staff. But code enforcement can involve many others, including:

- advocate members who write the codes
- boards who represent the public
- industry members who want a say in regulation

insignia, and will be happy to show identification. But there's no game program that describes exactly what function any particular inspector is performing on a given day. So, if you have any doubt, it's appropriate to ask. "Hi, Mr. Code Official. I don't believe we've met before. I'm Mr. Contractor with ABC Construction. This is one of our jobs. What's your position with the Department?"

- secondary government agencies

- associations of groups who have a vested interest in the codes — such as designers, architects, engineers and builders

- material standards associations that evaluate and adopt requirements for building materials

Code enforcement has many stakeholders — people who have an interest and want to exert influence. But these interests come together in the building department office. That's the tip of the code enforcement spear — where the work gets done.

The *building official* (sometimes called the *chief building official*) is the boss. He runs the office, managing both technical and administrative staff. His duties and powers are defined in the building code. The building official is appointed (hired) by people who run the jurisdiction (city, county, town or village). The building official is responsible to those people, usually a city or county manager and ultimately an elected city council or board of supervisors. The position of building official is politically sensitive. Anyone who answers to elected officials has to be a responsible public servant.

- The *assistant building official* works directly under the building official and usually manages department staff.

- The plumbing, mechanical, and electrical officials supervise specialists who enforce those parts of the code.

- The chief plans examiner and chief building inspector supervise plan review and the inspection staff.

- Plans examiners review plans before they're approved.

- The *building inspectors* do on-site inspections after a permit is issued. Their primary focus is ensuring that construction complies with approved plans.

That's the big picture. Now let's look at each of these jobs in detail.

The Building Official

The building official supervises code enforcement staff, as stated in *IRC* Section R103.1:

"The department of building safety is hereby created and the official in charge thereof shall be known as the building official."

The building official has authority to interpret the code and accept alternate materials and methods of construction not specifically identified in the code. *IRC* Section R104.1 details the duties and authority of the building official:

"The building official is hereby authorized and directed to enforce the provisions of this code. The building official shall have the authority to render interpretations of this code and to adopt policies and procedures in order to clarify the application of its provisions. Such interpretations, policies and procedures shall be in conformance with the intent and purpose of this code. Such policies and procedures shall not have the effect of waiving requirements specifically provided for in this code."

The building official establishes the code enforcement program and directs its operation. He has the authority of a law enforcement officer. *IRC* Section R104.3 declares:

"The building official shall issue all necessary notices or orders to ensure compliance with this code."

Every building official has a "right of entry" as identified in *IRC* Section R104.6:

"...the building official or designee is authorized to enter the structure or premises at reasonable times to inspect or to perform the duties imposed by this code ..."

Later in this chapter I'm going to explain the operation of the Board of Appeals. For now, just understand that the building official is an advisor to the Board of Appeals but has no vote on the Board. The building official advises elected officials and explains proposed code changes to the local adoption authority. The building official's boss is usually the city manager or a county manager.

The buck stops on the desk of the department's building official. He has final responsibility for building safety within the jurisdiction. Most building officials have years or experience in building code enforcement. There's no school for building officials. Nearly all are promoted from within the department, working their way up the ladder.

Though there's no school for building officials (yet), most have a heavy educational background, usually including a university degree in either architecture or engineering.

"Most building officials have a working knowledge of all areas of code enforcement, including plumbing, structural and electrical."

Typical work experience includes 10 or more years in a building department, with steady increases in responsibility. As a manager, the building official oversees all work done by inspectors and plans examiners. Most building officials have a working knowledge of all areas of code enforcement, including plumbing, structural and electrical. For highly technical issues, a building official may call on a code specialist.

Assistant Building Official

Larger jurisdictions will have an assistant building official. This individual is a senior member of the management team and will cover for the building official when he isn't available. The assistant building official is an operations manager, supervising, giving instructions and advice, setting schedules and assigning priorities. His academic credential may be no less than his boss, the building official. But the assistant building official probably has less experience in code enforcement.

Chief Mechanical Official, Chief Plumbing Official, Chief Electrical Official

Some large jurisdictions have specialist inspectors and plans examiners for each of the construction trades, such as architectural, structural, plumbing, mechanical, and electrical. These are technical specialists, experts in their field. The senior official over each particular trade is usually called *supervisor*, *chief* or *team leader*. These staff members normally serve under the direction of the building official or the assistant building official. The building official will rely on these experts for opinions or even interpretations in their area of expertise.

Plans Examiners

Plans for commercial buildings must meet engineering requirements for commercial buildings. Residential structures can be built under conventional standards outlined in the code. It is the responsibility of the plans examiners to see that these concerns are dealt with correctly.

Chief Plans Examiner

The chief plans examiner directs senior and junior staff in the plans examining section. No permit is issued until plans are approved. And final approval of plans is the responsibility of the chief plans examiner. Examiners have to verify that preliminary building plans comply with all codes and administrative rules in effect in the jurisdiction. These include structural, plumbing, mechanical, and electrical work.

The chief plans examiner assigns work and monitors progress of the review process. He plans, organizes, directs, and controls the building department's plan review operations.

Not all plan review will be done by building department staff. It's common in some communities for plan review to be done by plan review consultants working under contract for the building department. That's especially true during periods when work volume is heavy. If plans for your project are reviewed by independent consultants working for the building department, you'll probably be given a contact number. Don't be surprised if you get a call from a consultant during the plan review process. It's a benefit, in my opinion, to have an exchange of information between plan review staff, owners and contractors. For example, the plans examiner may feel that additional engineering calculations are required for some feature in the plans. Instead of noting the error in writing and requesting a re-submission, the examiner may informally advise you to submit additional data while plans are still in the review process.

Senior Plans Examiner

A senior plans examiner (also called a principal plans examiner) will review more complex building plans or plans for buildings that include unconventional design elements. Most senior plans examiners have years of experience in building code enforcement. Some are either an architect or engineer. Most senior plans examiners are experts in a particular trade — structural, plumbing, mechanical, electrical, or fire and life safety, for example. Senior plans examiners work with architectural and design firms and have to know as much about the code as the architects and engineers who prepared the plans. The senior plans examiner will also advise the chief plans examiner, or even the building official, on code issues.

Plans Examiner

A plans examiner checks plans that use conventional building design. A single plans examiner may review plans for all trades, including structural, plumbing, mechanical, electrical and architectural. A plans examiner may advise designers or junior members of an architectural or design firm on code compliance. A plans examiner takes direction from a senior or chief plans examiner. Plans examiners train and instruct permit or plan technicians studying to become plans examiners. I'll have more to say about the role of plans examiners in the next chapter.

Plumbing Plans Examiner

A plumbing plans examiner checks drain, waste and vent pipe, water supply pipe, and fixtures such as water closets, lavatories, sinks, showers, bathtubs, and clothes washers, as well as exterior yard line water distribution systems. The plumbing plans examiner will also review plans for gas piping. These are specialists. Most of the plans they review will be for larger commercial buildings.

Mechanical Plans Examiner

A mechanical plans examiner checks heating, ventilating, and air conditioning (HVAC) equipment, duct work, exhaust vents, and other air transfer systems. He coordinates with the plumbing plans examiner on installation of gas pipe and mechanical equipment. These are also specialists. Most of the mechanical plans they review are for larger commercial buildings.

Electrical Plans Examiner

An electrical plans examiner checks electrical service equipment, wiring materials and methods, lights, outlets, and other electrical devices. Electrical examiners are also specialists. Normally their work is limited to larger commercial buildings.

Accessibility Plans Examiner

Both state and federal law set accessibility standards for the disabled in both new and existing buildings. The accessibility plans examiner checks bathrooms, kitchens, work tables, benches, showers, walks, curbs, counters, parking and other features for code compliance for accessibility.

Plan Technician

Most plan technicians have more experience than permit technicians. Most have at least some construction background. But their code enforcement experience is usually more limited. Normally, plan technicians work at the service counter, where they interact with contractors and property owners. Both plan technicians and permit technicians can process permit requests. A plan technician has authority to approve simple plans right at the counter. That's good to know if you're eager to get a project under way.

A plan technician is a hybrid between the permit technician, who deals with more routine matters, and the plans examiner, who reviews plans almost exclusively. A plan technician does part of both jobs. He may accept an application, process it, review a simple plan (such as a retaining wall), and either make comments or approve the plan and issue a permit on the spot. For larger plans, such as a room addition or deck, the plans technician will do a quick review to be sure the basic elements are in place. Then he'll pass the plans to a plans examiner for more careful review.

There are two advantages to preliminary review by a plan technician. First, the plans are screened for obvious errors. If there's a serious problem, the plan technician can hand the plans back to the applicant immediately. That saves everyone's time. Second, the plan technician learns a lot about the nuts and bolts of building code enforcement. That usually opens opportunities for advancement.

Permit Technicians

Permit technicians work directly with the public on a daily basis. They need a basic understanding of administrative details that affect permit processing. They're often called on to give advice on zoning, addressing, flood plains, environmental quality as well as building codes. If you've got a question about anything that can delay issuance of a permit, start by asking a permit technician. A permit technician who is good at dealing with the public will be among the first promoted to a more responsible position.

The first face you see inside the door at a building department office will be the face of a permit technician. Permit technicians answer questions, accept applications, briefly review plans for compliance with basic submission standards, enter data for automated plan tracking, run errands, stock the supply shelf, answer the telephone, and handle other duties as required. When time and workload permits, a permit technician may have an opportunity to learn the basics of plan review by checking plans for a minor project such as residential porch or shed. Chapter 6 has more detailed information on the permit technician's job.

Building Inspectors

Many building offices classify inspection staff by experience level, such as Inspector I, Inspector II, Inspector III, and so forth. In some offices, more experienced inspectors are called *senior*, *lead*, or *team-leader* inspectors. Most offices have a well-defined career track for inspection staff.

> *"An inspector will check raw land for soil conditions, drainage and slope before excavation begins."*

An inspector's primary job is safety, ensuring that each project complies with the code and meets minimum safety standards. He inspects new construction, additions to existing buildings, remodeling and even demolition work. An inspector will check raw land for soil conditions, drainage and slope before excavation begins. He will inspect every part of the project, from foundation, floor and wall framing to the roof decking. He'll check chimneys, exterior siding, and the roof. He'll check all structural and architectural parts of a building to ensure compliance with minimum code standards. When work is done, the inspector will issue a certificate of occupancy. Chapter 5 has more on the building inspector's job.

Chief Building Inspector

A chief building inspector coordinates work of other inspectors and ensures that inspections are completed at each sequence of a project. He trains, directs, and supervises all building inspection staff. He monitors each building inspector's work to be sure that standards are uniform and in compliance with the code.

Building inspectors have different experience levels. The chief building inspector ensures that department assignments match skill levels. For example, a wise chief inspector will assign the most experienced inspector in the office to a major project, such as a multi-story bank building. For tract housing in a subdivision, the assignment could go to a trainee working with an experienced mid-level inspector.

The chief building inspector responds to complaints made about inspection staff. If you hit a roadblock with an inspector assigned to your project, ask for an introduction to the chief building inspector.

Specialty and Combination Inspectors

Inspection procedure varies from office to office. Some building departments prefer to use "specialty" inspectors with skill and knowledge in one specific trade, such as electrical installation. Other jurisdictions use "combination" inspectors who have a broad knowledge of the construction trades. Each method of inspecting has benefits and drawbacks.

A specialty inspector will be highly skilled in one trade, well-qualified for even the most complex work. But a department relying on specialists will need a larger staff to cover all trades. Combination inspectors are more versatile, covering the work of more trades — but probably not to the same depth as a specialty inspector. Some jurisdictions use both inspection methods. For example, a combination inspector may have adequate background to inspect all trades on a residential project. But a specialty inspector would be assigned on commercial projects with more complex inspections issues.

Public Works Inspector

A public works inspector will check, for example, excavation and earth fill and compaction on a highway project. He'll inspect installation of forms for concrete curbs, sidewalks, gutters, and similar facilities. He'll check placement of concrete reinforcing bars and review testing results for concrete samples.

Note that there's a very significant distinction between what a public works inspector does and what a building inspector does. A public works inspector and a building inspector will check the same forms, slabs, gutters, rebars and so on. But a building inspector's focus is always on safety and code compliance. A public works inspector focuses on quality control and contract compliance, ensuring that the public is getting what they paid for. Don't confuse the two functions.

Mechanical Inspector

A mechanical inspector checks HVAC equipment: appliances, air distribution equipment, exhaust systems, boilers, and water heaters. He

also inspects piping, flammable and combustible liquid storage, piping systems, fireplaces, chimneys and vents, refrigeration systems, and incinerators. He may even inspect indoor air quality standards.

Electrical Inspector

An electrical inspector checks the quality of materials and proper installation of electrical wiring systems. He looks for proper grounding, proper use of electrical equipment, appliances, and facilities. He inspects electrical service entrance wiring for residential and commercial facilities. He ensures that electrical loads are connected correctly by electrical contractors.

Plumbing Inspector

A plumbing inspector checks drain, waste, vent (DWV), and water supply pipe. He checks all sanitary plumbing and storm drains. He verifies that fixtures are the right type and that they're installed properly. He monitors pressure tests to be sure the piping system won't leak.

Fire Protection Inspector

A fire protection inspector checks for proper installation of fire suppression systems, such as sprinklers. He also checks fire alarm systems and other warning devices for proper operation. The local fire department will inspect these systems annually after occupancy. But the building department needs their own fire protection plan review and inspection staff for initial acceptance testing. Normally the fire code is enforced by the fire department rather than the building department.

Zoning Inspector

The building inspection staff usually won't have responsibility for enforcing local zoning ordinances. But the zoning inspector may report to the building official. Zoning ordinances control the location, size, height and character of buildings. For example, zoning rules usually specify how close a building can be to a property line, how tall a building can be and even how many square feet of floor space are allowed in a particular zone. The zoning inspector checks these issues and many others, all related to zoning ordinances adopted by the local jurisdiction.

Residential Energy Inspector

Energy efficiency has become a national priority over the last decade. About one-third of all energy we consume is used to heat, cool and light our buildings. It makes sense to design buildings that are energy efficient. Conserving energy is both in our national interest and a financial advantage to the building occupants. The code requirements in *IRC* Chapter 11 are enforced by an energy code inspector. He verifies that insulation is installed, the heating system is efficient, proper windows and doors are installed, and energy-sensitive material standards are met. To promote energy efficiency in both new and existing commercial buildings, the ICC has created a stand-alone addition to the ICC library, the *International Green Construction Code.*

One- and Two-Family Building Inspector

A one- and two-family building inspector will check all systems in residential buildings, including the structure, plumbing, mechanical, and electrical systems. This will be a combination (multi-trade) inspector. One- and two-family building inspectors need a broad range of knowledge about building codes. These inspectors usually have many years of field experience and will have passed an examination in this inspection category.

One- and Two-Family Specialty Inspector

A specialty inspector, such as electrical, plumbing, or mechanical, checks a single trade. For example, a one- and two-family electrical inspector will check only electrical work. Most trade inspectors have worked in the trade before becoming inspectors. A specialty electrical inspector will

check grounding and wiring, electrical boxes, conduit, switches, outlets, lights, and specialty equipment such as dryers, ranges and ovens.

The plumbing inspector will check the dwelling's DWV and water supply pipe for proper materials, fittings, and connections. He checks for unsanitary connections and backflow potential, and makes sure pipe is installed properly and isn't damaged by other construction.

The mechanical inspector checks all mechanical systems, including fans, blowers, exhaust venting systems and similar equipment, to be sure proper materials were used and correct installation methods were followed.

Miscellaneous Inspectors

Other inspectors at the building department include specialists in elevators, backflow certification, underground storage tanks, and abatement of dangerous buildings. These inspectors work under the authority of the building official. Existing buildings are normally checked by a property maintenance inspector if the *Property Maintenance Code* has been adopted by the jurisdiction.

Elevator Inspector

Elevator inspectors check for wear and unsafe operating conditions. By law, elevators have to be inspected at set intervals. Elevator inspectors perform these schedule inspections. Most elevator inspectors have experience working for companies that install and maintain elevators.

Backflow Certification Inspector

Backflow equipment must be checked regularly to be sure it's working properly. The backflow certification inspector will run checks on the system and then sign a certification for the period under inspection. The purpose of a backflow inspection is to prevent water contamination by a reversed flow of water. When water pressure drops due to a maintenance problem or planned outage, it's possible for the system to suck insecticide or contaminants back into the potable water supply lines. When water pressure is restored, contaminants can be distributed into adjacent buildings. Control devices should isolate agricultural water supply lines when water pressure fails. But these control devices must be maintained. The backflow inspector will verify that maintenance is being done and that the device is working properly.

Underground Storage Tank Inspector

Chemicals and flammables are often stored in underground tanks. Proper installation and maintenance of these tanks is critical to public safety. Regular inspection ensures that the public is protected.

Property Maintenance Inspector

Every construction contractor has met inspectors who check new construction. But you may not have met inspectors who check existing buildings. One type of inspector deals exclusively with safety of existing buildings. The property maintenance inspector or housing inspector's primary job is to check the condition of older residences. Most of these are rental units, either detached single-family residences or apartments. Property maintenance inspectors ensure that absentee owners maintain safe and sanitary building conditions for their tenants.

Abatement of Dangerous Buildings Inspector

These inspectors evaluate dangerous conditions, usually the result of poor maintenance. But a dangerous condition, with a risk of building collapse, might occur due to some other cause, like an earthquake or a hurricane, or an accident such as a car crashing through a storefront window. Faulty electrical equipment can also create dangerous conditions. These cases and others are investigated by the abatement inspector.

The *IRC* doesn't cover abatement. But *IBC* Section 115.3 requires that the building official serve the building owner with a written notice to abate any unsafe condition:

"If an unsafe condition is found, the building official shall serve on the owner, agent or person in control of the structure, a written notice that describes the condition deemed

unsafe and specifies the required repairs or improvements to be made to abate the unsafe condition, or that requires the unsafe structure to be demolished within a stipulated time..."

The building official can issue orders to protect the public, requesting that a building either be restored to a safe condition or be demolished. When there's imminent danger to the public from building collapse or fire hazards, the abatement inspector can use the court system to prosecute violations.

As of this writing, the ICC is developing a new guideline on abatement of dangerous buildings. Once this code is adopted by your state, county, city or town, the abatement inspector will follow legal procedures in the code to reduce the risk posed by unsafe buildings.

The *IPMC (International Property Maintenance Code)* covers public hazards from unsafe buildings and defines hazard categories. If any of these exist in a building, the building official is required to notify the building owner. If that doesn't resolve the problem, the building official has authority to abate the hazard. Abatement can include expelling residents, securing the building to prevent entry, or even demolition of the building.

The Board of Appeals

I promised earlier to discuss the Board of Appeals, a subject that will interest any contractor who's had a dispute on code interpretation. The Board of Appeals represents the public — the taxpayers. The Board serves as an arbiter between property owners and contractors on one side and the building official on the other. Think of the Board as a higher court with authority to reverse a decision made by the building official. Board members are appointed volunteers, not employees of the building department. Board members may have either technical or non-technical backgrounds.

The Board can accept for review any challenge to an interpretation by the building official. For example, suppose a property owner wants to use a new, alternative building material. The building official won't approve the plans, contending that the material isn't tested and has no record of performance. The property owner (or the contractor) can request a review of that decision by the Board. At the hearing, the owner, usually along with the contractor, will be invited to make their case. Their common claim is that the building official is being overly cautious. The Board could side with the building official or the owner. But more likely, the Board will ask the owner to re-apply for a permit, armed this time with an opinion from a registered design professional.

> *"In some cases, the Board may assist the building official in interpreting the code by accepting alternative building materials or methods of construction."*

The Board may also review and comment unofficially on policy decisions by the building official. The Board may help write and endorse local or regional changes to the model building code. In some cases, the Board may assist the building official in interpreting the code by accepting alternative building materials or methods of construction. Some appeal boards also help the building official make hiring decisions.

Material Standards

We've covered the title and responsibility of just about everyone you're likely to meet in a building department office. But before leaving the subject of titles, there's one more category of definitions you need to master.

You'll hear references to "material standards" if you hang around the building department office for very long. Material standards are something you need to understand. Here's why. Material standards relate to both the materials themselves and how those materials are installed. Use exactly the right material but install it the wrong way, and you're likely to have a surprise on inspection day. I'm also going to sketch out how material standards are developed. Every new material is tested for safety

before being made available for use by the public. We'll begin where materials begin, with a manufacturer who has a new product ready for market.

Every manufacturer of construction materials wants to make it easy for architects, owners and contractors to adopt their materials. But building departments are reluctant to approve plans that incorporate materials not widely accepted or that haven't been thoroughly tested. So, to simplify the plan approval process, manufacturers submit their products for testing and approval.

These tests won't be done at your local building office, of course. Test results will be submitted to one of the many associations, institutes, societies, boards, agencies, councils, bureaus, foundations, laboratories and commissions that publish building material standards. Collectively these are known as *Standard Developing Organizations* or *SDOs*. These *SDOs* follow standards and procedures accepted by institutes, government agencies, and councils. One of these institutes is *ANSI*, the American National Standards Institute. While many standards carry the "ANSI" name, *ANSI* is not an *SDO*. ANSI does accredit SDOs, that agree to follow its process and submit their documents, for the development of standards. Once SDO's follow the ANSI process, they may then call their standard an "American National Standard" or use the ANSI name and logo on their standard.

There are two types of standards for building materials, rating standards and test standards:

- Rating standards compare new products or materials with similar, already-accepted products or materials, using criteria in a published document as the basis for the comparison.

- Test standards identify a procedure to follow when testing a new material, and specify the methods to be used to determine whether the material or product meets the published product standard.

Here's the procedure ANSI requires SDO's to use when developing a new standard:

- The need for a new standard is identified.

- A request to develop (or modify) a standard is made.

- A committee is selected to review the proposal.

- A review, comment and appeal process is followed by the committee or other standards-making body and the new standard is published and sent to ANSI for acceptance.

- If the standard relates to construction products or materials, it may be submitted as a reference document in a proposed change to one of the model codes developed and published by the International Code Council.

Once a material is approved by a testing lab, or is evaluated and listed by ICC Evaluation Services (ICC-ES), plan approval at your local building office should be routine. But be aware that approval by a testing lab or ICC-ES is only a recommendation, not the law. Material standards become law only when they're referenced in the code. Building officials have authority to exercise their own judgment and may or may not accept testing lab or ICC-ES approval.

Standards Used by the IRC

Groups such as the American Gas Association, U.S. Department of Commerce and National Association of Home Builders have helped develop many standards used in the *IRC*. You'll find a complete list of agencies that contribute standards to the *IRC* in Chapter 44, Referenced Standards.

Adopting a Standard

Here's an example. The *Insulating Concrete Form (ICF)* wall system was invented in the late 1960s. But ICF didn't conform to any existing material standard and wasn't incorporated into the *IRC* until the 2000 edition. Between the 1960s and 2000, anyone could build with ICF. But a permit would be issued only if plans were submitted with an engineered design stamped by a registered engineer. For nearly 40 years ICF had to be engineered for each project. That took extra time and cost more. But beginning with the 2000 *IRC*, ICF is listed in the code. A design that follows the test standard should sail through the plan review process without the stamp of an engineer.

THE PLAN

C H A P T E R   4

Your Plans in Plan Review

Anyone can apply for a permit and submit plans for review and approval. But as a practical matter, contractors usually apply for the building permit, and thus have to submit plans for review. And there's a good reason why states encourage application by contractors: It helps enforce contractor license and registration laws.

In states where contractors have to register or be licensed, the building department usually requires a contractor's license or registration number on the permit application. If an owner applies for a permit, the owner may have to certify that contractors on the job will be licensed. Electrical and mechanical contractors (plumbing and HVAC work) will usually apply for electrical and mechanical permits for their work.

Construction Plan Submission

Each application must be accompanied by a plan, according to *IRC* Section R106.1:

"Submittal documents consisting of construction documents, and other data shall be submitted in two or more sets with each application for a permit. The construction documents shall be prepared by a registered design professional where required by the statutes of the jurisdiction in which the project is to be constructed. Where special conditions exist, the building official is authorized to require additional construction documents to be prepared by a registered design professional."

Then the code backs off this stringent requirement with an exception:

> *"**Exception:** The building official is authorized to waive the submission of construction documents and other data not required to be prepared by a registered design professional if it is found that the nature of the work applied for is such that reviewing of construction documents is not necessary to obtain compliance with this code."*

In essence, plans aren't necessary if the intent of the work is clear.

"Registered design professional" means an architect or engineer licensed under state law. States license design professionals who meet educational requirements and pass examinations for competency. When you see an architect's or engineer's stamps on a set of drawings, you know that design professional is certifying that the plans meet conventional design standards. He's accepting responsibility for the integrity of the design. That's important. No one at the building department may be qualified to do the required structural calculations. So the plans examiner is going to rely on the opinion of the architect or engineer.

In most states, nearly every commercial project requires the seal of a design professional. A detached single-family residence built with conventional materials and following conventional practice seldom requires the seal of a design professional. There won't be any engineering issues if a foundation extends below the frost line and if framing complies with tables readily available to every contractor and plans examiner.

Basic Requirements

Although building officials have the authority to waive the submission of construction documents, this is not common. Even for a simple retaining wall, you'll need to sketch an elevation view and plan view drawn to scale. Normally, plans will be drawn by a design professional. Be sure there's a data block on the plans — date, site address, drawn by, etc. More on that later when we get to plan review checklists.

In most building department offices, a permit technician will make a preliminary review of the plans before forwarding them to the plans examiner. The permit technician checks for obvious errors. Is there enough detail for the plans examiner to evaluate code compliance? Assuming your plans get past the permit technician, the next stop will be the desk of the plans examiner.

Like every law enforcement officer, the plans examiner has both authority and limitations on that authority. The plans examiner has to apply the code fairly and accurately. Anything a plans examiner requires has to be based on some section of the code. Obviously, every plans examiner has to be an expert on the building code.

Required Construction Plan Documents

IRC Section R106.1.1 sets basic requirements:

> *"Construction documents shall be drawn upon suitable material. Electronic media documents are permitted to be submitted when approved by the building official. Construction documents shall be of sufficient clarity to indicate the location, nature and extent of the work proposed and show in detail that it will conform to the provisions of this code and relevant laws, ordinances, rules and regulations, as determined by the building official."*

Plans must be readable and drawn on substantial paper. Don't try submitting sketches on the back of a napkin. Today, most plans are prepared with a computer using Computer Aided Design *(CAD)* software. If the plans are in digital form, it may be easier to submit a disk. Inquire at your local building department office about acceptable CAD formats. In any case, you're always safe printing the plans and submitting them the old-fashioned way. Either way, the plans must be complete enough to eliminate any doubt about code compliance.

Consistent Plan Review

Every plans examiner I know follows checklists when reviewing plans. That's the single best way to avoid forgetting something. Many jurisdictions have standard checklists for use by plans examiners. There will be one checklist for each inspection category, site plan, foundation, etc. But you should understand that there's no such thing as an absolutely foolproof and complete checklist for any type of building — except maybe a checklist which consists of the entire *IRC*. And that's not really a checklist at all. But even if there's no single perfect checklist, I recommend using the best checklist available.

The second half of this chapter is a sample plan review checklist, divided into inspection categories. If you're a plans examiner, compare my checklist with whatever checklist you currently use. If you're a contractor, use my checklist to review plans before submission. There's no advantage in submitting plans that can't possibly be approved. Save time by submitting plans likely to pass without revision.

The plans examiner will (should) quote a code section when citing any required change. That simplifies matters if there's any controversy about *why* a change is needed or exactly *what* change is required. My checklists cite many code sections.

Consistent Enforcement Standards

Consistency in plan review is important. No contractor wants to feel singled out for special scrutiny. A contractor has a legitimate question when some construction detail fails plan review in City A and would sail right through plan review in City B. Contractors who work in both City A and City B will be quick to discover inconsistent plan review standards. We're all enforcing the same code. Ideally, enforcement standards should be consistent regardless of who's doing the enforcement.

Even worse: Some detail may pass when checked by Examiner A and fail when checked by Examiner B in the same office.

So long as plans are examined by human beings, there will always be at least some margin for error and inconsistency. Examiners have various levels of experience. Some jurisdictions promote plans examiners from among field inspectors. Their feeling is that field experience helps plans examiners develop a better understanding

of the construction process. Other jurisdictions hire plans examiners with no actual field experience. Once seasoned as plans examiners, they'll be trained to perform inspections in the field. So it's reasonable to expect varying standards among examiners. They see things differently and react differently.

But I feel it's legitimate for contractors, builders, and developers to point out inconsistent enforcement practice, either within a single office or between nearby jurisdictions. If you're a contractor, feel free to ask, "Why are you making me do something *they* don't have to do?"

Consistency is a reasonable goal for every code enforcement official. Plans examiners have an open line of communication with examiners in the same office and with examiners in other jurisdictions. Examiners should use that line of communication to discuss enforcement standards and to develop consistent standards. What passes plan review shouldn't depend on who's asking.

Having made a case for consistency in plan review (to examiners), let me explain (to contractors) that there are legitimate reasons for variation in enforcement standards.

All jurisdictions are permitted to adopt policies under the code section *Alternative Materials and Methods of Construction*. For example, the code requires that attics be ventilated to reduce accumulation of moisture that can damage wood and insulation. In an area with high moisture conditions, good ventilation is essential. A jurisdiction on the coast, where the air is moist, needs to enforce air circulation requirements to the letter. Another jurisdiction, a few miles inland where the air is dryer, may not have the same risk. On the coast, they're enforcing the strict letter of the code. Further inland, the office may have a policy that modifies code requirements. In my opinion, both jurisdictions may be doing exactly the right thing.

You've probably detected that this discussion has come back to the theme explored in depth in Chapter 2, "the reason for the rule." It's simply common sense to modify a rule when reasons for that rule don't exist. Every building official has authority to make judgment calls and policy decisions. So it's naive to believe that code enforcement standards will be uniform throughout any state or region, no matter how desirable that might be.

Still, I feel that plans examiners have an obligation to share their thoughts on enforcement policy with peers both within their office and among offices in neighboring communities. With approval of your supervisors, discuss enforcement decisions with your counterparts. Meet regularly, if possible, to discuss code issues. Regional chapters of model code organizations have meetings that provide a perfect setting for interaction. Use seminars attended by examiners from other jurisdictions to ask questions about controversial issues in your area. Find ways to harmonize enforcement decisions wherever possible.

Architectural Drafting Symbols

The construction industry uses a unique language that's understood by few outside the field. When you see a term you don't understand, see the glossary at the back of this book. For drafting symbols, refer to the book *Architectural Graphic Standards.* But there's no complete list of graphic symbols used in construction. The number of symbols used by architects, designers and draftsmen must be nearly infinite. More are being created daily. Many architects, designers, and draftsmen include a legend listing the symbols used on the plan. If you're truly stumped, call the designer. The phone number will be on the plans.

The same is true for abbreviations. For example, an architect might use *GWC* as a label indicating gypsum wall ceiling, or *A.F.F.* for the finish height of a beam above finish floor. You'll see a lot of these abbreviations as you review plans. Generally, abbreviations will be referenced in a summary sheet included with the plans.

Generalist or Specialist Plan Reviewer

Most plans examiners come to the position with at least some related experience — such as carpentry, plumbing, mechanical or electrical work. Some have worked in an architectural or engineering organization. Whatever the background, plans examiners are usually best at identifying

defects within their comfort zone. No doubt, that's why larger building department offices divide plan review responsibilities among several specialists.

For example, a structural engineer may only review highly-complex structural calculations and designs. An expert in plumbing and mechanical work will review only those systems. An examiner with experience in electrical wiring may review only electrical work. An experienced fire inspector may review architectural, fire, and life safety issues in commercial buildings.

In smaller building department offices, a general plans examiner may draw responsibility for all trades — including structural, plumbing, mechanical, electrical, energy efficiency, and architectural. Most generalist plans examiners served as generalist field inspectors before being promoted to plan review.

A Typical Plans Examiner's Day

Most of a typical workday will be spent reviewing plans and talking with applicants. Workload and number of plans reviewed per day can vary widely. A plans examiner may review seven small house plans in one day and then spend several days reviewing a single commercial plan.

After reviewing plans, someone has to record information about the fees, building size and height, valuation, and other details. That someone is usually the plans examiner. Modern building departments record this information with permit-tracking software.

If a set of plans doesn't have all the proper information, the applicant should be advised, either by phone, email or in a comment letter. The best way to resolve problems quickly is with a phone call. Have the plans in front of you when making this call. Follow up with a checklist identifying each discrepancy and filling in comments where necessary.

Most jurisdictions have a standard checklist for use by plans examiners. Follow the checklist to be sure everything that's supposed to be on the plans actually *is* on the plans. The checklist that fol-

> ### *What Makes a Good Plans Examiner?*
>
> *I feel good plans examiners are more born than made. It's easier to learn the code than it is to develop the personality required for effective public service. I have the highest regard for plans examiners who exhibit the following characteristics. I've had the good fortune to know and work with several.*
>
> ■ *Works well with others, regardless of education, status or background*
>
> ■ *Performs duties in a professional manner and with a positive attitude*
>
> ■ *Never argues with an applicant or gets angry if the applicant disagrees with a decision*
>
> ■ *Has the ability to recognize his own errors and admit a mistake*
>
> ■ *Finds ways to resolve potential conflicts by building a consensus*
>
> ■ *Makes good use of the tools available, including computer applications and the Internet*
>
> ■ *Shows genuine interest in the needs of applicants and keeps in close contact during the plan review process*
>
> ■ *Is genuinely interested in new ideas, materials and construction methods*
>
> ■ *Is not afraid to use his deputy status to make sure the law is upheld*
>
> ■ *Enjoys sharing experiences with fellow associates*
>
> ■ *Is eager to learn from those with more experience in code enforcement*

lows is intended for use when reviewing plans for a detached, single-family dwelling. Most items include the *IRC* section, table or figure that applies.

Save the completed checklist under the tracking number assigned by the permit office. When plans are resubmitted, you'll know exactly what you asked for. It's good practice to cite the applicable *IRC* code section in your comments so the applicant can research what has to be changed. Remember, a plans examiner's role is to *assist* applicants, not judge applicants.

When the comment letter has been written, the checklist filled out and saved, and the initial set of plans red-lined, the entire package should be returned to the applicant for correction. Everything should be in writing. When the amended plans are resubmitted, it's easy to check off each correction and spot any issues that remain to be resolved.

What if ...

It's common to have an applicant question a decision reached in plan review. For example, suppose the plans examiner asks for a wall framing detail for a particular structural connection. The examiner may be concerned about how a load will be transferred to the footing. The plans examiner may think the load is resolved through wall framing when, in fact, it's resolved through a drag strut in the roof framing. The load path will be resolved across the room. But a plans examiner won't know that without asking the question and listening to the answer.

The best plans examiners listen carefully and keep an open mind. Many times, the applicant will be right. This shouldn't be a problem, so *don't make it one.* Don't try to defend yourself if it's likely that you're wrong. Offer genuine thanks and appreciation for the explanation. Scratch that requirement and be done with it! No one likes to dwell on their mistakes, especially those in positions of authority. Don't be defensive.

But if you see fault in the argument, say so and show the applicant why you believe your point is correct. An applicant is more likely to compromise once you've demonstrated respect for his point of view. If you can't convince the applicant, take the matter to your supervisor, the final authority.

Technical Design Review

Not many contractors and only a few plans examiners qualify as design professionals. But every plans examiner and every contractor should look for obvious errors made by a licensed design professional. If you find a mistake, present the problem tactfully and professionally. Deal with it jointly. Most of the time, a team attitude will yield positive results. Show glee about finding a mistake and you'll surely be sorry.

Some design professionals may consider changes in plan review to be an indignity. Good human relations skills will resolve most of these disputes. But be careful with your comments, especially on the first few encounters. When challenged, don't become defensive. Listen carefully. Reply with an "I understand" or "I hear you." Of course, you don't have to agree. But showing respect for the opinion of a design professional will earn reciprocated respect. Research the issue collectively. Finding the answer should be a joint discovery — a learning experience for both of you.

Architects normally limit their work to selection of materials, shape and form. Engineers focus on utility and structural integrity. The building code deals with both engineering and architectural issues. A plans examiner without training in structural analysis or design should leave most structural review questions to an engineer in the department.

Technical review of an engineer's work is more complicated than architectural review. Unless you're properly qualified, pass structural issues to someone who's qualified. Structural engineering is no place for an amateur.

Wood framing is an exception. Many of the basic rules for wood framing can be reduced to tables anyone can follow.

When in doubt, take disputes with a design professional to your supervisor. You're not required to accept a design professional's opinion on code issues. Remember, the building official has the final word on interpreting intent of the code.

Sample Plan Review Checklists Based on the 2009 *IRC*

Every plans examiner, every contractor and every design professional needs a checklist when reviewing plans for code compliance. Many building departments publish a plan review checklist and recommend that contractors use that checklist before submitting plans. If the office where you submit plans recommends a specific checklist, by all means, follow their recommendation. The checklist they recommend probably includes items that

touch on local ordinances, zoning or office policy and that won't be covered anywhere else.

You should also be aware that the ICC publishes an exhaustive plan review checklist, *2009 IRC® CheckList: Building and Energy Provisions Chapters 1-11*. This book is available direct from the ICC Web store for under $50.

So why have I included another checklist in this manual? Easy. I call it the three bears approach to plan review:

The checklist published by your local building department is likely to be short, maybe too short, covering only the high points. The ICC checklist is very complete, as complete as the code itself. In essence, it nearly *is* the code — and is more than required for most jobs. In my experience, the value in this published checklist is that it can be whittled down and customized to cover the key items most likely to be caught in the plan review. I feel the checklist that follows strikes a happy medium between the short (free) checklists you'll find at some building department offices and the exhaustive checklist published by the ICC. I hope you agree that my checklist is "just right."

Site Plan Checklist

Note: *Many items in this checklist involve IRC Section R106.2, which directs you to the site plan and construction documents.*

☐ Number and address (including legal description). *IRC* Section R319

☐ North arrow and unit drawing scale

☐ Lot, block, subdivision name, and vicinity map. *IRC* Section R106.2 (site plan)

☐ All adjacent streets, rights of way, and easements

☐ All existing and proposed structures on the property

☐ Required fire separation distance to nearest structures and property lines. *IRC* Section and Table R302.1

☐ All walls and fences

☐ All proposed driveways and parking areas

☐ Areas for onsite retention of rain water or similar control of storm water. *IRC* Section R401.3

☐ Utility locations for water, electricity, gas, sewage, or septic tank

☐ All required setbacks, including local zoning requirements, per *IRC* Section and Table R302.1 and local zoning ordinance

☐ Percent of land covered by development, including any grading. Zoning Code

☐ Survey of property, if requested by the Administrative Authority

☐ Tax assessor's parcel number for identification for taxing purposes

☐ Location of septic tank or sewer connection

☐ Elevation heights in topographic style to show terrain features such as hills, valleys, and drainage

☐ Any native plants targeted for protection, if required by local ordinance

☐ Major landscaping or trees and other significant flora targeted for protection, if required by local ordinance

Foundation Plan Checklist

☐ Soil is treated to prevent termite damage. *IRC* Section R318

☐ Foundations will transfer all loads to the supporting soil. *IRC* Section R401.2

☐ Surface drainage is diverted, so as not to create a hazard. *IRC* Section 401.3

☐ Report of soil test if area is likely to have expansive, compressive, shifting, or similar soil. *IRC* Section R401.4

☐ Soil design follows *IRC* Table R401.4.1 if there's no geotechnical report

☐ Concrete has minimum strength. *IRC* Table R402.2

☐ Concrete exposed and subject to weathering is air entrained. *IRC* Section 402.2

☐ Exterior walls are supported on continuous solid concrete, fully-grouted masonry, or other approved footings. *IRC* Section R403.1

☐ Footings are at least minimum size and shape. *IRC* Table 403.1

☐ Braced walls required for lateral forces are supported by continuous reinforced footings. *IRC* Section R403.1.2

☐ Foundations with stem walls and slab-on-grade in seismic zones are reinforced with steel bars. *IRC* Section R403.1.3

☐ Exterior footings and foundation systems go below the frost line, or 12 inches below the undisturbed ground surface. *IRC* Section R403.1.4

☐ Shallow footings are protected from frost with insulation. *IRC* Section R403.3 and Table R403.3

☐ Tops of footings are level and bottoms of footings don't slope more than 1:10. *IRC* Section R403.1.5

☐ Wood frame wall is anchored to the foundation with ½-inch anchor bolts 6 feet oc. *IRC* Section R403.1.6

☐ Anchor bolts embedded 7 inches into concrete or masonry foundation. *IRC* Section R403.1.6

☐ Special anchorage if required for seismic conditions. *IRC* Section R403.1.6.1

☐ Footings adjacent to slopes meet the setback requirements (3:1). *IRC* Section R403.1.7

☐ Foundation height is 12 inches higher than the street gutter at a point of discharge. *IRC* Section R403.1.7.3

☐ Masonry foundation walls meet size and shape requirements. *IRC* Tables R404.1.1(1) and (2)

☐ Masonry foundation walls meet reinforcement requirements. *IRC* Tables R404.1.1(2), (3) and (4)

☐ Concrete or masonry foundation walls in any seismic regions meet requirements. *IRC* Section 404.1.4

☐ Finish elevation of foundation walls is a minimum of 4 inches where masonry veneer is used, and a minimum of 6 inches elsewhere above adjacent grade. *IRC* Section R404.1.6

☐ Special foundation design meets the requirements of engineered design and manufacturer's specifications

☐ Concrete and masonry foundation walls are dampproofed to prevent moisture penetration. *IRC* Section R406

☐ Crawl space is ventilated by openings in foundation wall that are 1 square foot per 150 square feet of floor. *IRC* Section R408.1

☐ Crawl space is provided with an access panel that is at least 18 inches by 24 inches. *IRC* Section R408.4

☐ Provide foundation details that are tied to foundation plan. *IRC* Figure R403.1(1)

Floor Plan Checklist

☐ All rooms, labeled with their uses

☐ Large equipment such as refrigerators, ranges/ovens, dishwashers, clothes dryers, water heaters, and furnaces

☐ Plumbing fixtures such as tubs, toilets, washing machines, and lavatory bases

☐ Overall dimensions of structure and interior dimensions of each room

☐ Natural lighting (window sizes) for each room not less than 8 percent of floor area of that room, unless artificial light is provided that meets the requirements of *IRC* Section R303.1

☐ Natural ventilation at least 4 percent of floor area for operable portions of windows, unless mechanical ventilation is provided that meets the requirements of *IRC* Section R303.1

☐ At least one room at least 120 square feet. Other rooms must be at least 70 square feet. *IRC* Section R304

☐ Minimum dimension at least 7 feet for any habitable room. *IRC* Section R304.3

☐ Ceiling height at least 7 feet in habitable rooms. *IRC* Section R305

☐ Smoke detectors on each floor, in each bedroom, and each hallway leading to a bedroom. *IRC* Section R314

☐ Door and windows labeled for energy code compliance. *IRC* Sections R308.1 and N1101.5

☐ Equipment capable of maintaining room temperature of 68 degrees F. *IRC* Section R303.8

☐ Attic access is at least 22 inches by 30 inches and opens to where there is at least 30 inches headroom. *IRC* Section R807

☐ If mechanical equipment is in the attic, the opening is large enough to allow for removal of the largest appliance, and all the applicable requirements of *IRC* Section M1305.1.3 are followed

☐ Attached garages separated from dwelling by not less than ½-inch gypsum board on the garage-side and a solid core or rated door. *IRC* Section R302 and Table R302.6

☐ Garages beneath habitable rooms have not less than ⅝-inch type-X gypsum board or equivalent on the ceiling, and any wall supporting that floor/ceiling not less than ½-inch gypsum board. *IRC* Section R302

☐ Stair location and shape showing width, rise of step, length of run, handrail locations, and landings. *IRC* Section R311.7

☐ Bathroom ventilation (windows totaling not less than 3 square feet, half of which must be openable, or mechanical). *IRC* Section R303.3

☐ Bedroom emergency egress windows not at grade have a minimum 5.7 square feet clear opening; bedroom emergency egress at grade; 5 square feet minimum operable windows at grade level. *IRC* Section R310.1

☐ Maximum 44-inch sill height for exit windows. *IRC* Section R310.1

☐ Walls and soffits of enclosed accessible space under stairs protected with ½-inch gypsum board. *IRC* Section R302.7

☐ Shower enclosures finished with a nonabsorbent finish to a height of 6 feet above the floor. *IRC* Section R307.2

☐ Shower enclosures have a minimum dimension of 30 inches and floor area of at least 900 square inches. *IRC* Figure R307.1

☐ Only tempered glass enclosures, including windows, within shower. *IRC* Section R308.4 Item #5

☐ Each water closet has a clear space not less than 15 inches from either side and not less than 21 inches in front. *IRC* Figure R307.1

☐ Fireplace location, hearth size, and materials. For factory-built or zero-clearance fireplaces; cut sheet, make, model number, and the approval number of the testing agency. The required clearance to combustible material. For masonry fireplaces; cross-section with vertical steel and solid grout specified. *IRC* Section R1001

☐ Comply with requirements for landings at doors. *IRC* Section R311.7.5

☐ Appliances having an ignition source installed in garages are mounted on platforms so that the ignition source is at least 18 inches above the floor. *IRC* Section M1307.3

☐ Locations of skylights. Manufacturer's listing provided on all skylights over 2 feet by 4 feet. (Plan review looks for a listing or a note on plans that a listing will be provided.) *IRC* Section R308.6.9

Stair Detail Checklist

☐ Maximum rise of step is 7 ¾ inches. *IRC* Section R311.7.4.1

☐ Minimum run of tread is 10 inches. *IRC* Section R311.7.4.2

☐ Width of stair may not be less than 36 inches. *IRC* Section R311.7.1

☐ Headroom of stairwell not less than 6 foot 8 inches. *IRC* Section R311.7.2

☐ Handrail diameter at least 1¼ inches and not more than 2 inches. *IRC* Section R311.7.7.3

☐ Handrail height not less than 34 inches and not more than 38 inches above nosing of the tread. *IRC* Section R311.7.7.1

☐ Stair landing width not less than the width of the stairway served, and a minimum dimension of 36 inches measured in the direction of travel. *IRC* Section R311.7.5

☐ Pre-fabricated metal stair manufacturer's specifications are attached to the plans.

☐ Illumination provided for landings and treads. *IRC* Section R311.7.8

☐ Maximum variation in tread width or riser height is no more than ⅜ inch. *IRC* Section R311.7.4

Exits and Guards Requirement Checklist

☐ Required exit doors are side-hinged and not less than 32 inches wide by 6 feet 6 inches high. *IRC* Section R311.2. However, to achieve these minimum dimensions, you'll need a door 3 feet wide and 6 feet 8 inches high

☐ Required guards are not less than 36 inches high. *IRC* Section R312. Note the exception for stairs

☐ Openings in guards have intermediate rails or ornamental closures which do not allow passage of a 4-inch-diameter sphere. *IRC* Section R312.3

☐ Exterior stairway landings are at least 36 inches wide and 36 inches long. *IRC* Sections R311.7.1 and R311.7.5

☐ Ramps have a maximum slope of 1 in 12 (8.3 percent) unless it's technically infeasible to meet the slope and requirements for the exception, in which case the slope may go as steep as 1 in 8 (12.5 percent) as long as a handrail is provided. *IRC* Section R311.8.1

☐ A minimum 3 foot by 3 foot landing must be at the top and bottom of each ramp, where a door opens onto the ramp, and where the ramp changes direction. *IRC* Section R311.8.2

Electrical Plan Checklist

☐ Location of main service disconnect. Service disconnect is required to be readily accessible. *IRC* Section E3601.6.2

□ Location and sizes of sub-panels. Sub-panels (service disconnecting means) may not be in a bathroom. *IRC* Section E3601.6.2

□ Show all lights, outlets, and electrical devices with circuit designation number that matches the panel schedule

□ All GFCI and arc-fault circuit interrupter (AFCI) outlets identified where required. *IRC* Section E3902

□ Enlarged drawing of service panel and meter base, showing grounding and bonding. *IRC* Sections E3601.6.2, E3607, E3608, E3609, E3610, and E3611

□ Panel schedule showing circuit size, conductor size, overcurrent protection and circuit identification in panel. *IRC* Table E3603.1, Section E3601.6.1, Table E3702.13 and Section E3705

□ Show load calculations. *IRC* Table E3602

□ Note the service equipment manufacturer, type and amps of the panel. Service equipment must be listed for this use. In order to be listed, it will be labeled. Look for manufacturer's data on nameplate. *IRC* Section E3601.6.1

□ Note the grounding conductor is the proper size for the electrical service size. *IRC* Section E3603.1

□ Note that a bonding conductor is connected between service panel and any non-current carrying metal parts. *IRC* Section E3609.2

□ At least one wall-switch-controlled lighting outlet in hallways, and stairways. *IRC* Section E3903.3

□ At least one wall-switch-controlled lighting outlet in all habitable rooms and bathrooms. *IRC* Section E3903.2

□ At least one wall-switch-controlled lighting outlet in attached garages and outdoor entrances. *IRC* Section E3903.3

□ No point along any wall in a room such as kitchen, bathroom, habitable or similar room is more than 6 feet from a receptacle outlet. *IRC* Figure E3901.2

□ At least one receptacle outlet in hallways 10 feet or more in length. *IRC* Section E3901.10

□ An exterior weatherproof GFCI outlet, at grade level, at both front and back of house. *IRC* Sections E3902.3 and E3901.7

□ GFCI receptacle outlets at each kitchen counter space wider than 12 inches. These outlets must be spaced so that no portion of wall is more than 24 inches from an outlet. *IRC* Sections E3902.6 and E3901.4, and Figure E3901.4

□ GFCI receptacle outlet in each bathroom on a wall adjacent to the wall where the lavatory basin is located, and within 36 inches of the outside edge. *IRC* Sections E3902.1 and E3901.6

□ Bathrooms have a minimum of one outlet on a separate 20-amp circuit with no other outlets. *IRC* Section E3703.4

□ Receptacles in bathrooms, kitchens, unfinished basements, garages, and carports are the GFCI type. *IRC* Section E3902.6

□ Outlets in habitable rooms must be the arc-fault interrupter type. *IRC* Section E3902.11

□ A minimum of two 20-amp-rated appliance circuits to serve all outlets located in the kitchen, breakfast, and dining room. *IRC* Section E3703.2

□ Minimum of one 20-amp branch circuit to serve only outlets in the laundry room. *IRC* Section E3703.3

□ A light controlled by a switch at the attic entrance for the HVAC equipment. *IRC* Sections M1305.1.4.3 and E3901.11

□ A service outlet for HVAC equipment within 25 feet of equipment. *IRC* Sections E3901.11 and M1305.1.4.3

□ Where ceiling fans are specified, approved outlet boxes are supported. *IRC* Section E3905.9

□ Light fixtures in clothes closets meet clearance requirements. *IRC* Figure E4003.12 and Section E4003.12

□ Smoke detectors, with circuit designation numbers, are wired to building power. *IRC* Section R314.4

Plumbing Plan Checklist

☐ Water service pipe material and size, based on friction loss and developed length. *IRC* Section P2903.7

☐ Location of all plumbing fixtures, piping material, sizes, and layout. *IRC* Chapter 27

☐ Minimum water supply pressure is 40 psi. *IRC* Section P2903.3

☐ Maximum water supply pressure is 80 psi. *IRC* Sections P2903.1 and P2903.3.1

☐ Water heater installation according to *IRC* Chapter 28 that includes the following:

  ☐ Location to provide access for observation, maintenance, servicing and replacement. *IRC* Section P2801.3

  ☐ Where a leak could cause damage, a pan must be installed under water heater. *IRC* Section P2801.5

  ☐ Water heaters in any garage having an ignition source must be elevated 18 inches above the garage floor. *IRC* Section P2801.6

  ☐ Water heaters in seismic zones must be braced. *IRC* Section P2801.7

  ☐ Where required, a pan with a discharge pipe under water heater. *IRC* Section P2801.5

  ☐ Relief valve and discharge line at water heater. *IRC* Section P2803

☐ Piping protected from physical damage or from freezing. *IRC* Sections P2603.2.1 and P2603.6

☐ Piping properly supported. *IRC* Section P2605

☐ Proper materials are used in DWV system. *IRC* Section P3002

☐ Drainage pipe fittings meet standards for change of direction. *IRC* Section P3005 and Table P3005.1

☐ Drainage pipe sizes meet limitations for maximum fixture units. *IRC* Section P3004 and Table P3004.1

☐ Plumbing relief vents are at least 4 feet below any door or window or air intake and 10 feet horizontally from all air intakes, unless it's 2 feet above top of opening. *IRC* Section P3103.5

☐ Vent pipes meet minimum size requirements based on drainage pipe size. *IRC* Section P3113

☐ Water pipe fittings have only approved joints. *IRC* Section P2905.6

☐ Total fixture demand and maximum developed length for water lines follow *IRC* Sections P2903.6 and P2903.7

☐ Water supply pipe size is based on water supply fixture-unit values according to *IRC* Table P2903.6, available water pressure, friction loss and developed length, and can be based on acceptable design methods in Appendix P

☐ Showers and tub-shower combinations have a thermostatic mixing valve. *IRC* Section P2708.3

☐ Atmospheric-type vacuum breakers must comply with referenced standards. *IRC* Section P2902.3.2

☐ Waste line is as high as possible under the countertop for dishwashers. *IRC* Section P2717.2

☐ Shower is at least 30 inches in any dimension. *IRC* Figure R307.1

☐ Trap size of each fixture in compliance with *IRC* Table P3201.7

☐ Specified distance between traps and vents within limitations of *IRC* Table P3105.1

Mechanical Plan Checklist

☐ HVAC equipment is sized according to recognized standards. *IRC* Section M1401.3

☐ Heat pump and other mechanical equipment is labeled (by labeling appliance "listed and tested" on plans). *IRC* Section M1303

☐ Appliance installation methods comply with manufacturer's listing (label appliance "listed and tested" on plans) and *IRC* Section M1307

☐ Appliances in garage or carport are protected from possible damage due to impact. *IRC* Section M1307.3.1

☐ Appliances are installed with a clearance from unprotected combustible materials. *IRC* Section M1306.1

☐ Baseboard heaters (convectors) installed per manufacturer's specifications (by labeling appliance "listed and tested" on plans). *IRC* Section M1405

☐ Fireplace stoves installed according to *IRC* Section M1414 and manufacturer's listings (by labeling appliance "listed and tested" on plans). Note that a fireplace stove is defined in Chapter 2 as one that burns solid fuel such as wood

☐ In certain seismic zones, appliances are anchored. *IRC* Section M1307.2

☐ Heat pump equipment installed outside supported at least 3 inches above grade. *IRC* Section M1403.2

☐ Installation and support of each supply register, return air grill, and all ductwork. *IRC* Section M1601.4

☐ Material, size and routing of all ductwork. *IRC* Section M1601

☐ Ducts meet the minimum size return air requirements, per the referenced standards and *IRC* Section M1601.1 and ACCA Manual D

☐ Solar energy systems installed per *IRC* Chapter 23

☐ Evaporative cooler location and installation methods are shown. *IRC* Section M1413

☐ Access, clearances, and working space around HVAC equipment in accordance with *IRC* Section M1305

☐ Condensation drains for HVAC units are per *IRC* Section M1411.3

☐ Provisions for, and route of, secondary condensate drain, if needed, are shown. *IRC* Section M1411.3.1

☐ Mechanical exhaust vents terminate not less than the distance permitted by *IRC* Section M1804.2

☐ Exhaust fan size and locations for bathrooms, water closet compartments, and laundry rooms. *IRC* Section R303.3

☐ A minimum size and shape moisture exhaust vent for dryer. Exhaust type is regulated by dryer manufacturer's instructions. *IRC* Section M1502

☐ Any range hood is exhausted to atmosphere according to the standards of *IRC* Section M1503

☐ Ducts for exhaust vents for range hoods comply with the material limitations. *IRC* Section M1503.2

☐ All exhaust vents terminate to outdoors. *IRC* Section M1501

☐ If HVAC equipment is in attic, access shown per *IRC* Section M1305.1.3

☐ If HVAC equipment is in attic, show passageway and working platform. *IRC* Section M1305.1.3

☐ If HVAC equipment is in attic, switched light and service outlet are shown. *IRC* Section M1305.1.3

☐ Fuel gas piping and equipment is installed according to the provisions of *IRC* Chapter 24

Structural Floor Framing Plan Checklist

☐ Layout and identification of structural support system, including girders, joists, posts, beams, and decking

☐ Species of wood being used, its strength properties and grade. *IRC* Section R502.1

☐ Identify bearing wall locations. Make sure these walls match foundation plans for footing requirements

☐ Center spacing of repetitive members such as floor joists. *IRC* Tables R502.3.1(1) and (2)

☐ Minimum bearing for floor joists 1½-inch wood and 3-inch masonry. *IRC* Section R502.6

☐ Joists prevented from rotating with bridging at points of support. *IRC* Section R502.7.1

☐ Joists under bearing partitions doubled. *IRC* Section R502.4

☐ Girders and headers are within span limitations. *IRC* Tables R502.5 (1) and (2)

☐ Framing anchors, clips, and other structural connectors for joists framing into girders. *IRC* Section R502.6.2

Structural Roof Framing Checklist

☐ Layout and identification of structural support system, including trusses, rafters, posts, beams, headers, and decking

☐ Type of wood to be used, its strength properties and grade. *IRC* Sections R802.1 and R602.2

☐ Identify bearing wall locations. *IRC* Sections R601.2, R602.2, R602.3 and R602.4

☐ Bearing walls match foundation plans for footing requirements. *IRC* Sections R401.2 and R403.1

☐ Center spacing of repetitive members such as rafters. *IRC* Tables R802.5.1(1) through (9)

☐ Rafters are prevented from rotating with lateral support (blocking) at points of support. *IRC* Sections R802.1.1 and R802.8

☐ Rafters are within span limitations. *IRC* Tables R802.5.1(1) through (9)

☐ Girders and headers are within span limitations. *IRC* Tables R502.5.1(1) and (2)

Structural and Non-Structural Wall Framing Checklist

☐ Type of wood to be used, its strength properties and grade. *IRC* Section R602.1

☐ Wall bracing for exterior bearing and non-bearing walls. *IRC* Section R602.10

☐ Type and location of wall bracing. *IRC* Section R602.10 and *IRC* Table R602.10.1

☐ Any trusses must be engineered and factory assembled. *IRC* Section R802.10

☐ Stud size, spacing and wall height. *IRC* Table R602.3(5)

☐ Nailing schedule for wall components. *IRC* Table R602.3(1)

☐ Required blocking to keep joists or trusses from rotating at points of support. *IRC* Section R802.8

☐ Required fire blocking. *IRC* Section R602.8

Elevation Views (all sides) Checklist

☐ View from grade to sky of all sides of proposed structure

☐ Windows, doors, roof lines, chimney, and all other features visible from a side view

☐ Dimensions for height, width, and length of the overall structure

☐ Material and type of exterior finish proposed. *IRC* Section R703

☐ Required lateral bracing (shear walls). *IRC* Section R602.10

☐ All structures such as porches, balconies, roof overhang, and parapets

☐ Roof covering material such as shingles, roll roofing, etc. *IRC* Chapter 9

☐ All roof slopes that depend on roofing material type. *IRC* Chapter 9

☐ All roof drains or scuppers on flat roofed areas. *IRC* Section R903.4

☐ Fireplace chimney ends at least 3 feet above roof at roofline and at least 2 feet above roof at 10 feet. *IRC* Table R1001.1 and Figure R1001.1

☐ Roof vent area is $\frac{1}{150}$ of roof area. Show location of all vents. *IRC* Section R806

☐ Safety glass in hazardous areas; within 24 inches of the door or 18 inches of the floor. *IRC* Section R308 (Hazardous location #2 and #3)

☐ Note veneer and specify type. *IRC* Section R703.7

☐ Detail and anchoring method for any wall veneer, backing, and vapor barrier. *IRC* Sections R703.2 and R703.7.2

☐ Note and specify the water-resistant barrier under stucco and over siding. *IRC* Section R703.2

Cross-Sectional View and Detail Checklist

☐ Wall section with details of construction, such as treated bottom and double top plate. *IRC* Chapter 6

☐ Wall sheathing, interior drywall, insulation, and connection of wall to rafter or truss. *IRC* Sections R702.3 and R802.11

☐ Draft stops and fireblocking in walls to prevent smoke and fire in walls from entering attic. *IRC* Sections R602.8 and R302.11

☐ Attic ventilation opening is at least $\frac{1}{150}$ of roof area. *IRC* Section R806

☐ Under-floor ventilation opening is at least $\frac{1}{150}$ of floor area. *IRC* Section R408.2

☐ Attic access is 22 inches by 30 inches for roofs, with at least 30 inches of clear height. *IRC* Section R807

☐ Foundation crawl space access is 18 inches by 24 inches. *IRC* Section R408.4

☐ Structural wood located closer than 18 inches is treated to resist decay. *IRC* Section R317.1

☐ Roof pitch and roof covering material. *IRC* Chapter 9

☐ Roof drains and overflows. *IRC* Section R903.4

☐ Grades adjacent to exterior walls. *IRC* Section R404.1.6

☐ Insulation required for energy code compliance. *IRC* Table N1102.1

☐ Termite protection. *IRC* Section R318

☐ Flood-resistant construction. *IRC* Section R322

☐ Treated plate in wall framing. *IRC* Section R317.1

☐ Interior drywall attachment method. *IRC* Section R702.3

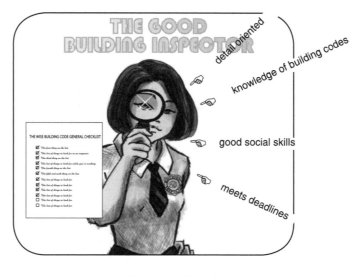

THE GOOD
BUILDING INSPECTOR

detail oriented

knowledge of building codes

good social skills

meets deadlines

THE WISE BUILDING CODE GENERAL CHECKLIST

C H A P T E R   5

Building Inspections

In my opinion, the best building departments can be identified by the consistency of their inspections. Everyone can agree: Whether you pass or fail an inspection shouldn't depend on who does the inspection. Also true: If two adjacent communities are enforcing the same *IRC*, whether you pass or fail an inspection shouldn't depend on which building department does the inspection.

Unfortunately, achieving that goal isn't easy. As mentioned in Chapter 4, inspectors come from varied backgrounds. Most have significant experience in one or two construction specialties and very limited practical experience in other areas of construction. Expect a very thorough framing inspection from an inspector with years of experience as a framing contractor. But that inspector may not notice a defect in the plumbing work. The next inspector,

who may have been a plumbing contractor, will spot the discrepancy immediately, even though it passed the previous inspection. If it's your job that's being inspected, treatment like that hurts. Every builder who passes an inspection wants to assume that anything on site at the time of the inspection was judged to comply with the code.

We all wish that were true. Unfortunately for contractors, that's not how building departments understand their role in the code enforcement process. Also unfortunately, inconsistency in inspections isn't a defense contractors can use to their advantage. Having said that, I'll admit that inconsistent inspections waste time and materials, delay project completion, increase costs, upset schedules and expose weakness in the training of building department staff.

Consistent Building Inspections

So, what can a building department do to make inspections more consistent? I'll name the ways.

Many wise building officials and chief inspectors keep a general checklist for their inspectors to follow. Any checklist, even if less than complete, is a good step toward consistent inspections. Another is to emphasize training by supervisors and interaction among inspectors. Every new inspector who joins a department will have both strengths and weaknesses. Most newly-hired staff members can both help existing inspectors and benefit from the counsel of existing staff members. It's a little like mixing new ingredients into a cake recipe. When selected carefully and blended well, everyone should benefit from each addition.

New inspectors have to understand which code provisions are strictly enforced in your office and where contractors are given more latitude. For example, are seismic bracing or footing depth hot issues in your community? What issues have been resolved or policies adopted recently? Are there enforcement problems that remain unresolved? Maybe most of all, what do the best and most knowledgeable contractors expect from your office? Generally, it's good policy to reward reasonable expectations. If a contractor should expect that a particular construction detail will fail an inspection, it's a mistake to overlook that detail. The converse is also true.

While it's always reasonable to enforce the entire code, it's equally important to remember the goal — the intent of the code. That's general building safety. Inspectors who count nails in roof decking and then fail to catch poor wiring practice will be a torment to both the chief building inspector and contractors trying to make a living in the community.

Some departments require an inspector to cite a code section when writing up an infraction. That's good policy, in my opinion, and should be followed consistently. Requiring documentation for each defect prevents an overzealous inspector from enforcing his own notions about quality construction. Remember, the code sets minimums required for safety. Code compliance isn't intended as a guarantee of top quality construction.

Coordination With Nearby Departments

When a large metropolitan area has many cities, each with dozens of inspectors, poor coordination between jurisdictions can make the results of any inspection seem random and capricious. Your local department is missing an opportunity if not represented at local ICC chapter meetings. Almost certainly, the ICC has chapter meetings in your area. Most meetings offer ample opportunity to discuss common issues and coordinate enforcement policy.

Some metropolitan areas have a building code review committee that spans municipal boundaries. Representatives are usually appointed from each of the participating building departments. Some of these committees are granted authority to rule on appeals or questions that affect the larger community. All of these review committees can have a positive influence on consistency in code enforcement throughout the area.

As a building official, I make it my policy to record the most common mistakes made by inspectors in my office. I keep these notes confidential, of course. But each note serves as a reminder to (1) monitor similar occurrence that affect the inspector involved, and (2) cover similar topics at regular staff meetings. My confidential list is also useful in the indoctrination of new hires or the transition of staff members from one function to another.

For the benefit of contractors who are reading these words: Many of the mistakes recorded on my list of mistakes are based on a conversation I've had (or heard about) with contractors, usually based on an enforcement decision made by a staff member. A well-considered complaint from an experienced construction pro, especially when backed by a careful reading of the code, carries weight at your local building department office.

Enforcing Installation Standards

As discussed in Chapter 2, the *IRC* is loaded with standards written by SDOs (Standard Developing Organizations). These standards identify how equipment and materials should be installed. As construction work gets more complex and as materials become more specialized, designers and code officials have to rely more and more on industry standards. Anyone who worked in construction before getting into code enforcement will be well-acquainted with many of these standards. You may have assumed that many of these installation standards were company policy — simply how things are done. More likely, these rules are mandates in the *IRC* based on work done by an SDO.

> *"The best building inspectors are detail-oriented and persistent without being abrasive."*

Building inspectors have to enforce these standards even though the reason for the rule may not be obvious. Many of these standards are referenced in the *IRC*. It's hard to argue with such a requirement. Inspectors, like contractors, have to take code requirements at face value. Nearly all standards are based on an engineering study and careful testing. That's why it's important for both inspectors and contractors to follow the standard as written (including all the exceptions) — not the inspector's opinion of quality workmanship.

Another consistency issue: Unless the department has adopted job safety standards, inspectors aren't authorized to enforce safety rules on the job site. An inspector I know once wrote a project up for frayed electrical wiring on a portable circular saw. I admire the zeal of that inspector. But it's not part of an inspector's job. Offering friendly advice is one thing. Code enforcement is something entirely different. One sure way to know the difference is to locate the code section for every violation you cite. If you don't have a law to back you up, you don't write the citation.

Finding an Inspection Address

Building inspectors are among the first to visit most job sites, usually right after the start of excavation. In some cases, the only access to a job site will be over an unpaved road or rough trail. Outside of developed urban areas, there may be no street, no street sign and no street address.

Worse, the street may not even be listed on current maps. It's a waste of valuable time if the inspector has to search to find the site.

A word to the wise for contractors: Help the inspector arrive when scheduled and with as few wrong turns as possible. If the site is remote, mark a scrap sheet of plywood with arrows that show the way. At the access point to the construction site, identify the site address with a sign. A little common courtesy will be appreciated.

I recommend that inspectors not leave the office until they're sure of directions. The person who logs each inspection request should identify the nearest major cross streets and note directions from that intersection to the site. If there are direction signs to the site, that fact should be recorded with the request for inspection.

What Makes a Good Inspector?

In the last chapter I identified characteristics of a good plans examiner. In this chapter, I'll do the same for field inspectors.

As in every profession, you'll meet great people who are a joy to work with and who really like their careers. It's easy to work with these people because they enjoy working with others.

You'll also encounter people with poor social skills. Some of these shouldn't be working with the public. There are misfits in every profession. Building inspection, as a profession, is no exception.

A good building inspector is able to work well with all kinds of people and enjoys being helpful, even when under time pressure. The best building inspectors are detail-oriented and persistent without being abrasive. There's no advantage in getting emotionally involved in any dispute. An angry inspector brings out the worst in others. The less drama and intrigue, the more effective an inspector is likely to be.

I value an inspector who's always willing to listen, study and grow. Show respect to those you work with. As a public servant, you can't allow personal feelings to influence your decisions. You're obligated to inspect accurately and make unbiased judgments.

I feel that contractors have the right to know the "why" of any unfavorable inspection decisions. When you explain violations to a builder, be sensitive and open-minded. The last thing you want is to be caught demanding something that isn't required. An inspector who is too picky and quick to find fault is encouraging reciprocal behavior from contractors.

You may recall a statement I made in the last chapter: Plans examiners are more born than made. I don't believe the same is true for field inspectors. Building inspection is an equal opportunity job. Nearly anyone willing to invest the time required to develop the requisite skills (including social skills) can become an effective building inspector.

As with most code-enforcement positions, knowledge of the building code is essential. The second half of this book will cover the building code in detail. But what other skills belong in an inspector's portfolio?

I recommend joining a local group or chapter organized for people interested in code compliance and development. You'll benefit from the opportunity to discuss compliance with others in your field. You'll gain insights unlikely to be found in this manual — or anywhere else, for that matter. Develop a network of people in positions similar to the position you hold. Using email, that's easy. Connect with code enforcement user groups on the Web. There are many. Enter the keywords *building code blog* in your search engine. You'll find both local and national user groups that focus on code compliance. Join a user group to make contributions or get responses from others.

Generalist or Specialist Inspector

A specialist inspector usually concentrates on one of four basic trades — structural, plumbing, mechanical, or electrical. Specialist inspectors are normally highly experienced in the particular trade they inspect. They're also generally certified in that category by the ICC.

Some other specialties are:

- abatement of dangerous buildings

- property maintenance and housing inspector
- accessibility inspector
- zoning inspector
- residential energy inspector
- one- and two-family dwelling inspector
- one- and two-family electrical inspector
- one- and two-family plumbing inspector
- one- and two-family mechanical inspector
- fire code inspector
- underground storage tank inspector

A general inspector has experience in all types of construction but will have less experience in structural, plumbing, mechanical, and electrical inspection than a specialist in one of these trades. Many general inspectors worked as project superintendents or general contractors before getting into code enforcement. Of course, a general inspector has authority to identify code violations in every area of construction, including structural, plumbing, mechanical, and electrical work.

Electrical work that includes 480/277 volt service or service over 2,000 amps serving heavy motor loads should be inspected by an electrical specialist. More examples: Inspection of a combination waste and vent system in a high rise building should be performed by a plumbing specialist. A tilt-up concrete wall that's 20 feet high with pick points at strategic locations should be inspected by a structural specialist.

A *general combination inspector* (different from the general inspector) is qualified to identify code violations in *every area* of construction. This saves the department and the builder both time and money. In a single visit, the combination inspector can review all parts of a construction project.

A Day in the Life of a Building Inspector

Let's run through a typical day for a general inspector. There are lessons to be learned here, for both prospective building inspectors and contractors.

Most inspectors start work early, often as early as 7 a.m. Inspectors usually gather at the building department office for a morning briefing and distribution of assignments.

When assignments have been passed out, each inspector will develop a preliminary route plan and schedule for the day. The goal is to complete all assigned inspections before the end of the day. The chief inspector will normally review the work assignments and approve the list of inspections for each inspector. If any inspector has more work than can be completed in a day, the chief inspector may transfer an assignment to an inspector with a lighter load. Most inspection groups find ways to balance the workload among available personnel.

Once you have the route planned and an approximate schedule, call each builder to suggest the approximate arrival time. If detailed directions to the site aren't available, ask for directions. Also, ask where project plans and the permit record card are kept on site.

Making the Rounds

Start with the closest project, typically within 10 miles. The first stop is a stucco lath inspection. Look for proper installation of exterior wall substrate, insulation foam board, and stucco lath nailing to framing members. Compare the manufacturer's installation standards with actual installation practice. If installation is complete and in compliance with applicable standards, pick up the installation certificate and note approval of work on the permit record card.

The next stop is five miles away. The site is fenced and the gates are closed but unlocked. Be sure to close both gates after entering the site. Meet the project supervisor on the way in. The project is a remodel of a 100-year-old ranch house. Check the bond beam steel on top of the rammed earth wall. The plans show the size, spacing, and placement of the required steel. Check that everything is in place. Then note approval on the permit record card.

The next four inspection sites are all in the same subdivision. Inspect a foundation on the first house, groundwork and plumbing on the second, a roof sheathing connection on the third,

and perform the final inspection on the fourth. You've seen plans for these homes several times. The same plans have been used by the developer throughout the subdivision. But just to be thorough, check the plans and permit paperwork on every house. Three of the houses pass inspection, including the one final inspection. You call in approval of the final inspection so utility companies can start service. That helps the developer transfer title a day sooner.

In the second of the four houses, the pressure test for the groundwork plumbing system shows an almost-complete loss of pressure. There must be a leak somewhere. Note on the permit record card that the plumbing pressure test failed. On the inspection failure ticket, cite the code section violated. Then mention the problem to the project superintendent.

An Intermediate Inspection

After a lunch break, check five more houses in another subdivision in the same neighborhood. Two are roof decking inspections and two are stucco lath inspections. The fifth is an intermediate inspection. As it turns out, the roof decking isn't ready for inspection. The framer didn't show up for work today to finish nailing the deck. So both roof jobs fail inspection. The stucco lath inspections are OK. The installer's card is complete and signed for your review. You sign off on these two inspections.

The last inspection, the intermediate, is four separate inspections rolled into one: structural framing and the rough-in for plumbing, mechanical, and electrical. This inspection takes considerably longer than the others — about an hour. Several items were overlooked by the mechanical and electrical subcontractors — six discrepancies in all. Fill out a request for a follow-up inspection and list the six corrections.

Leave the corrections list with the superintendent. The superintendent is upset, of course. These corrections will cost money and add another day's work to the job. He has to contact each subcontractor and schedule repairs.

Your next stop will be to check installation of temporary electrical service for a new single-family home. Check the equipment, grounding, bonding, and general safety of the electrical pedestal. It meets all safety requirements. So approve the work and call in clearance to your office to expedite utility connection.

The next inspection item is a footing for a 12-foot-high retaining wall. The wall was designed by a registered engineer and approved by the plans examiner in your office. The plan detail shows width and depth of the footing and the grade, size and placement of reinforcing steel. Measure carefully when checking rebar spacing. Steel placement is critical in retaining walls. In this case, spacing is within tolerance. Approve the work.

The last stop of the day is four more residences in another subdivision. Three of these are new homes. The fourth is a home improvement project. The three new residences are a mixed bag — checking stucco lath, trench depth for a yard water supply line, and drywall installation. The home improvement project is adding a third garage to the two on the existing home. Only carpentry and electrical work need inspection. So it takes just a few minutes.

Back at the Office

You're back at the office by 4 p.m. to turn in paperwork on the day's inspections and check any messages that came in during the day. The chief inspector asks about the intermediate inspection you did after lunch. The project superintendent called the office to complain. You explain to the chief inspector why the job failed inspection. Together, you discuss each of the six items on the follow-up inspection request. You agree that one of the discrepancies cited could probably have been approved.

You and the chief inspector agree to visit the site early the next day to meet with the superintendent.

That brings me to the final point in this chapter. Building inspectors have a lot of authority. In most communities, the building official grants to building inspectors the status of law enforcement officers, like a policeman. *IRC* Section R103.3 says:

> *"In accordance with the prescribed procedures of this jurisdiction and with the concurrence of the appointing authority, the building official shall have the authority to appoint a deputy building official, the related technical officers, inspectors, plan examiners and other employees. Such employees shall have powers as delegated by the building official."*

Like nearly all law enforcement officers, every decision you make is subject to challenge. That's the way it should be. It's also a good reason to avoid overzealous application of the code. Be too quick to reject work and you're going to be challenged occasionally. There's always a chance your supervisor will side with the builder. When that happens, don't take it personally. Everyone makes mistakes. Humility is a virtue among building inspectors. Work *with* the builder. Discuss your concerns openly. Take the view that every discrepancy is both your problem and the contractor's problem. Working together, *both* of you can resolve the issue. Then, if you're overruled, both you and the builder can share in the relief.

When your decision is overruled, accept the change with grace. Think of it as a favor. Your supervisor is helping you understand an interpretation of the code accepted in your jurisdiction. You learned something, and will be a more skilled inspector tomorrow than you were today.

THE FACE OF
THE BUILDING DEPARTMENT

C H A P T E R 6

Building Permit Technicians

Back in Chapter 3 I promised more information on the first person you're likely to see when walking through the door at the building department office: the building permit technician. You can think of a permit technician as the "face" on most building departments. Permit technicians interact with the public more than anyone else in the office — giving advice, making recommendations, and referring questions to appropriate staff members. I'll use this chapter to explain a permit technician's role in the building department.

Rely on a permit technician to help when you have an issue with code compliance, easements, zoning, setbacks, obstructing rights of way, special inspections or appeals. There's no one at your local building department office more willing to help when you need guidance on issues like these. Maybe best of all, the advice you get from a permit technician will be both authoritative and free.

If you've got a question on any of the topics covered in this chapter, I recommend talking with a permit technician. The most experienced, most professional contractors I know are on a first-name basis with at least one permit technician at their local building department office. By the time you finish this chapter, I expect you'll understand why you should too.

Your Permit

But before getting into the role of permit technicians, I need to explain something that's obvious to everyone working in code enforcement — but that may not be so obvious to construction contractors: Do you really need a building permit?

Most contractors and more than a few property owners have been tempted to do work without a permit. After all, there was a time within memory of many active contractors when building permits weren't necessary for small jobs, especially small residential jobs. That's not true any longer, as *IRC* Section R105.1 makes it clear:

"Any owner or authorized agent who intends to construct, enlarge, alter, repair, move, demolish or change the occupancy of a building or structure, or to erect, install, enlarge, alter, repair, remove, convert or replace any electrical, gas, mechanical or plumbing system, the installation of which is regulated by this code, or to cause any such work to be done, shall first make application to the building official and obtain the required permit."

That means nearly any task a contractor is likely to do for a homeowner requires a building permit — with only the exceptions described in *IRC* Section R105.2:

*"**Work exempt from permit.** Permits shall not be required for the following. Exemption from permit requirements of this code shall not be deemed to grant authorization for any work to be done in any manner in violation of the provisions of this code or any other laws or ordinances of this jurisdiction.*

Building:

1. *One-story detached accessory structures used as tool and storage sheds, playhouses and similar uses, provided the floor area does not exceed 200 square feet (18.58 m2).*

2. *Fences not over 6 feet (1829 mm) high.*

3. *Retaining walls that are not over 4 feet (1219 mm) in height measured from the bottom of the footing to the top of the wall, unless supporting a surcharge.*

4. *Water tanks supported directly upon grade if the capacity does not exceed 5,000 gallons (18,927 L) and the ratio of height to diameter or width does not exceed 2 to 1.*

5. *Sidewalks and driveways.*

6. *Painting, papering, tiling, carpeting, cabinets, counter tops and similar finish work.*

7. *Prefabricated swimming pools that are less than 24 inches (610 mm) deep.*

8. *Swings and other playground equipment.*

9. *Window awnings supported by an exterior wall which do not project more than 54 inches (1372 mm) from the exterior wall and do not require additional support.*

10. *Decks not exceeding 200 square feet (18.58 m2) in area, that are not more than 30 inches (762 mm) above grade at any point, are not attached to a dwelling and do not serve the exit door required by Section R311.4."*

Minor electrical repairs and installation of portable electric and gas appliances are also exempt under *IRC* Section R105.2. Clearly not exempt: jobs such as replacing a water heater or garbage disposer that is hard wired to the electric source.

Notice that there's no exemption for work by homeowners. If the work requires a permit, it makes no difference whether work is done by a licensed professional or by an owner or by an unlicensed tradesman. A permit is required.

If you've worked in construction for a while, you've probably heard stories about work being done without a permit. You may even have heard contractors boast about not pulling a permit for some specific job. I don't recommend that for several reasons.

First, where contractors are licensed, a contractor working without a permit risks discipline by the state board — maybe even revocation of a license. If an owner insists that no permit is necessary, or makes award of the job contingent on your pledge not to file for a permit, I recommend walking the other way. The same is true of any code compliance issue. Don't do any work that you know to be a violation of the code, even under pressure from a homeowner. The risk isn't worth the reward.

Second, starting work without a permit will usually double the permit fee if your job is discovered before completion. That's *IRC* Section R108.6. And building departments have very clever ways of discovering work in progress without the benefit of a permit. Many building material dealers and lumber yards cooperate with building departments by reporting delivery of substantial quantities of building materials to existing residences. Even if your delivery isn't reported, a pile of building materials or a dumpster on the front driveway of an existing residence will attract the attention of every building inspector and every city official who passes by.

Third, a home remodeled or improved without a permit is a lemon. No lender will be eager to lend on residential real estate that doesn't comply with the code. Appraisers usually have instructions to disregard the value of any improvement done without a building permit. Savvy buyers will check with the building department before investing in a building that's obviously been remodeled and improved. If no permit is on file, or if no final inspection is recorded, expect potential buyers to look elsewhere.

Many states now require a transfer disclosure statement when a home is sold. In California, this is Civil Code section 1102.6. Home sellers have to reveal to potential buyers any work that was done without a building permit. No one wants to buy a headache. If the home is remodeled later under a permit, the inspector is likely to spot bootleg work done earlier and demand an upgrade to old work before signing off on the current job. Getting an inspector to sign off on work completed years earlier may require opening up wall cavities long closed with finish materials. Even if building codes aren't strictly enforced in your community today, that's not going to last forever.

If you're convinced of the importance of applying for a building permit, it's time to meet the permit technician at your local building department office.

Role of the Permit Technician

First, I'll offer an admission. Permit technicians are on the bottom rung of the code enforcement career ladder. But that doesn't means you can ignore most what you hear explained by a permit technician. In fact, it may mean exactly the opposite. The permit technician is the department staff member most likely to appreciate your side of many issues. And for good reason. A permit technician was probably on your side of the counter not too many months or years ago.

To understand the role of a permit technician, have a look at the sidebar. This is similar to a *Help Wanted* advertisement that ran not too long ago in my home state of Virginia. The ad in the sidebar defines pretty well the responsibilities of a permit technician.

Customer Service

As I said, the permit technician is the "face" of the building department. A good permit technician is a salesman for the department — explaining, when

---

Job Title: ***Permit Technician***
Location: *Any County, VA*
Yearly Salary: *$32,669 to $39,861*
Contact Info: *Human Resources Dept.*
Any County, VA
123 Main Street
Any City, VA

Job Description:

Any County, VA is seeking a self-starter to join our progressive team in the Building Codes Department. The successful applicant will use computer permit tracking software to process building permit applications, and will issue certificates of occupancy, process contractor license information, perform cursory plan review for completeness, and organize and maintain property files for active construction permits. Must demonstrate respect and courtesy while assisting applicants, customers, and the public with building permit applications, general information, permit procedures, and various building permit request issues. Will network with engineers, architects, contractors, builders, developers and owners/builders daily. Experience in an office environment, effective verbal and written communication skills, and familiarity with word processing and database software are essential.

necessary, the "how" and "why" of working with the code enforcement staff. The permit technician is also a problem solver and will be the best point of contact for a builder with a code compliance issue.

Call any building department office and you'll probably connect with a permit technician. Permit technicians routinely deal with applicants by phone. Many permit technicians are hired for their verbal skills. A good permit technician will listen without interrupting and show exceptional patience. My advice to permit technicians is to let the builder explain the problem. Get the facts: who, what, when, where, why, how, and how much? Here are some specific questions to ask:

- Do you have a permit? If so, what is the number of the permit? Is it in this jurisdiction?

- Have you already talked with anyone about this problem? If so, what were the results of the discussion?

- Exactly what are you trying to achieve? What would you like our department to do for you?

If you need help with a problem or a request, don't just transfer the call to another extension in hopes that someone will be available. Transfers to voice mail leave a poor impression. Instead, get the facts and tell the builder the name and title of the person who can help. Then put the caller on hold. Talk to that staff person. Quickly sum up the problem. Then ask that staff member to assist the caller. If you have time and won't be abandoning your post, listen to the staff member respond to the question. That way, you'll be better prepared the next time there's a similar question.

Terms and Vocabulary

Step into any building department and you'll hear both construction terms and the language of the code. That can be confusing. The code is a law, written more to be enforced than to be instructive. Part of a permit technician's role is to help others understand what the code means. The glossary at the back of this book is intended to serve as an introduction to the language of code enforcement. The building code itself defines many terms used in the code. Where a term isn't defined in the

code, *IRC* Section R201.4 recommends using the dictionary definition.

> *"Where terms are not defined through the methods authorized by this section, such terms shall have ordinarily accepted meanings such as the context implies."*

The Permit Technician as a Teacher

Part of the role of every permit technician is to help builders understand code requirements. Obviously, permit technicians need to know the code. But no one knows every code section. And it's unreasonable to expect any newly-hired permit technician to have an answer for every code question. But it's entirely reasonable to expect permit technicians to know where to look in the code for answers. If a permit technician can't answer a question to your satisfaction, ask for a referral to someone who *can*. That's entirely reasonable. Permit technicians should *never try to wing it*. It's better to admit that you can't answer a question than provide incorrect information.

Fee Calculation

Every permit technician has to quote building permit fees. This is one of the most common questions asked by builders. Permit fees aren't set by the code. Instead they're set by municipal government to cover the cost of administering the building department, processing permits and conducting inspections. These expenses include building rental, employment expenses (recruitment, salaries, benefits, taxes, insurance), utilities (electricity, gas, and telephone), vehicles, administrative costs, and legal services. Building permit fees usually scale up as the estimated value of the project increases.

Scheduling Inspections

Permit technicians usually schedule building inspections. Contractors phone in inspection requests as the work progresses. The permit technician will record the builder's name, the address to be inspected, the permit number, the type of inspection or inspections requested, and the time requested for the inspection. Be sure to get a telephone number from the caller in case there's a question the inspector must ask before visiting the site. Get directions or major cross streets for projects in remote areas.

Certificate of Occupancy

Permit technicians also review and approve applications for Certificates of Occupancy (C of O). A certificate of occupancy is normally required any time a new building is ready for occupancy. But a C of O will also be required when a new commercial activity is proposed for an existing building. For example, suppose a shoe retailer plans to lease space in an existing vacant commercial building. The retailer signs a contract to lease the space. Before he can open for business, he must have a C of O.

A C of O will be issued once an inspector has visited the site and verified that the building meets minimum requirements for the proposed occupancy. To get a C of O inspection, an applicant will have to answer a few questions about the intended use. The building department needs to figure out the occupancy classification. This classification will determine the specific requirements for that particular use. Most building code questions will have been resolved when the previous C of O was completed. But if there's a change of use, such as from office space to retail, the occupancy classification may have changed. The C of O review will identify any change in occupancy classification.

When occupancy changes, fire-resistive separation requirements may change. Also, the building's egress requirements may change. The occupant load for the new use may be over limit for the space available. Here's an extreme example: An applicant wants to convert a warehouse previously used for storing cement and sand into a day care center for mentally and physically handicapped children. Changes will include additional exit doors and better fire protection, such as fire-resistive construction and sprinklers. The permit technician will need information about neighboring buildings and a floor plan of the building being converted.

Special Inspection Certificates

In addition to the routine inspections that we'll cover in later chapters, the code may require special inspections. For example, high strength bolts on a metal building must be torqued to a specified measurement. A special inspector will verify this before those bolts are covered with exterior substrate or interior finish. Permit technicians review and process special inspection certificates when required by the code.

The design professional may also identify points at which a special inspection is required. In that case, a statement of special inspection will be prepared by the design professional before the plan can go into plan review. The statement will include a list of materials that require special inspection, the inspections needed and the names of individuals or firms qualified to make the inspection. The plans examiner will review this statement. When the department approves a request for a special inspection requested by a design professional, the department is accepting the credentials of the person or firm nominated to perform the inspection. The building permit will be issued noting the special inspection required.

The special inspector will perform the inspection when required and will provide documentation that the work was done in an acceptable manner. The contractor must fix any problems the inspector finds. Anything not corrected will be referred to both the design professional and the building official before that part of the job is approved. Field notes should be used to document job conditions during a special inspection. The special inspector will submit a final report to the building department verifying that work was done according to approved construction documents. A request and a final report can be a single sheet that serves both as a request for special inspection and the inspection report.

Checking Status for Permit Applications

Nearly all contractors and property owners will be eager to know when their permit will be issued. That's a legitimate question that permit technicians should be prepared to answer. By the time the job gets to the building department, both the owner and the contractor are likely to be fed up with delay in the zoning and land use departments. Plans for construction usually take longer to review than zoning or land use issues. Getting a construction permit can take a while — almost always longer than the applicant wants to wait. Fortunately, most building departments have good tracking software that makes it easy to document progress all along the way.

Most building departments set an estimated completion date for plan review when the plans are accepted. This date isn't arbitrary. It's based on staff level, work volume and other factors such as holidays, vacations and even training schedules. If an estimated target date is missed, get an explanation from the plans examiner.

Plans are usually processed in the order received. But not always. There may be circumstances that call for advancing a particular project ahead of others. For example, if plan review isn't completed by the forecast date, it's legitimate to request that the project be accelerated to the front of the line. Most departments will accept responsibility for missed deadlines and will respond appropriately. If you have a project with a missed deadline or if you have a good argument that the project is time-sensitive, make that argument to the permit technician. You're almost certain to get a sympathetic hearing and may even get positive results. Only a supervisor has authority to advance a particular permit request to the front of the line. In really egregious cases, remember that every building department has a formal complaint procedure.

Administrative Policy Statements

Most building departments issue policy statements intended to answer common questions about code enforcement. These statements often include both written explanations and drawings showing an approved installation method. Policy statements are usually circulated to all staff members, and should be available to the public.

For example, many building departments have policy statements on the minimum width, thickness, and depth of standard monolithic concrete slabs and footings. Another common policy statement covers basic submittal requirements for metal buildings. A third common policy statement

will cover requirements for special inspections. Every permit technician should make these policy statements available for review by the public, preferably on the department Web site.

Keep these policy statements current. Check handouts periodically for obsolete code references. In many building department offices, permit technicians draw responsibility for updating policy statements.

If you're a contractor, be sure you have access to the policy statements issued by building departments where you do business.

Plan Routing and Permit Processing

When an applicant submits plans for review, a permit technician will usually route the plan to the best-qualified plans examiner. Obviously, plans for a new plumbing system shouldn't land on the desk of an expert in electrical systems. But most routing questions won't be that easy. To be effective at routing plans, a permit technician needs to understand the various occupancy classifications and types of construction. And, obviously, you need to know who is best qualified in your department to perform each type of plan review.

Plan Review

Every set of plans needs a quick review before being passed to a plans examiner. This review is the responsibility of a plans technician. It isn't a building plan review in the formal sense. It's just an initial check for obvious errors. Are all the plan sheets present: structural framing, foundation, cross-sectional views, elevations, plumbing, mechanical, electrical, etc. Check the project application to be sure any previous submissions have been approved.

Comment Letters

A plans examiner who denies an initial request for a permit will usually write a comment letter identifying defects by code section. The permit technician draws responsibility for explaining these code citations. Work like this requires both knowledge and tact.

No permit technician can be expected to explain every part of every comment letter. But offering the best explanation possible will help ease the sting of rejection. Every builder is entitled to a sympathetic hearing and clarification on exactly what's needed to comply with the code. A good permit technician will both help the builder understand what's requested — in language the builder can understand — and explain *why* those provisions are important. Knowledge of the history of the code — how it was developed — will help. No contractor wants to put up a building that's a hazard to life and property. A builder who understands the *why* is less likely to question the *what*.

Plan Reading

Permit technicians have to be able to read plans and topographic maps to check slope setback, hillside ordinances and even flood plain elevations. For this work, you'll need some type of scaling device. Use an architectural scale to measure architectural features. Engineering scales are used for measuring terrain and land features.

Legal Aspects of the Job

Few permit technicians have a legal background. But permit technicians are routinely asked legal questions. For example, it's routine for permit technicians to be asked about permit application procedures, plan approval, inspections, design requirements, approved materials and methods of construction. Every answer will be considered an official interpretation. That's fine, assuming your answer is correct and well-founded in the code. But no building official is going to feel bound by a faulty interpretation rendered by a permit technician. If you don't know, don't pretend you do. Simply say that you don't have an answer and will try to respond by the end of the day — or whatever you consider a reasonable time. Of course, having correct answers on the tip of your tongue is best — and helps gain the respect of applicants. Just be sure you're correct.

Liability and Jurisdictional Exposure

What happens if you offer an opinion on a legal questions and it turns out that you were wrong? A building department is responsible for its negligence. But unless you were guilty of malice, you won't be held personally liable for misstatements. Still, your casual statements can put the department and the city or county on the losing end of an expensive lawsuit. That won't happen very often before changes are made.

Record Keeping

State and local laws require the building department to keep and maintain a record of actions. *IRC* Section R104.7 says:

> *"The* building official *shall keep official records of applications received, permits and certificates issued, fees collected, reports of inspections, and notices and orders issued. Such records shall be retained in the official records for the period required for the retention of public records."*

These records are legal documents and have to be handled carefully. Record management is commonly a part of a permit technician's job description. Understand the department's record-keeping policies. You'll be asked daily to check records for builders and staff. These files should be readily available. It's better if they're in cabinets in the office rather than in crates in the basement. Many building departments run out of storage space and have to commit plans and permit records to microfilm or digital storage. No matter the storage method, records have to be kept for the period set by state or local law.

Appeals to the Building Official

When a builder asks for a code modification, the permit technician will prepare the request. You'll record the date and time the request was received. If help is needed, assist the builder with wording of the request. Again, you'll need to follow guidance in the code. Enter applicable code sections on the appeal form. Help the applicant by finding the relevant code sections and entering that information on the appeal form.

Permit Extensions

If construction activity has been suspended for more than 180 days, the permit expires. However, any builder is entitled to submit a written request for a permit extension. Permit technicians usually process these requests. Be sure you date-stamp the request to record the day the request was made.

Abatement of Dangerous Buildings

If your department investigates dangerous buildings, the permit technician will be required to deal with abatement issues. The *International Property Maintenance Code (IPMC)* provides specific rules for abating a dangerous building. However, your department may follow different policies. In either case, you'll need to stay current on local policy and help the abatement inspector with administrative duties.

Alternate Materials and Methods

Unconventional construction presents special problems. Typically, an owner wants to build using a unique design he's seen in a magazine. *IRC* Section R104.9 says, in part:

> *"Materials, equipment and devices approved by the building official shall be constructed and installed in accordance with such approval."*

And *IRC* Section R104.11 says, in part:

> *"...An alternative material, design or method of construction shall be approved where the building official finds that the proposed design is satisfactory and complies with the intent of the provisions of this code, and that the material, method or work offered is, for the purpose intended, at least the equivalent of that prescribed in this code. ..."*

The department's building official has authority to approve alternative materials and methods.

But approval will set conditions for acceptance and inspection. The building official makes the final decision on these questions.

Zoning and Site Development Duties

Every permit technician needs to understand zoning and land use terms. Zoning has its own vocabulary. Some terms used in zoning have definitions entirely different from definitions used for similar terms in code compliance. The definition of *kitchen* is a good example. Zoning is intended to prevent single-family homes from being used by multiple families. For example, a single-family home in an area zoned for detached single-family homes shouldn't be converted to use as a duplex. So, for zoning purposes, a *kitchen* may be any room with major appliances and a double sink. Any home with two kitchens would qualify as a duplex and would be prohibited in an area zoned for single-family homes. A wet bar with a single sink wouldn't qualify as a kitchen and wouldn't violate the single-family zoning ordinance. For building code purposes, a kitchen sink can have either one or two compartments. The two different laws regulate different conditions.

Application Procedures

The site plan review process can be complicated. Permit technicians can help take the mystery out of the procedure. Make a quick review of the site plan to:

- check the structure location on the building site
- check the particular zoning classification for the parcel
- check allowable lot coverage for the zone
- check for any irregularities on the land that may require an engineered design

Alert the builder right away if any of these issues presents a problem. If, for example, the builder wants to put a duplex on a lot zoned for single-family residences, you'll need to explain the zoning appeal process.

Rights-of-Way

Permit technicians need a working knowledge of right-of-way issues. A right-of-way is a legal public access to some property. A public street is built on a right-of-way. Zoning codes usually define a right-of-way as (1) any street or alley or other parcel of land (2) open to the outside air (3) leading to a public street that's deeded, dedicated, or otherwise permanently appropriated for public use, and (4) with a clear width and height of not less than 10 feet. Any construction activity within a public way or right-of-way is regulated.

In some communities, the city or county owns rights-of-way. In other communities, the right-of-way is owned by the state. In still others, the federal government has control of the property. If you're a builder and need to obstruct a public right-of-way, get the counsel of a permit technician at your local building department.

Easements

An easement is the right to use land you don't own for some purpose. For example, a utility company may accept an easement to run power lines across private property. Without an easement, a public utility usually won't install power lines across private property. The significance of an easement is that access can't be obstructed by the owner. For example, you wouldn't want to pour a slab over an easement granted to a utility company. Easements are granted by the property owner and will be recorded at the county recorder's office.

Setbacks

Most communities require that buildings be set back from the street by a certain number of feet. For example, in residential zones, a 40- or 50-foot setback is common. Setbacks vary with the type of zone. The *IRC* also specifies setbacks. But zoning setbacks are usually greater than *IRC* setbacks. Don't make a mistake about setbacks. Double-check *everything*, including the address, the correct zoning and the proposed setback distance. A mistake on the setback requirements can affect the entire project.

Advice for a New Permit Technician

Everyone's your boss when you're new to a job. It may seem like everyone's asking you to do something. Every permit technician is required to support the department's professional staff. I recommend following your supervisor's direction in assisting other staff members. Staff members may be architects, engineers, or licensed contractors. Most will have worked in construction. If you're new to the construction field, ask questions. Become an attentive listener and eager learner.

When you deal with the public at the building department counter, give each customer your full attention. Listen carefully. Don't be distracted by other people or discussions nearby. Don't take phone calls while serving a customer. That's a sign of disrespect.

How's Your Attitude?

Some customers arrive at the building department with prejudices about bureaucratic waste and poor treatment from public agencies. Other customers are just the opposite. Every permit technician deals with both types of customer every day. Be quick to reassure an angry applicant before emotions get out of control. It's easy to develop good working relationships with most customers. But as a public servant, you have to work with *everyone*. Difficult customers aren't always right. But every applicant deserve respect, courtesy and fair treatment.

Look for ways to make a customer's experience easier. If a customer is frustrated, ask questions about the cause of the frustration. Ask "How can I help?" Find ways to turn antagonism and aggression into friendly cooperation. Collect success stories about dealing with hostile customers and share those stories with your supervisor.

How to Deal with Complaints

Everyone can tell a story about difficulty in dealing with a government agency: delay, confusing or conflicting requirements, inadequate staff assistance, poor attitude, etc. Don't give customers at your counter reason to develop hostility and resentment.

Let an angry customer explain the problem. Be generous with your time. Be positive. It's hard to stay angry at someone who's listening attentively. Don't be judgmental. Develop an understanding of the problem from the customer's perspective. Once you understand the complaint, you're more likely to find a solution that satisfies all concerned. Avoid pointing out weaknesses in any argument or point of view. Be patient. Don't interrupt.

Remember, you're the expert in the eyes of every customer at the building department. You're experienced in solving problems just like this. Ask the question, "How can we resolve this?" Listen to the answer. If a customer has some document that supports his side of the story, examine the document carefully. Then check your own records.

When a customer's finished explaining what the trouble is, summarize the problem as you understand it. This assures your customer that you've listened carefully, and understand. A second explanation isn't needed. Then work with the customer toward a solution. Find a single point of agreement and build on that. Try to keep discussions simple. Adopt a straightforward approach to the problem. Discuss any specific laws that apply. Suggest alternatives. If necessary, explain why you may not be able to do exactly what a customer wants.

Many irate customers have good reasons to be angry. Maybe someone in your department dropped the ball. Maybe a requirement specified by a staff member was incorrect. Maybe someone overlooked something in the plans or an application that's already been approved. Customers feel that mistakes made by the building department should be at the expense of the building department, not builders. Unfortunately, it doesn't always work that way. Sometimes all you can offer is an honest admission and apology. If you're wrong, apologize and take responsibility. Don't blame others. If someone else in the department made a mistake, you can't apologize for them. But you can apologize for the department as a whole.

In spite of your best efforts, occasionally a customer will reach the boiling point. My advice is to move that customer to a conference room or at least out of the reception area. This shows respect for the customer and saves embarrassing others. Some angry customers prefer to blow off steam in public just to draw an audience. If you remove that audience, the anger may subside. Avoid using threatening language or delivering non-verbal messages to any customer.

Try restating the demands made by an angry customer. The weakness in many arguments will be obvious when expressed by a code enforcement staff member. Use this tactic when you're sure the customer's demand is absurd. For example, "Okay, you'd like us to reinstate a permit that lapsed five years ago with no additional fees, right?" Restating the request in the customer's own words may make a customer recognize how silly the request sounds.

When used appropriately, humor can be disarming. But be careful. Humor that's off-color or sarcastic can aggravate the situation. Simple humor is best. Sometimes a good one-line joke or humorous remark can calm a customer and put the two of you on a friendly footing. It's always easier work in a friendly, casual environment. That's where you want to be.

Finally, I'll offer the same advice to permit technicians that I offered to contractors. Get to know your customers. The best, most professional permit technicians know several dozen contractors by first name. I recommend that you do the same.

BRIBES START OFF SMALL...
DON'T GET CAUGHT UP

C H A P T E R   7

Careers in Code Compliance

This chapter is a slight detour along the way to mastering the details of code compliance. I believe this chapter will be of particular interest to anyone with experience in construction but who is not yet settled into a career. I'm going to trace the career path of 11 people who ended up in code enforcement. Nearly all of these people found their career almost by accident. Most didn't set out to become a code enforcement official. But all found satisfying careers working with the building code.

I've asked each to distill what they've learned into a few paragraphs — advice they would give to someone in construction who's considering a career in code enforcement. You may see something of your own personal history in this chapter.

Career Change by Accident
— *Lynn Underwood, Virginia*

Here's a brief summary of my own career: I'm a native of New Mexico. As a young man, I built my own home and enjoyed doing it so much that I decided to become a licensed contractor. I studied the building code and educational material from the Construction Industries Division in New Mexico. I passed the New Mexico license exam without too much trouble. As a licensed general contractor, I built several homes and did hundreds of remodel and room addition projects.

For several years, I enjoyed real success as a builder. But in 1984, I was injured in a car accident. While recovering, I couldn't manage existing projects or compete for new work. I needed a different job — at least until I was fully recovered. One day I was in the County Engineer's office. One of the engineers I knew suggested that I apply for an opening as a building inspector. I passed a New Mexico code exam and was hired.

Having a degree in engineering, I felt right at home with engineering issues in the code. Before too long, I was promoted to building official, and supervised several inspectors. I reviewed plans and filled in when inspectors were overloaded. Then I saw a Help Wanted ad in *Building Standards* magazine for a plans examiner in Pima County, Arizona. Taking that job would have been a promotion for me. Pima County includes Tucson and most of southern Arizona. I got the job but faced a layoff within three years.

In 1989 I was hired by Clark County, Washington as a Plans Examiner II. While in Washington, I passed three more ICC certification exams: plans examiner, plumbing inspector and mechanical inspector. That qualified me to work as a combination inspector.

I didn't adapt very well to the rain in Washington and was eager to move into a leadership role. Eventually, I accepted a building safety manager position in a municipality in central Arizona. During this time, I learned a lot about the unwritten rules of building code enforcement — the *intent* of the code.

After a year, it was clear that the goals of that community — which was made up mostly of winter visitors with no tolerance for rules and regulations — were at cross purposes to mine. I moved back to Tucson and worked as a combination inspector. Later, I worked as an abatement inspector and then as senior plans examiner. I now serve as Building Official for the City of Norfolk, Virginia.

Over the last 27 years I've worked in six jurisdictions — all good positions and all in building code enforcement.

What I've Learned

The duties and obligations of every building inspector extend to the greater community. But your boss has to accept responsibility for every deci-

sion you make. Keep him or her informed of every problem that may require intervention. Listen carefully to directions. Then follow those directions.

As with just about any job that you plan to turn into a career, work longer than required. Come in early. Stay late. Don't abuse break periods. Be honest, moral, respectful, honorable and ethical in your actions. Support the boss's decisions. Don't gossip about the boss (however tempting it may be). During every conversation with others, imagine that your boss is sitting next to you. Office gossip travels, especially to the person who's the topic of that gossip. And the name of every person who repeats gossip travels just as fast and just as far.

Learn Something New Each Day

Always be open to learning something new. Don't pretend to be a master of the code or the profession. Relax and learn. It takes a lifetime to become a code expert. We're all learning every day.

Join Professional Associations

I recommend joining a code enforcement chapter in your community. Most members will be inspectors, plans examiners or building officials. Most chapters hold regular meetings to discuss the code, both formally and informally.

As a group, these chapters have an influence on code development — changes being considered by the voting membership. Network at chapter meetings. You'll learn about the problems and issues others have and how they handle those problems.

Get Certified

It's becoming more and more important to pass building code qualification exams. Many jurisdictions now require as a condition of employment that inspectors be certified. Even once certified, you'll have to take continuing education courses offered for inspectors and plans examiners. Many are offered by vocational and community colleges. Certification is also the key to increased responsibility and better pay.

Keep a Professional Distance from Clients

Don't let emotions or familiarity influence your judgment or lead to favoritism. This doesn't mean you can't be on a first name basis with contractors in your community. But it *does* mean you can't play favorites.

Just as a person who works at the Motor Vehicle Department wouldn't issue a license to a blind friend, you can't let friends get away with code violations. Remember, you're enforcing rules that benefit the public.

Don't become a target for special favors. Favors may be small at first — coffee, doughnuts, and so on. But favors tend to grow in value. Eventually you begin to feel you should reciprocate — by overlooking some minor code violation.

Don't get caught in this trap. True professionals don't ask for favors that could compromise your integrity. If a builder makes what seems to be an inappropriate request, think about your responsibilities as an inspector. Enforce the code fully and without partiality. You integrity is worth more than coffee and doughnuts.

Keep Asking Questions

— John H., Connecticut

I worked in construction to put myself through the University of Connecticut. My degree was in education and my first job was teaching industrial arts and auto mechanics at a high school in Rhode Island. I must have developed a good reputation as teacher, because out of the blue, I was offered the job of building official in Putnam, Connecticut.

Eventually, I transferred to the Connecticut State Health Department as a building and fire safety inspector of health care facilities. I was certified as a federal health facilities inspector.

In 1996 I left Connecticut winters for the City of Tucson to work as a Permit Specialist. My job was to review plans for single-family residences (SFR). I joined Pima County two years later as a

senior plans examiner. Three years after that, I was appointed building official for the City of Marana, a city of about 40,000 in the northern suburbs of Tucson. Here are some things I've learned over the years.

Don't be Afraid to Ask for Help

I remember the first time I looked at an electrical equipment cabinet with 480/277 service and 208/120 transformers throughout. The service was over 2,000 amps with big motor loads. I thought, *"How in the world do I inspect this?"*

> *"True professionals don't ask for favors that could compromise your integrity."*

Instead of trying to bluff my way through the inspection and making an absolute fool of myself, I asked the electrician to walk me through the installation process. He was glad I asked and was happy to show me his work. I asked questions, listened to the answers and asked more questions. Eventually I recognized what I was looking at. As a building official in a small city, I'm always learning. Very few inspectors outside of metropolitan areas feel qualified to inspect 480/277 volt cabinets. Many intentionally avoid those inspections. But even a non-specialist can accumulate enough knowledge to perform good technical inspections.

Keep Learning

I can't emphasize enough the importance of asking questions when you don't know or understand something. Read the code. Join an inspectors' organization like the ICC or the International Association of Electrical Inspectors (IAEI). Participate in regular meetings and discussion groups. Take study classes and attend seminars offered by building inspectors' organizations in your community. If classes aren't available at a local community college, enroll in an interactive course on the Web. Certification exams are administered in many parts of the country. Most of these are scored immediately so you can get the results before leaving the examination site. Before you know it, you'll have a reputation as the guy with the answers.

Beware of Political Solutions

Everyone working in code enforcement is responsible to an elected official. Politics can be a minefield for any building inspector. Politicians are experts at doing favors for their political supporters. Beware when an elected official asks for a "favor" or rather "cooperation." Maybe a buddy of his who helped him get elected is having trouble getting a C of O for a building he owns. Maybe the building doesn't quite meet code without expensive alterations.

"If you're not willing to invest a lot of your own time in training, you probably won't go far as an inspector."

You're employed by the city. Your friend the politician can influence who stays on the payroll and who gets promoted. All the politician wants is some "flexibility" to make the problem go away. You know exactly what that means. It means you're in a tough spot.

What do you do?

Remember that you work for the public, not for the elected official. Explain that the code was adopted by the city. Your authority extends only to enforcing that code. You don't have the authority to change it. Anyone who wants a waiver has the option of going through the proper channels. If the request is reasonable, expect a waiver will be granted. You'll even help process the application for a waiver. You're not being uncooperative; you're being helpful! That's your job.

Once established that you can't be corrupted, you probably won't get asked any more. And that's exactly the way it should be.

The first position you take may not be a perfect fit. Don't assume every job will be the same.

They're not. Try another community and another organization. Don't give up. Quality, dedicated people are always in demand.

Don't Expect a Pat on the Back

Code enforcement can be a thankless job. Do you thank the police officer for writing you a speeding ticket, even though slowing you down might save your life? Probably not. Building inspectors have similar responsibilities and rewards. Never expect a pat on the back, even when what you do promotes public safety and well-being. You won't be loved by everyone.

Starting as an Intern
— Terry V., California

I applied for a job as a building inspector right out of college. At that time, the competition for jobs was fierce. The market was flooded with experienced inspectors looking for work. I applied at many cities and towns and got no offers. Eventually, I gave up asking for a job and simply asked for a chance to work as an intern for no pay, just to get job experience.

Hesperia, California took me up on my offer. They let me spend time in the office with the staff and in the field with building inspectors. I spent about three months with them and gained a tremendous amount of experience: working at the counter, answering the phone, watching building inspections, attending staff meetings. I developed an appreciation of the inner workings and problems of a building department. With those three months of experience, specialized training, persistence, and a strong construction background, I was hired as a building inspector in Burlingame, California.

While working in Burlingame, I continued improving my skills and learning the code. I attended night school at the local community college, two semesters a year for two years, taking code classes. I went to every educational seminar offered by my employer. If you're not willing to invest a lot of your own time in training, you probably won't go far as an inspector. Certainly, you have to qualify yourself even before applying for the job. I got where I am by committing a lot of my personal time to training and study.

I became active in the local ICC chapter. I attended monthly plumbing code, mechanical code and electrical code lunch meetings with other building officials. Only a few building inspectors attended these meetings. And not many took evening classes. Those who did advanced much faster in their careers.

Learn all you can about the codes. I found a specialized school that taught the building, mechanical, plumbing and electrical codes. Students visited job sites once a week to learn how to make inspections.

I continue to be very active in local, state, and national ICC activities and donate a lot of my time to code development committee work.

What I like best about code enforcement: There's always something new to learn. Every day brings a unique challenge — new technology, new construction method, or new code section. There's never a dull moment. I always face new challenges.

If you like working with people, this is the best job you could ask for. When most people think of public safety, they think of police and firemen. But code enforcement people have a similar impact on public safety. Everyone wants to trust that the buildings where they live and work are safe. Code enforcement makes that possible.

Starting as a Secretary

— Barbara Piller

It's hard to remember when I first considered a career in code enforcement. Like most of us, I never realized the profession existed. I assumed all contractors were licensed and knew what they were supposed to do.

After serving in the army at Fort Huachuca, Arizona, I got a job with the City of Sierra Vista as a secretary in the Building Inspections Department. That job opened up a whole new world for me. I'd always loved building things as a child. Getting into a profession where I'd be dealing with con-

struction methods and materials was a natural. When a position opened for an inspector, I applied and was hired. I've never regretted that decision.

Was I ever green when I started out! But I studied the code, talked with contractors, and discussed code with my peers in the office. I used the ICC certification exams to measure my knowledge of the code. It wasn't long before I could talk intelligently about the code with contractors, architects, and engineers.

After I'd worked seven years as a combination building inspector, the building official retired. He told me I was ready to step into his shoes. And I did. As building official, I discovered an entirely new set of issues — employee supervision, contractor complaints, and politics.

I truly love my job — most of the time — and look forward to the variety that each day brings. The job is challenging. Every project comes with something new to learn. A career in public service is very rewarding; I love the cantankerous fellow who walks up to the counter assuming I know nothing and then leaves City Hall delighted with all my assistance. I chalk him up as another success story.

Passing Exams Doesn't Make You a Super Inspector

Even after 20 years, every day brings something new. Contractors and inspectors keep discovering code issues I haven't faced before. I try to listen carefully to everyone's story. But don't always take the code interpretations and advice of others at face value. Check it out for yourself. Use all your available resources — codes, handbooks, evaluation reports, the Internet, and even a respected inspector or building official. Make sure the information you're given is correct.

And pursue the ICC certifications. They say a lot about you:

1. Passing an exam tells your supervisor and peers that you're qualified to make good decisions about code enforcement.

2. Certification will give you confidence to stand up to a contractor who's belligerent and won't agree with you.

3. On your resume, certifications give you the edge over other applicants.

Choose Your Battles Wisely

Think every dispute through carefully. Brainstorm with your supervisor. Understand how issues will play out politically. Then make your decision. Remember, sometimes you must lose a battle to win a war.

Follow the Golden Rule

Treating people as you'd like to be treated wins them over. Be fair, honest, and professional. Remember, the minute you begin to believe you have dictatorial power is the minute you start making your life (and your supervisor's) difficult. That feeling of power breeds arrogance. None of us needs that.

One last thought: You'll deal with many "old-timers" who learned the trade when the code was a slim little pamphlet that fit nicely in your pocket or purse. Be especially respectful here. These old-timers may not know the code as well as you do, but they almost certainly know twice as much about construction. Help them understand the code and you'll tap into a lifetime of construction savvy.

The Best Job You'll Ever Have
— Lincoln T., Chief Inspector

I started building when I was a teenager, helping the contractor who built my family home. In high school my favorite subjects were woodworking, welding, metalworking and electronics. Out of high school, I worked for a couple of pre-cast concrete companies. Then I started working as a framer.

A couple of years later, I got a general contracting license and started a business with two partners. We built custom homes and remodeled existing homes. Later, I sold my interest in that business and, for the next 20 years, worked with my brother, building houses.

Around age 40, I started to get a little burned out with construction. Building is a young man's game, at least the way I was doing it. My love for walking on the narrow edge of a 2 x 12 was begin-

ning to fade. It took me a little longer each day to limber up and simply stand when I got out of bed in the morning.

It seemed to me at the time that working as a building inspector might be a good alternative. Building inspectors are still part of the construction industry. I had absorbed a lot of code knowledge in my 20-plus years working on job-sites. Inspectors work on salary and draw benefits. I could enjoy a week off and still get paid while I was relaxing on the beach in Mexico. That part still tickles me!

Now that I'm a chief inspector for the county, I'm still surprised at the rewards in this job. When I hire and train new inspectors, I tell them this is the best job they'll ever have.

At my first interview for an inspector's job, I was given a written exam to test my knowledge of the building code. I had followed the code many times — but usually to check a rafter span table. Like most people in the trades, what I knew about the building code came from rejection notices written by an inspector.

When results of the exam were released, I was surprised to learn that I had tied with one other applicant for the highest score. Turns out, you really *can* learn a lot from those rejection notices! However, since there was a tie, the job would go to the applicant with the best interview. My competition helped me a lot by showing up for the interview in casual attire — very casual. I still have the note my boss made while he interviewed me. He scribbled a remark about my appearance: "Appears well-qualified ... wears socks." I learned to take interviews seriously and dress nicely.

The ICC offers certification exams in each category of construction. Having these certifications is like having a graduate degree. In the interview process, it gives you a huge advantage over those who don't have the certificates. Passing at least one certification exam during the first year of your employment is usually a condition of keeping your job. So it's better to take the exam as soon as possible — even before you apply.

You can get information about these tests from the ICC or at almost any building department. Your toolbox as an inspector will be filled with codes, product catalogs, and evaluation reports —

not hammers, saws and levels. This job requires continuous study to keep up with the codes. They change all the time. Inspectors need to know about both code changes *and* the hundreds of new building products introduced each year.

Understanding the codes is a fundamental part of being an inspector. Applying the codes is another necessary part of the job. Not everyone gets both of those right — certainly not the first time.

You may think it's secondary. But I've learned that interacting with builders is a vital part of my job. Success as a code enforcement professional requires people skills. You need code compliance. But you have to get it without antagonizing builders. That requires constant effort and even more patience. Be as flexible as possible within the limits of the code. And be positive and helpful. Always take time to explain a specific code requirement. Open the book on a jobsite. Let the builder read the appropriate sections. Don't give the impression that you're improvising or are on an ego trip. Show the contractor what the code requires. You're just following the code.

Four Rules to Follow
— Larry R., Building Safety Director

I'm retired now. My last job in code enforcement was as a building safety director. In my opinion, a successful career in code enforcement is built on technical knowledge, managerial savvy, stellar customer service and good personal presentation. Here is my advice on each.

Technical Knowledge

Inspectors have to be at the top of their game. There's no margin for improvising. Keep improving your knowledge of the codes, construction materials and construction methods. Keep studying, attending seminars and asking questions. Review manufacturers' materials and ICC ES Reports. Understand the intent of the code. Keep a library of each year's proposed code changes. Review proposed code changes, the reasons for the change, staff analysis and challenges.

Managerial Savvy

Keep complete and clear records and observe proper office procedures. Understand the department's budget so you can make cost-effective recommendations to your supervisor. Learn the legal aspects of code enforcement.

Customer Service

Good communication skills begin with accurate listening. Be eager to assist the public. Both seasoned contractors and homeowners appreciate courtesy, a positive attitude and encouragement.

I feel every building inspector should treat every code violation as an honest mistake. That's true even though you know many violations are a deliberate disregard of the code to save time or money. When you find a code violation, don't embarrass the contractor, even if you're sure he was cheating. Remember, your task is to inspect installations and ensure code violations are corrected. You're not the contractor's disciplinarian. Think of your work as a positive member of the construction team, helping others get it right.

Appearance

A professional building inspector must dress for the part. The image an inspector presents will greatly influence how council members, contractors, supervisors, and the public view him. Be neat and clean. Dress appropriately for the type of work performed.

Barney Fife or Andy Taylor
— Steve B., Arizona

After completing a two-year Architectural Technology college course, I applied for, and got, a job as a residential plans examiner in a small suburban community. The building commissioner and his assistant helped me learn plan review. I also typed letters, scheduled inspections, answered phones and logged in plans.

A year later, the building commissioner left to become the building official in another, larger jurisdiction. He recommended me as his replacement. I took the job and responsibility for plan review, code enforcement and building maintenance. Fortunately, the town was small and just beginning to grow. I had time to learn on the job.

After 10 years, I accepted a job as a plans examiner with a county just outside Chicago. The job also included being senior inspector and assistant building official. After several years, the building official retired and I moved into that position.

> *"If you never admit that you're wrong, people will do their best to prove that you are."*

In 1995, I became chief building official in Goodyear, Arizona. I can honestly say that I've never had a day when I regretted my career choice. Here's the advice I can pass along.

Watch Out for the Barney Fife/ Andy Taylor Syndrome

If you ever watched the Andy Griffith Show, you know Sheriff Andy Taylor (played by Andy Griffith) and Barney Fife (played by Don Knotts). New inspectors start out as Barney Fife, following the exact letter of the code, presumably to impress people — or maybe just impressed with their own authority.

Unfortunately, this is exactly the wrong way to get results. Try to act more like Sheriff Andy Taylor, confident in your ability. You know what the code is trying to accomplish and the reasoning behind it. Try to figure out a way to *approve* the inspection rather than find a way to fail it.

Don't Quote the Code, but Know Where to Find an Answer

I think it's a mistake to quote the code from memory. Eventually you're going to misquote it.

Look up the section and read it. Read all of it. Don't guess. If you *do* guess, *my* guess is you'll be wrong.

Admit it When You're Wrong or Don't Know

If you never admit that you're wrong, people will do their best to prove that you are. And believe me, they'll succeed. Never paint yourself (or anyone else, for that matter) into a corner. Leave an escape route. Take your time. Research the question. Then make a decision. Quick decisions rarely pay off.

Politics are Part of the Game

If you don't want to play, find a different game. Assume that every person you meet is going to serve on the city council. There's nothing worse than making an enemy and then seeing his or her name on your local election ballot.

Keep Your Inspection Reputation Clean

The code industry is a small world. Give respect and you'll get it back.

Get Certified

When I started out in this business, it wasn't *what* but *who* you knew that counted. Now jurisdictions want professional code enforcement. My guess is they got tired of lawsuits over unqualified inspectors. Being certified doesn't make you an expert, but it shows incentive and provides a basis for your decisions.

Join Local Code Chapters and Committees

You'll learn a lot by meeting colleagues at local code organization. Every code official you meet is a potential resource when you have a problem. Collect phone numbers and email addresses of experts in nearby communities.

Always Carry a Clipboard

Few people will question someone with a clipboard! Besides, it will come in handy for any notes you may need to make.

No Prima Donnas Needed

— Chuck King

I have several bits of advice for anyone setting out to become the best building inspector possible.

Be Consistent

There are few things more frustrating to a general contractor, subcontractor, or homeowner than an inconsistent inspector. One day he calls it this way. The next day, well, who knows? That inspector fails some detail on one site and passes a similar detail on a different site the same day. This looks like favoritism, and sometimes it might be.

An inspector who doesn't know what to look for will be an inconsistent inspector. A good construction background is an asset for any inspector. It's easier to recognize problems that you've seen many times before.

Another reason for inconsistency is lack of time. An inspector who doesn't have the time necessary to do a quality inspection will miss violations at one location and catch the same problem at the next job. Even worse, the same inspector visiting a job a second time may catch a violation missed on the first visit. The result will be more aggravation and delay.

To be consistent, cultivate good inspection habits. When training new inspectors, I recommend following the same routine on every job. Whether I'm outside a residence getting ready to check the lath or inside checking the wiring, I always start at the same location and follow the same specific route and routine.

For example, when inspecting a residence, my first task is to find the approved plans and permit. Then I walk to the left corner of the garage, circle the residence to the right, ending up where I started. When I go inside, I follow the same routine, starting in the front left corner of the first room, circle to the right and end up in the place where the inspection began. With a routine that specific, it's very rare that I miss something. Repetition equals consistency. And that's important, no matter what you do.

Some inspectors I've trained have experimented with working at random, checking first whatever caught their eye. Without fail, they soon realized just how important consistency is in helping them do their job properly. It also demonstrates to builders just how meticulous and consistent you are. My advice is to be both methodical and thorough.

Keep an Open Mind and Be Ready to Learn

An inspector with a closed mind is usually an inspector with a know-it-all attitude. This type of attitude benefits no one and can earn the label *Prima Donna*. You can't learn while you're talking. If a tradesman is trying to explain something to you, listen.

A journeyman who has worked for years in a specific trade will know more about that trade than any inspector. Let the journeyman teach you. Building codes are built on the practical experience of proficient tradesmen.

An inspector who shows up at a jobsite with a professional attitude and confidence in what he's doing gets the respect of those whose work he inspects. Respect isn't given automatically. It's earned.

Be fair and consistent with people. They'll be more willing to work with you and will have a better appreciation of your role on the construction team. As enforcement officers, we police the building industry. If you're pulled over by a police officer who is friendly and respectful, you'll still feel pretty good when you're back on the road.

There's no reason why an inspector can't leave the people at a construction site feeling good, even if the work wasn't approved. The way you approach and treat people demonstrates whether your goal is to help or to hinder.

No Experience is a Bad Experience
— *Timothy W., Wichita*

In high school, I enjoyed building things out of wood. In woodshop I learned to respect the structure of wood and the tolerance of the material. I could have become a cabinetmaker or finish carpenter. But I wanted a job with normal working hours, steady employment and job security. Construction certainly didn't offer any of those. I found office positions even less appealing. Then my father suggested I look into the Building Inspection program at Butte Community College. It turned out to be just what I was looking for.

Following graduation, I started out as a zoning inspector in Wichita, Kansas. I went on to work as a building inspector, a combination building inspector, and a deputy building official. After passing the certification exam, I was promoted to building official.

I learned the value of training offered by local chapters of the ICC. I learned that networking with other building officials is absolutely essential. I enjoy the camaraderie. And I enjoy being an active member of the local ICC chapter. I feel good going home every night, knowing that buildings where people live and work are safer places. It's not easy work, but it's certainly rewarding.

Here's my advice for new inspectors:

No experience is a bad experience. Learn from every inspection. When a builder or citizen is upset, listen carefully. Learn what you can about the problem. I can't remember a day when I didn't learn something new.

Join your local ICC chapter. These chapters provide networking opportunities. Learn from people with many years of experience. Local chapters also offer educational opportunities and involvement in code development.

Take the time to make sure your answers are supported by the code or other government regulation. Learn where to find answers in the code. The more you know about the code, the more you'll need to refer to your code book. Codes keep changing to incorporate the best protection with the most flexibility.

Try not to give a flat-out "No." Suggest options. Help your builder figure out how to tailor a problem to fit the code, or how a small change in design could meet code requirements. Builders, developers and citizens are already intimidated by the Building Department. Do what you can to ease the tension. Provide assistance. Use your knowledge, experience and people-skills to get compliance without making demands.

Finally, remember who the boss is. It's easy to criticize some decision by a senior building official. But you may not understand or know all the circumstances leading to the decision. Many decisions I questioned as a rookie make better sense to me now. Learn from a situation. Listen to the advice of others. If you don't understand, ask. Once you learn why a decision was made, remember it. Learn from it. Support it.

Looking back, would I change anything? Not one thing.

A Profession to be Proud Of
— *Bob L., Carrying the Code*

Some people think building inspectors ride around in a department truck all day, spend hours in small talk with contractors and take unlimited breaks. It seems like an easy job. Anybody would love to do that! But that isn't the real world.

The truth is that many departments use vehicles that should have been scrapped long ago. Some conversations are anything but technical and can get downright unpleasant. And those "unlimited" breaks usually consist of eating lunch on the road between jobsites.

Inspectors like to believe they know every word in the code. They consider themselves diplomats in dealing with upset customers. They feel they complete 10 hours of inspections in less than eight hours. They wish they could complete all paper-work while waiting for the traffic light to turn green. But that isn't so, either. Inspectors aren't superhuman. They're normal human beings.

I've heard that some inspectors don't carry a code book in their vehicles. In my opinion, that's the worst mistake an inspector can make. There's no way anyone can remember all the fine points of the codes. When you recognize something at a project that's questionable, get an answer before writing a violation notice. Research the point in the book. Find exactly the section that covers the issue. Be able to show the on-site supervisor, in writing, what the code requires.

To make the best use of your time, organize your route of inspections. Arrange your paper-work in same order as the inspections.

Uniformity of code-interpretation is the ideal. But it's unrealistic to expect that every inspector will catch the same violations. Be confident that you're prepared for the work at hand. But listen and learn from both other inspectors and those with experience in the trades.

The code is written to be precise and is intended to be followed closely. But in the real world, everything isn't black or white. The code allows modifications in some circumstances and recog-nizes equivalency in others. Sometimes a building official participates in those alterations. At other times, an inspector will have responsibility for making the decision.

Studying the code before taking a certification test can be intimidating. It helps to break the code down into segments. Concentrate on each section and subsection one at a time. That makes the task more manageable. When studying, try to imagine the circumstances called out in the code. As you read, visualize what the components look like in a building under construction. The requirements make more sense when you have a picture in mind. No matter how successful you are at accu-mulating certifications, don't think the learning is done. In fact, it's never over.

Yes, the inspector's job can be tough. But it can also be the most rewarding job you'll ever have. As a construction worker in any of the trades, you usually work on one building at a time. At the end of the year, you can look at work completed and

feel satisfied that you've done so much good for so many people. As an inspector, you'll have the same feeling — and about many, many more buildings.

No, the pay isn't going to make you a Rockefeller. Yes, the stress level is high. No, the people you work with and the people you work for won't always appreciate what you do. Yes, the work is hard. But no one else does as much to make buildings safe. It's a rewarding profession — one to be proud of.

Be a Teacher ... Be a Joiner
— *Bill Dupler*

I'm the Building Official in Chesterfield County, Virginia. But I didn't grow up wanting to be a building official. I don't believe any kid ever has. My mother tells me as a child I wanted to be a garbage man so I could ride on the back of the garbage truck. As a teenager and a young adult, I joined the volunteer fire department and rode on the back of a truck. Our fire trucks were much cleaner than any garbage truck. But the work was just as dirty and tough.

In college, I planned to become an accoun-tant — *actuarial science* we called it. But I stayed active in the local volunteer fire department and remained interested in fire protection. I had been on site at a number of structure fires, taken several fire department training classes and was inter-ested in building construction from a fire service perspective. While still in college, I learned of an opportunity to earn a college degree in fire protec-tion — something that really interested me. As a fire-protection professional, I could wind up work-ing for a fire department, for an industrial firm, or as a fire protection system designer. I never con-sidered that my preparation and background were well-suited to a career as a building official.

Every building official has a *technical* job. Much of what we learn comes from books and studies. But a lot of what we know about code enforcement comes from others. As a building offi-cial, I never stop learning. When I think I know some code subject from top to bottom, I can be sure it's going to change, either because new products are available or because someone in authority wants to try something different.

To stay effective in code enforcement, take advantage of every learning opportunity available. If you truly have mastered a subject, share what you know with others. You'll be surprised at how much more you can learn simply by preparing to teach others.

Four points I want to make for anyone considering a career in code enforcement:

First, you have an important job. Your technical experience helps avoid mistakes that can put lives and property at risk. But be more than a brake on the wheel of progress. It's easy to say "No." Instead, find a way to say "Yes." Your job is to approve work, not to reject it. Say, "Yes, I can approve this if you'll change ..." That takes more creativity and a better understanding of the code. It also adds value. Everyone wins. Suggest multiple options, all of which result in code compliance. Let the contractor decide which solution is best. Then explain why the code requires something. Sell a builder on the reason it has to be done that way, something he hadn't considered. The code is quality construction. Every construction contractor wants to be known as a quality builder.

Second, accept the fact that the code doesn't have a solution for every construction detail. Use the intent of the code and your modification or equivalence authority when confronted with an unconventional situation.

Third, find a way to participate in code development. Learn firsthand why the code was approved with the current language. Team up with others who take an interest in the code. Study proposed code changes. Develop comments that you or a representative can present at a code development hearing.

Volunteer to serve on one of the many ICC code development committees. Beg, borrow or get a grant to attend and vote on the code changes at the final action hearings. Participate! Exercise control over the code you enforce. After all, once a code change is approved, both you and your department have to support and defend the change.

Fourth, be a joiner. Get involved in professional associations at the local, state and national level. Encourage associates to do the same. Find ways to help subordinates grow in their jobs the same way you're growing in your job. Contribute your skill and energy to code development. It's not only rewarding. It's a way to give back to your profession.

CHAPTER 8

A Job Description for Inspectors

Back in Chapter 4 I outlined what plans examiners do for a living. The following chapters, 9, 10 and 11, will do the same for building inspectors. But before we go there, I want to make the point that building inspectors do considerably more than inspect buildings and write up violations. In this chapter I'm going to cover tasks common to building inspectors — many you may never have considered.

Never a Dull Moment

One of the reasons I like my job is the variety. Every day brings new challenges — and usually a few surprises. In part, that's because every code enforcement official wears several hats. Each of these roles has a distinct set of rules. I'm going to cover six distinct functions of a building inspector that don't involve inspection of buildings:

1. A law enforcement professional serving your jurisdiction

2. A building safety expert for those who have questions

3. A teacher and advisor to those who are unfamiliar with building codes

4. A student, learning about codes from various sources

5. An expert witness in a legal setting, such as in court or mediation

6. A public servant

These roles may change several times during the course of a single day. And sometimes you'll wear more than one hat at a time.

Law Enforcement Professional

First and foremost, you're a law enforcement professional. The building safety codes you enforce are laws passed by the elected officials in your state and ratified by the elected political leadership in your community.

You have to understand, enforce and be ready to explain these laws. The code is a law written in legal language. So, you may have to think like a lawyer. Some rules are written in inverse form: Exceptions to a basic code requirement establish the minimum standard. Some terms have a legal meaning that's different from the usual meaning. You may need a law dictionary as part of your code library. When you see a word you can't define, research the meaning. That avoids misunderstandings.

As a law enforcement professional, you have an obligation to avoid personal bias. The law applies to your friends and relatives just as it applies to everyone else. Everyone has to comply with the law. You have the same obligation. Avoid showing favoritism. Don't succumb to the temptation to show how important you are by giving your buddies a break. The news will be out before the sun sets.

Building Safety Expert

You'll be regarded as an expert in every field of construction. You're the technical authority whose advice and recommendations are accepted when questions arise. You'll be asked questions about construction details that you may not know a lot about. Financial decisions will be based on your opinion. To maintain your authority, be accurate when rendering an opinion. Here are some rules to follow:

- Carefully think through each problem and code issue.

- Take time to research code provisions.

- Write everything down for clarity.

- Call others in the field for advice.

- Discuss each problem and its implications with everyone involved.

- Be sure your decision is fair.

- Avoid snap decisions. Give it your full consideration.

Advisor, Teacher, and Counselor

It's not your role to design a building. However, as your experience grows in a number of directions, you may find yourself giving guidance to builders. To them, you're an authority. They'll ask all kinds of questions. Many common safety issues are completely foreign to most construction contractors. The complexities of the bureaucratic process that you could recite with your eyes closed may have them stymied. Listen carefully to their questions. Give them your time. Be the best guide you can be.

Even veteran builders will need your counsel from time to time. Revisions in standards, changes in code requirements, new product application and use, and alternate methods of construction can perplex even the most experienced builder. You're on the cutting edge of code enforcement. Your knowledge and patience will set the tone for future interactions. Explain the reason for a code provision when your ruling is questioned. If a builder sees your point and trusts your judgment, you'll be more likely to get his cooperation.

When deviating from the strict letter of the code is still safe, consider accepting an alternate construction detail. If you haven't been given authority to accept that particular detail, get the opinion of your supervisor. *IRC* Section R104.11 gives the building official authority to accept alternative building materials or methods of construction.

Try to avoid becoming attached to any decision you make on a code violation. If your supervisor changes your ruling, think of it as an opportunity to improve your knowledge. Learn from the mistake.

Student

Every inspector has many teachers. Expect to learn something new about the code every day. Your supervisor will review your comment letters and inspection results for accuracy. You'll attend training seminars offered by model code organizations and state and regional code associations. From material suppliers you'll learn what constitutes an acceptable — or unacceptable — installation. You'll take courses and examinations that test your skill. And every day in the field, you'll learn from builders.

Builders, contractors, architects, and engineers aren't code experts. But they can read code sections as well as you can. Debates over the meaning of code sections are common. You'll refer to the code book every day. Don't feel challenged if a builder gets out his code book to question your decision. You don't know everything about the code. Pretending otherwise will serve as a challenge to builders to prove you wrong. Turn any dispute into a joint learning session. Both you and the builder, as a *team*, not as adversaries, are trying to figure out what the code requires. If you can't agree on the meaning of a particular code section, your supervisor will help make the decision. Learn the art of compromise by listening to your supervisor.

"Don't feel challenged if a builder gets out his code book to question your decision."

Builders have good memories and remember very well lessons learned from previous inspections. For example, a builder will remember all the details about a previous ruling that was appealed and overturned. Contractors don't forget a lesson like that. So what happens when you come on the scene and ask, once again, for the same change? This is a case when roles will be reversed. Your character will be assessed by the builder based on your response to his request. Accept this as a learning situation and move on. Compliment the builder for his code knowledge. Apologize for the inconvenience. Learn from your mistake. Don't make the mistake of becoming a sore loser.

It's common, in my experience, to see new inspectors bristle at any challenge to their authority. An experienced inspector who feels more secure about his authority won't take offense when challenged. Admit you're not sure. Don't feel obligated to demonstrate superior skill and knowledge to maintain authority. A contractor experienced in a particular field will see through this false bravado instantly. No one respects an inspector who's a faker.

As a new member of the building code enforcement community, you may be like a fish out of water when inspecting some types of construction. For instance, if your background is carpentry, and you have only a passing knowledge of electrical installations, you may be overwhelmed with the first 270/480 volt, three-phase service you're asked to inspect. The dilemma you'll face isn't new. But how does a novice inspector pass judgment on something he's never seen before? How do you, a greenhorn in this field, tell an experienced tradesman that something needs correction? Hopefully, you won't be put in such situations very often. But it's bound to happen occasionally.

When this happens, admit that you're not an expert at this type of work. Everyone is an expert at something and a novice at most everything else. Ask for help in understanding the installation. The installer has a wealth of information on the work completed. More often than not, he'll be happy to teach you something about his work. Ask questions, listen, write notes, and follow up by restating what you learned. Have the tradesman draw sketches and point out details of a proper installation. He'll be happy to show you mistakes others make and may point out common code violations. It's also a good idea to ask more than one installer for an opinion. A second opinion is verification that what you're learning is correct. An installer who's cut a corner probably won't educate you on how to spot such corner-cutting.

Testifying as a Witness in Court

Most building inspectors prefer to stay out of court. But nearly every experienced building inspector has been asked to testify, either in court or in an arbitration hearing. More than likely you'll be asked to serve as a witness in matters you've reviewed or inspected. Interrogation by opposing counsel in the presence of judge and jury can be exhausting work.

Prepare for the appearance by researching your involvement in the case thoroughly. Memorize the facts, dates and events (or have them available for reference). Bring to court all written records and documents available that can confirm your testimony. You'll be allowed to refer to these records when on the witness stand. Discuss your testimony with the legal representative from your jurisdiction — a city or county attorney. Expect to be asked the same question in a variety of ways by the attorney for each side.

Listen very carefully to each question. Don't respond right away. Think about the question for a few seconds. Then, if possible, answer yes or no. Try to avoid long, drawn-out answers unless it's absolutely necessary. If an attorney asks you for an opinion on something, avoid criticism of the work of others.

If you're asked for the facts, state only the facts, not opinions. For example, if an attorney asks you to describe the events leading up to your action that resulted in your denial of an inspection, think only about the things you did in your official capacity that led to the denial. Don't speculate. Here's an example:

1. Received an inspection request
2. Drove to the site
3. Found the approved plans and reviewed them
4. Began inspecting the building
5. Found numerous code violations
6. Recorded them specifically on the inspection request

Don't say anything that would indicate your prejudice for or against either party. Don't say something like "He's always trying to cut corners to save a buck." Showing bias or prejudice reduces your credibility. The attorneys are the advocates. You're in the courtroom to help others understand the facts. Be very cautious about your answers. Answer questions with facts that are clear in your mind. Don't fill in the blanks by embellishing your testimony. Of course, when called on, it's perfectly acceptable to express an opinion. But qualify that statement as your opinion based on what you know about the facts.

Public Servant

Working for a government jurisdiction makes you a public servant. The title comes with responsibilities you may not have consid-

ered when working in the private sector. If you used to be a carpenter and opened a cold beer on the job site at quitting time on Fridays, no one really cared. But as a public servant, you can't do that any more. Having a friendly chat with a construction crew at quitting time can be misinterpreted — or even exaggerated. The contractor whose job you just failed has reason to do some exaggerating. Your supervisor isn't going to be happy to hear those exaggerations.

"Showing bias or prejudice reduces your credibility. The attorneys are the advocates."

You represent your employer to everyone you meet, whether during or after work hours. Public opinion of your jurisdiction will be based, at least in part, on the impression you give as a private citizen. A good public official is honest, moral, respectful, friendly, hard working, cooperative, smart, considerate, and enthusiastic.

The Well-Equipped Office

A building inspector will have two offices — one indoors and one mobile. Plan review and administrative staff will generally be inside a building that serves as both a customer service center and an office to perform plan review functions. Building inspectors will generally gather at the office in the morning to get their assignments and meet with supervisors to discuss problems. When the meeting breaks up, inspectors will drive to various inspection sites. At the end of the day, inspectors will usually return to the office to turn in inspection results. Each of these functions requires specific office equipment.

Electronic and communication equipment is essential. Computer-based permit tracking software is used just about everywhere now. Word processing, using a boilerplate checklist, lets plans examiners compose comment letters very quickly. Most plans examiners have access to a digital library of building code reference materials, including standards, products listings, testing laboratory results and manufacturers' product information. Code interpretation manuals, illustrated commentaries, guide manuals and periodicals will help improve the accuracy of your inspections. Electronic calculators, clocks, and cellular phones are staples in every building department office.

A field inspector's outdoor office is usually a sedan or light truck. A cell phone is essential, and maybe a pager. You need to be available to answer questions or give your location. Take along at least the basic code books your jurisdiction enforces. Organize your inspection requests before beginning the route. Use a street map to plot your course. If not stored at a record center, keep all active permits in a file in the car. Other tools your outdoor office needs are:

- 25-foot-long tape measure
- screwdriver
- circuit polarity testing device
- level
- camera
- a ladder for climbing to roofs

- drinking water, if you inspect in remote areas
- extra pens
- bad weather gear
- a shovel (in case you get stuck in fresh dirt at a construction site)
- an extra spare tire — construction sites usually have plenty of nails

Be Prepared for Change

Codes change. Construction materials and methods change. An inspector's job is going to change. Don't try to resist these changes. You may see others on staff who can't handle change. When offices converted to the digital age, some engineers and inspectors were at a loss with the new technology. They found ways to take early retirement. Get comfortable with the new technology.

As one smart building code instructor told me, "Doing it wrong for 30 years is no reason to continue doing it wrong for another 30."

Code of Conduct for Inspectors

Most of this book — and most of the *IRC* — consists of rules builder have to follow. If you're a building inspector, these are the rules you enforce. But as a building inspector, you have to follow rules too. You need to observe both written and unwritten standards. I'm not talking about the building code. I assume you have good technical skill and a working familiarity with the building code. That's how you got the job. I'm talking about how you fit the role of code enforcement professional. That's the subject of this chapter — the rules inspectors have to follow. I'm going to define a standard of practice for building inspectors.

If you're a contractor, not a building inspector, is there any reason to breeze through this chapter? In a word, yes. I'm going to lay out a code for inspectors. This code doesn't have the same force and effect as the building code. But what I'm going to explain is a code, nonetheless. Contractors have to comply with the building code. I think good inspectors comply with the code of conduct outlined in this chapter. As a contractor, when you see an inspector violating any of the principles in this chapter, it's fair to point that out. I hope (but can't guarantee) that it will do some good. But everyone, contractors and inspectors alike, have a vested interest in improving professionalism among building inspectors. On that, we can all agree. And that's the focus of this chapter.

A Code of Conduct for Building Inspectors

First, understand that code enforcement requires teamwork. You're a member of a team. As with most teams, those who work with you truly want you to succeed. When asked, your supervisor will be eager to help. Your peers will also help. Listen to them carefully. If you don't understand something, don't be afraid to ask questions.

Second, understand that every code enforcement official makes mistakes. You can't possibly know every code section you'll be enforcing, especially in the beginning. The written code is complicated and can be ambiguous. When you deny an inspection, it's based on your interpretation of the code or building practice. If your supervisor points out you're wrong, accept it! How you react reflects on your professional character. Resolve not to make that particular mistake again. That's how to grow in this profession, and as a person.

Character Traits

Building inspectors are hired for their education, experience, motivation and skill. But to succeed, you need to show integrity, respect for others, and an ability to get along.

If you lack integrity or your integrity is compromised, you lose the ability to enforce the rules. When others see you're not willing to abide by the rules, they're not about to let you enforce the rules. One inspector with compromised integrity can damage the entire building code enforcement program throughout a community.

Good inspectors show respect for others. In the public's eyes, you're the government. If you're known for conflict with builders, the public will assume you lack respect and consideration. A lack of respect toward the public is long remembered. Other improper behavior may be forgiven and forgotten. But treat the public with disrespect and you earn the same disrespect. You definitely reap what you sow. Have respect for others and they'll show the same respect for you and your position.

Good communication skills are essential for code enforcement officers. That means you must learn the art of listening. Most people want to talk about themselves and their interests. So take the time to listen. Show interest. Others will *want to do* what you ask when they feel you're on their side. Try to avoid giving opinions or judging others. Judgments tend to create adversaries.

Explaining a Code Requirement

There are two ways to get code compliance: Coercion and leadership. Coercion relies on fear to enforce compliance. Leadership gets compliance voluntarily. You already know which of these I recommend.

When you take time to explain the purpose of a code provision, most builders will want to comply. A builder who always argues with the building inspector develops a reputation for being uncooperative. Most builders and contractors genuinely want to develop and keep a reputation for cooperation by complying with all the rules and laws. For you, it's much easier to lead others to a higher standard than it is to coerce obedience. If you rely only on coercion, you'll never get voluntary cooperation.

Explaining a code requirement, off the cuff, at any time, takes experience. So, if your jurisdiction allows it, mark reference notes in your code book. Start a loose-leaf binder with notes, reference material, drawings, sketches, and memos. Collect copies of articles from industry trade journals and building inspection periodicals. Use these notes and articles when you need to explain the "why" of the code. With the permission of the property owner, take pictures of unique construction problems that demonstrate either code compliance or code violation. Use these visual aids when you need to explain proper methods of installation.

Sometimes, even after you've explained a requirement, a builder may decide to take his case to a higher-up. You may have to explain to an elected official the reasons for a decision. It's the elected official's job to hear a builder's claim of unfair treatment. Your job is to explain the code requirements calmly and professionally. A lawyer would say that good facts win cases. It's your job to collect and document the facts to make a persuasive presentation.

Construction-Speak — Deciphering Terms

The building code has an entire chapter on definitions of commonly-used terms. Many construction books have glossaries that define terms. Articles in trade journals usually include definitions of the terms used. You'll learn a lot just noting the labels on building materials as you walk the aisles of a building materials store. Immerse yourself in sales brochures, do-it-yourself programs on television, radio talk shows on construction, and home and garden shows.

Some terms are unique to a particular region of the country. Be careful using terms you've never heard pronounced. Improper pronunciation or incorrect use of a construction term identifies you as a novice.

In the United States, many people speak English as a second language. I'm not going to recommend that building inspectors need to learn a second language to be effective. But I recommend that you learn the names of common construction materials in the second-most-common language spoken in your community. If that language is Spanish, I recommend the handy-sized translation dictionary, *Constructionary*, published by the *ICC* (International Code Council). It translates common construction terms from English to Spanish and Spanish to English.

Making Communication Easier

Frequently you'll have to work with clients who are confused about a code provision and its effect on them. They may not understand your jurisdiction's policies or actions. They may not be able to understand the problem and what they have to do. Helping them may be your task.

Put yourself in their shoes. If you had to get a building permit and you had no experience, how difficult would it be for you? Learn what it's like to seek a permit and pass inspections. Apply for a permit yourself and go through the inspection process. I guarantee this will help you understand why the public can be confused about the obligations of your office.

Another approach: Follow an applicant through the process. When the applicant calls for an inspection, go with the inspector to see what it's like from a builder's perspective. Think

about costs as if you were the property owner or contractor. How would you react to an inspector who says you're not complying with the code? Would you be outraged at the cost of what the inspector wants?

Some builders have trouble putting questions in a form that inspectors can understand. Until you understand the question, you can't offer an answer that makes sense. When that happens, ask a fill-in-the-blank question like, "You came to see me because ...?" Keep asking questions until you understand the problem. Then help the builder ask the right question. Your experience in similar situations will help bridge the gap to better understanding.

> *"Think about costs as if you were the property owner or contractor."*

Suppose you're in the office on the phone with a builder who's trying to tell you about a problem or situation. You're having trouble understanding what the builder is describing. That's normal. We don't all use the same words to describe the same things. Learn to hear with your experience as well as your ears. Try to visualize the problem without actually visiting the site. Close your eyes and imagine you're on their building site looking at the problem. Ask questions. Then work out an answer or solution based on acceptable practice and code requirements.

Answers to Tough Questions

The ICC has a toll-free phone number available to ICC members. You can get help from a qualified expert on a wide variety of code questions. The ICC website has extremely useful information, and a chat room where you can ask other professionals questions online. These are called *Communities of Interest*.

One important thing to remember about what you learn from others: The ultimate authority on the meaning of a code in your jurisdiction is the building official. The code gives the building official sole authority to interpret the code.

Liability for Your Actions

Being *liable* for an action means you're legally responsible. Being *culpable* for an action means you deserve blame. While you may be culpable for a mistake, you're legally protected from liability by *IRC* Section R104.8. It states, in part:

> *"The building official, member of the board of appeals or employee charged with the enforcement of this code, while acting for the jurisdiction in good faith and without malice in the discharge of the duties required by this code or other pertinent law or ordinance, shall not thereby be rendered liable personally and is hereby relieved from personal liability for any damage accruing to persons or property as a result of any act or by reason of an act or omission in the discharge of official duties."*

Your protection from liability ends if you're guilty of malice. Dictionary definitions of malice include the desire to harm others intentionally. If you deliberately intend to harm someone, you'll be liable for your actions. The jurisdiction won't be required to defend you in a legal action. You could be held personally liable for any harm you cause. In addition, you could be subject to a criminal penalty and lose your job.

"Your protection from liability ends if you're guilty of malice."

No one sees himself as malicious. Yet we all have the ability to act with malice. That's just human nature. Under a difficult circumstance, anyone can be malicious. It's hard to be even-handed with a builder who's always trying to cut corners or who challenges you on every point.

Suppose a builder gets belligerent every time you show up for an inspection. So you finally find a way to shut down his job as payback.

Who wouldn't be tempted to stretch the point a little? Payback is simply human nature. But it's also malice and something you need to avoid.

Common Customer Complaints

In any service-related profession, there will always be customer complaints. In a government agency enforcing building safety laws, there will be *many* complaints. Everyone has the right to complain about government. Some complaints will be about the building code. But the most common complaints will be about those who enforce the building code. People love to complain about someone they barely know who works in a government agency.

Let's look at some common complaints:

■ **"I've been doing this for 35 years and you're the first inspector to ask for this."**

Not every builder makes an effort to learn the code. Instead, they rely on past code enforcement to help them predict what will be required. So, if a certain code provision hasn't been aggressively enforced, some builders may interpret enforcement as a new requirement. Suppose, during a code seminar, you find out about a code requirement that's never been enforced in your community. Enforcing it on a builder who's never heard of it before can be a challenge. Expect to spend some time getting your point across — explaining the "why" of the code.

■ **"Why are you so overbearing?"**

A builder accustomed to working with one inspector or plans examiner may be confused when the inspector or examiner changes. An earlier inspector may have been too cozy with a builder, letting him get away with minor code infractions. If a new inspector insists on compliance to the letter, the builder will think the inspector is being unfair. If you're accused of this, take up the issue with your supervisor. There may be a policy that will help you solve the problem. Otherwise, convince the builder of the *reason* for the requirement. That should resolve the issue.

■ **"Why are you being so nit-picky?"**

This is another version of the previous question. New staff members are usually eager to catch every code violation. So they hunt through every nook and cranny to find one. Some *assume* there's a code violation and then set out to find it. The fact is, every construction project will have code violations if an inspector looks hard enough and long enough. Use your judgment. Be thorough yet considerate in your application of the code. Sure, the code establishes maximum center spacing on nails for roof decking. But do you really need to count every nail in an 1,800-square-foot roof to verify code compliance? Select a section at random and use that area as a test sample. Were there any nails left out in that section? If so, continue to look. If not, just check a few more sample areas and approve the inspection.

■ **"It's my property. Why can't I use it the way I want?"**

Every law and ordinance is enacted, we can assume, for a purpose. All law can be seen as an invasion of personal rights and liberties. As inspectors, we don't make the law. We simply enforce it. Elected officials write the laws, such as setbacks and zoning codes. Limits on usable portions of land exist, for example, because of proximity to a flood plain or an ascending or descending slope. Potential landslides or mudslides limit the use of some properties. Endangered species protection may limit construction, type of work and location of a proposed building. Scenic restrictions and view ordinances may limit the usable portion of a tract of land. To win

the point, explain the basis for a restriction. Most restrictions are easy to explain. For example, setbacks reduce the risk of flooding and collapse due to landslides or a fire spreading from one house to the next.

■ **"Why do I have to fix that when you let it go on the Smith job?"**

A builder who believes he's singled out for enforcement is going to charge you with favoritism. Any preferential treatment you give to one builder may have to be explained to other builders. If you accept an alternate method for one project, it's not logical to turn down another builder's request to use the same method. For example, suppose one builder made a mistake. The fix will be very time-consuming and expensive. So you decide to let that builder use an alternate method that more or less meets the intent of the code. Then, another builder comes along and knows all about the exception you made. This builder requests permission ahead of time to use the same alternative. You turn down the request. Now what? You've worked yourself into a box. There's no easy way out. Just be thankful you're not the building official, the person who has to resolve issues like these.

■ **"You never told me about this code violation the first time. It was fine then."**

Few things exasperate a builder more than a neverending list of requirements. Here's an example: As an inspector, you perform an inspection and write a list of code violations. The builder fixes those items and calls for another inspection. When you return to check those items, you discover some different code violations you missed the first time. You write up a new list for the builder, who wonders, rightfully so, if this will ever end. The solution is obvious, though not easy: Catch everything the first time.

Build a professional relationship with builders. Approach your job from the perspective of a referee. Call fouls when you see them, don't take sides, and stay calm.

When partners in the construction trade have a dispute, it's common to call in the inspector to settle the issue. As you arrive on the scene, you're immediately approached by two or more people who want a decision in their favor. I can't stress enough how important it is to be able to give the correct answer in this situation. But if you don't know, say so. Don't make something up to look smarter than you are. An off-the-cuff answer will result in a loss of respect. Even worse, there'll be consequences if you're wrong. Don't respond until you're sure of the answer. Look it up in the code.

The Appearance of Impropriety

As mentioned earlier, you'll be judged by everyone who sees you throughout the day, even when you're off-duty (according to the clock). Let's look at some actions that seem innocent but can be misinterpreted:

- On payday, you get your check first thing in the morning. While driving between inspections, you stop at a convenient bank to make a deposit. Someone sees you in a government vehicle conducting private business.

- On your way home from work in a government vehicle, your spouse asks you to pick up some milk and bread. Now you're buying groceries with the taxpayer's dollar.

- You have a flat and mount the spare. You take the flat to a gas station, since the government service bay is 40 miles away. Someone may think you're using your government vehicle improperly.

- You come to work ill and need a rest midday. You park, stretch out, and fall asleep. Guess who will appear in a picture on the front page of the local paper with a caustic headline?

There are many ways you can get in trouble without really violating any laws or policies. Let's say you intend to build something on your property. Just like everyone else, you want to save money. Being in the construction field, you have an edge. So, when you approach the supplier, you ask for a discount. If you mention that you know discounts are given because you're a building inspector, the supplier might think you're trying to get a special deal based on your job. Remember, it's not what you say; it's what people hear and think they see that matters.

Disagreements

The line between code compliance and code violation isn't always sharp. Anyone who has skinned an animal knows that it can be difficult to remove the skin without cutting into the carcass. To avoid cutting into the carcass, you may leave some skin behind. Enforcing the building code can be like removing skin from an animal carcass. You want to remove all code violations and leave the safe construction intact. But it's easy to leave a code violation or to cut too deeply into what's perfectly acceptable.

There are times when you'll be right and times when you'll be wrong. We all make mistakes. The codes we enforce have thousands of pages. No one is correct every time on every subject. That's the nature of code enforcement. Accept that you'll be wrong occasionally and be ready to admit it.

Keeping on Schedule

Any action that delays construction will increase costs. Every inspector has the authority to delay a job. That's the nature of code enforcement. For example, the plans examiner may return a plan with comments requesting changes. Or maybe an engineered design for some part of the job is outside the scope of conventional design. Or a permit technician may deny the permit application until zoning has been approved. The building official may be asked to approve an appeal for some part of the project that hasn't been recognized as acceptable in your community. As an inspector, you may cite code violations that require extensive changes.

All of these delays are necessary. But they're still delays that cut into a builder's profit. Most delays will be legitimate requests required to comply with the code. It's the *unnecessary* delays that code enforcement officials need to avoid. For example, requesting something that's already been provided or that isn't actually required is unnecessary delay. Your responsibility is to avoid mistakes that add unnecessarily to the cost of construction. Unnecessary delays caused by the building department are high on any builder's hate list.

How do you avoid delaying the job any more than absolutely necessary? Respect builders' deadlines. A builder may set a deadline based on your timely inspection. Keep to your scheduled inspection time. If you tell a builder that you'll be at his construction site by noon to inspect the footing trench, don't show up two hours late. If you tell a builder that you'll review his plan by the fifth of the month, get it done by the fourth. Car problems, illness, and other unexpected delays will always crowd your schedule. So plan for the unexpected. Call a builder in advance if you can't make your appointment on time.

Keep in touch with builders about your schedule. If your workload increases, causing a delay, tell them. Let them prepare. In my area, concrete pours are usually scheduled about 10:00 a.m., before the hottest part of the day. If I can't be on the site until 1:00 p.m. to inspect the footing, I'm going to advise the builder. On most jobs, the concrete crew can work around a change like that. But if I don't advise the supervisor of my schedule, the builder has a legitimate grievance.

Remember that you're part of the construction team. Don't let the team down. Do your part to keep the job on schedule.

Working with Other Agencies and Utilities

You'll often have to deal with professionals in other quasi-governmental or utility agencies. These include electric and gas companies, the state fire marshal and the county sheriff. As an inspector, you may be asked to approve a utility connection to a building or verify some additional land use requirement. You may be asked to give an elected political official a tour of some natural disaster in your community. You'll be asked to participate in many tasks that don't fit precisely in your normal job description. I consider assignments like these to be a privilege and recommend that you do the same. As a public servant, you'll have many opportunities to serve the public in ways you haven't yet imagined.

Practical Experience vs. Training and Education

Until fairly recently, construction was considered the best possible background for a building inspector. Builders were hired from the construction trades because they knew code requirements from practical experience. Unfortunately, many didn't know the actual code language very well. Today, more inspectors are hired based on their formal education and certifications.

To improve understanding of the code, the ICC offers training seminars and certification exams. Many jurisdictions agree to hire and promote based upon successful completion of these courses. These exams are designed to test an inspector's knowledge and understanding of the code.

When these exams were first introduced, passing scores were low. Independent institutes got into the business of teaching students how to pass ICC exams. An unfortunate result was a flood of "code experts" who qualified for jobs but who had no practical experience and knew very little about construction — they were just good at passing exams. Without actual construction experience, they could only follow and enforce the letter of the code. Not surprisingly, problems developed. A builder could detect immediately that a new inspector knew nothing about construction. Some builders made it a practice to protest every unfavorable decision by a novice inspector. Others would try to snow the novice into passing anything and everything.

The best inspectors have a combination of practical experience and thorough knowledge of the code. This takes time. Practical construction experience, continuing education and training are required. A well-rounded inspector understands both the code and how the code should be applied.

"Take correspondence courses. Answer test questions available in various trade journals."

How can you improve performance as an inspector? Join inspector associations. Attend meetings and seminars. Take tests and become certified. Learn as much as you can about all the codes, not just the one code you're most familiar with. Deal with every code question you're asked. If you don't know an answer, look up the code section. Discuss it with your peers or your boss. Or, if necessary and with the boss's permission, call the model code organization in your area and get an official interpretation.

If you can, attend the ICC's annual conference meetings. Listen to the debates. Discuss the issues with other attendees. Subscribe to periodicals such as the *Building Safety Journal*, *Fine Homebuilding* and *Builder*. Join national associations. Take correspondence courses. Answer test questions available in various trade journals. Keep a notebook to record answers to questions you've researched.

Good Record Keeping

Every inspector has to make notes and keep records. Your notes are legal documents. Make sure your writing is clear and legible. If you don't have a digital keyboard in the field, you'll be recording comments by hand on an inspection request form. As a plans examiner, you'll have to write notes by hand about anything missing from the plans. Your handwriting has to be clear and legible.

Keep your verbal and written reports clear and brief. Be precise in your answers to questions from the public and your boss. State the problem as concisely as you can. Trust your boss' ability to understand the big picture. Just make sure your statements are correct. Your boss can't defend you if he doesn't know the truth. If you're at a loss for an explanation, don't be afraid to admit it.

Most plans are submitted, reviewed and exchanged in electronic format. Many larger jurisdictions post inspection results electronically. Approvals or denials of inspection results can be entered by an inspector in real time. A builder can access the inspection results on the Web and make plans based on results of the inspection.

Pace Yourself

As with most jobs, there will be days plagued with fatigue and frustration. Enforcing the code isn't easy, even when the construction community considers you part of the building team. And many communities aren't exactly thrilled with building code enforcement. Building codes get a lot of bad press, mostly undeserved. There isn't much praise for doing the job right.

Building inspection should be correct, thorough, low-key, efficient, and conducted in a manner that's professional and dispassionate. It will sometimes seem like a thankless job. After all, few of us give thanks when someone points out our mistake, especially when correcting a mistake costs money.

What constitutes a bad day for any building inspector? For some, it's when a supervisor finds fault with their work. Think of it as a training experience — another step along the way to learning the correct code interpretation, policy, or procedure. For the novice inspector, it's a blow to have a decision overruled. Try not to take it personally. Your supervisor doesn't. It's just part of your job.

Another common source of conflict will be an angry client. You don't intend to antagonize anyone when making an inspection. Sometimes it just happens. Most building inspectors develop a thick skin. But even for the most seasoned inspector, an ugly confrontation can ruin the day. For the novice who's less secure, an experienced builder throwing a tantrum can be devastating. Once you've been in the business a while, and you're sure of what you know, it's not such a big deal. Plus, most builders don't try it more than once when they know it won't get them anywhere. But when you're new, expect open hostility, at least occasionally.

Interactions with Co-Workers

Sometimes, especially when you're starting out, you think the process would go much smoother if some other division of the department did their work some other way. There's no other way to say this — *keep your opinions to yourself.* Never enter the domain of another division without the consent of the supervisor in charge. In other words, don't tell other sections what they should and shouldn't do. They probably know, better than you, how to improve. If you're spending time telling them what to do, you're neglecting your own duties and responsibilities.

If you have some serious difficulty with something done by a co-worker, discuss it with that person. Two people can solve a problem better than three. A personal discussion in a calm and detached manner gets the best results and can lead to positive changes without resentment. Don't go up the ladder to complain unless personal discussion doesn't work.

Never Forget Who You Work For

When it comes to dealing with your boss, there are just two rules:

- Rule 1: The boss is always right.
- Rule 2: If the boss is ever wrong, see Rule #1.

The boss is, in the end, *the boss.* You have an obligation to perform the job you were hired to do within the limitations established by law. But following an unlawful directive from your boss may leave you with some responsibility for your action. This is where good judgment is essential. Listen to that little voice in your head that says: "Let's think about this a second."

Hopefully, these times will be rare. Assume your boss didn't get to be boss by handing out unlawful directives.

Keep your boss advised of the critical events that affect his operation. If you can't do any part of the job because of some unforeseen event, such as a dead battery or a flat tire, keep your supervisor advised. Develop a feel for how much involvement your boss wants in your decisions. As you develop more experience, you'll be given freer rein. Initially, plan to run just about any significant decision by him. Later, just advising him of the situation and your decision will be enough. Discuss the limitations of your authority with him and find out when he wants to be consulted. For example, he may only want to be consulted when you're ready to suggest razing an unsafe building.

Always give an honest answer. Never lie, even if it hurts your pride or endangers your position. Tell the truth. You messed up. The builder dug his heels in. You made a decision, realized it was wrong, but didn't want to back down and lose face. Everyone does it ... and that includes your supervisor. To avoid losing the trust of your supervisor, tell it like it is. Don't shade the truth to save face.

If you're asked a question about the code and you don't know the answer, don't try to bluff. Say straight out that you don't know but will find out. If you're not certain, but believe something is true, express your answer as an opinion based on the facts you know.

Finally: Make Yourself Invaluable

As with any job, there are ways to improve your success. Work to impress your supervisor or manager by striving for excellence in the field. Showcase your talents by:

- Being enthusiastic
- Getting to work early and staying late
- Being organized
- Never saying "No." Say "Well, maybe, if ..."
- Proposing new ideas, being creative, searching for solutions

- Staying on top of assignments and promised deadlines

- Never participating in gossip

- Offering to do the extraordinary tasks, like attending an evening or weekend Builder's Association meeting

- Smiling and being friendly

- Keeping informed

In the next chapter, we'll see how inspectors and builders can work together to create safe, comfortable buildings that comply with all code requirements, and that are constructed efficiently and cost-effectively.

DO BE OBJECTIVE

DON'T USE PROFANITY

DO BE CONSISTENT

DO BE CORDIAL AND PROFESSIONAL

DON'T FAULT FIND

DON'T GET MAD

THE DO'S AND DONT'S

C H A P T E R   1 0

Inspectors & Inspections

As a professional builder, do you wonder, "Am I getting my money's worth when I pay the permit fee?" Or, do you consider building permits and inspections to be just one more necessary evil, like insurance or taxes?

Personally, I think builders get good value for their permit dollars. How much would you have to pay for a dozen site visits by technical experts, each doing a one-hour investigation, each resulting in a written report citing specific problems and violations?

Plus, your fee buys professional plan review. That's important. I'll admit that plan review can be a time-consuming annoyance, especially when you're eager to get started. The plans examiner will help resolve design problems with the architect or engineer. Once construction starts, you don't need any more plan changes than absolutely necessary. Obvi-

ously, the best time to iron out any code problems is in the design stage, not during construction. Careful screening by a registered architect, engineer or certified plans examiner will eliminate most design errors before the first spade of earth is turned. That's always to your advantage.

My recommendation: Think of plan review and inspections as *benefits*, not a compromise of your independence or a drain on your profit. Listen to the safety experts in the building department. Think of inspection reports as assets. Consider carefully any words of wisdom offered by the building inspector.

Most of the remainder of this chapter will be advice to building inspectors when actually doing inspections. Obviously, I'll be talking (mostly) to inspectors. But I think builders will appreciate what I'm going to say to inspectors.

Building Inspections and Teamwork

I've been on both sides of the building code enforcement counter. Soon after I finished college, I went into business building spec houses. The only part of building that I didn't like was doing a walk-through with the building inspector. It always made me feel like I was taking my driver's test all over again.

I'll admit that professional builders often have a love-hate relationship with building inspectors. On one hand, the inspector's job is to eliminate problems that pose a safety issue for the project. That's good. On the other hand, fixing problems will slow the construction process and may increase costs. But the truth is, both builder and inspector have the same goal: a safe, durable home. Of course, no one likes to have a job stopped because of a technicality. But wise builders understand that building inspectors and plans examiners add value and help control quality. Every construction pro can use a second set of eyes trained to search out and prevent serious and expensive construction problems.

Good inspectors detest shoddy work and love to see quality construction. Inspectors respect professional builders who are dedicated to delivering a quality product. And they're thankful when they find it. But safety is an entirely separate issue. No matter the quality, inspectors can't compromise on safety. An inspector's signature is confirmation that the project is safe. Every owner is entitled to confirmation that their building will be safe. Building inspectors provide that confirmation.

Violations: Finding an Acceptable Fix

Every inspector has authority to halt a construction project. That's the last resort, of course. I know inspectors who have completed a career without ever issuing a stop work order. Usually, when an inspector points out a

violation, the builder (or framer, or plumber, or electrician) will probably ask how to correct the problem. It's safe to assume the builder didn't know the solution. Otherwise he'd have built it right in the first place.

Many inspectors, especially those with less experience, avoid offering alternatives when they spot a violation. Novice inspectors don't want to get involved with the builder's problem. The builder did it; it's on him. But there's another reason for reluctance to suggest alternatives. There's a possibility that any fix an inspector suggests could create another code violation. For example, the remedy for too little roof insulation is to add more roof insulation. But adding too much insulation at the eaves could compromise ventilation.

What code inspector needs that? This is why many inspectors won't risk helping a builder out of a tight spot. And since builders have an emotional and financial connection to their projects, they may feel helpless and at the mercy of the inspector.

Less-experienced building inspectors have been taught that the building code is the absolute minimum standard for constructing a building. Anything less should be regarded as unsafe. But seasoned inspectors usually have a broad range of experience, especially in their area of expertise. They've seen a lot. Most are willing to help builders get it right. They regard themselves as building partners. Their job is to assist in completion of the project. I like that. I also recognize that no inspector has a solution to every problem on every job site.

Is a Fix as Good as Following the Code to Begin With?

The short answer is "No!" For example, when you patch a shirt, it never looks or wears as well as it did before the patch. Construction is no different, with the possible exception of framing patches or utility repairs that can be hidden with siding and drywall. Still, fixing a construction flaw is never as good as doing the job right the first time. Adding a mechanical patch won't restore the full strength of the member that's been cut and notched too much already. If a joist must be lapped with another to make an adequate connection, installing a metal strap may not be enough.

Fixing a construction mistake can be risky, especially when the correction hasn't been well thought out. For instance, adding nails to a joint between wood framing might help in some cases. But too many nails will weaken one or both members. Adding large stones to a concrete pour will stretch the available concrete and may be a safe alternative. But it breaks up the way loads are distributed in a foundation. Sometimes the more you try, the worse it gets. Even so, I recommend advising builders on fixes required to resolve a violation. But I also recommend being cautious.

There are usually several ways to correct nearly any code violation. For framing issues, metal connectors, straps, hold-downs, retrofit-anchoring devices and bracing mechanisms will overcome most problems. Many material suppliers offer fixes for construction mistakes. These manufacturers work with builders and inspectors to identify how materials are mis-used. Then they develop retrofits for mistakes and omissions.

Suppose an owner decides to enlarge a corner bedroom window. That shortens a shear wall. The engineer can substitute a manufactured shear wall brace panel for a site-built assembly. In the case of a shear wall anchor, substitute a device engineered to resist overturning forces of the shear wall. Another example: An anchor bolt is omitted by accident during a concrete pour. A builder can't put a traditional anchor bolt in hardened concrete. So, drill a retrofit anchor bolt into the concrete.

Talking with a Builder About a Fix

I recommend discussing violations with any builder willing to listen. Ask questions about the builder's construction methods. Discuss the code violation. Here's how to get the conversation started:

- Strike up a conversation with the builder (and anyone else within earshot). Discuss the purpose of the code requirement and the safety advantage.

- Define the code requirement clearly. A precise definition of what the code requires is the first step in problem solving.

- Test the definition or intent of the code. Does the requirement apply to *every* situation? Maybe you don't really have a code violation after all.

- Be considerate. Don't come across as a fault-finder.

- Consider alternatives. Ask questions about equivalent safety measures. Offer to work together to find a solution.

- Examine problems that could result from an alternate solution.

Treat the situation as you would if you were helping a friend. Be objective. Discuss the facts. Consider the alternatives.

What Not to Say

- *Don't tell me that's the best you could do.* Builders do things wrong occasionally. If they didn't, there wouldn't be any need for building inspectors. Inspectors find construction problems. But the number one way to alienate a builder is to criticize his work or his integrity. While you may have to reject the work, don't attack a builder's character. The problem is the building, not the builder. Be objective. Talk about each problem. Explain the reasons.

- *Profanity.* Never, under any circumstances, use profanity. Builders may use colorful language when talking to inspectors. In fact, you can almost count on it! But you're a government official and need to maintain high standards when dealing with the public. Be dignified and polite.

■ *I've never seen it done this way before!* Some building inspectors in large jurisdictions inspect the same thing every day. When you see something different, it doesn't necessarily mean it's wrong. It's just different. Builders experiment with alternative materials and methods of construction, always trying for greater structural integrity, ease of installation, efficiency and economy. Open your eyes to new ideas. Your judgment will be final on new materials and methods. Don't stifle ingenuity.

How to Work with a Builder

Justice is blind. The law should be enforced the same way for everyone. Every job should be subjected to the same scrutiny. Consistency is the gold standard for building code enforcement. As an inspector, you're in a good position to evaluate the competence, skill, and dedication of builders. You'll see builders who are entrepreneurs and risk-takers by nature. They'll stretch the envelope at every opportunity. Good builders, bad builders ... you'll see them all.

> *"Consistency is the gold standard for building code enforcement."*

Builders have to be careful about profits and losses and are always concerned with the bottom line. Good builders want a quality, safe project that satisfies the client and meets the terms of the contract. Following the code isn't always their top priority.

As a human being, you'll trust, or not trust, certain builders. Most follow the rules when the rules are fair and reasonable. Most have worked hard in their profession and hope to stay in business for many years. Regardless, every builder deserves respect and consideration. Be fair and even-handed with everyone. To be otherwise is to jeopardize your reputation. You'll pay for that in a loss of trust and cooperation.

■ Learn about the type of construction you're inspecting. Many projects will include new or alternative building materials. Some materials may require a little homework on your part. Take the time to learn about these materials. Read product listings and be alert to new installation standards.

■ Don't panic if you and a builder knock heads. Builders sometimes get locked in by contract terms or financial obligations. Don't be quick to settle on a single way of complying with the code. Find out how a builder would like to handle the problem. Brainstorm with him. Show that you're sincerely interested in helping.

■ Regard the builder as your teacher. I guarantee you'll learn plenty. True, you're a regulator. But you're not an expert on everything, especially if you're new to inspections. Ask questions, listen, then ask more questions. Confirm what you learn by checking with your supervisor.

■ Be reasonable when discussing any point of contention. Rigid interpretations don't win arguments. Don't get mad. Builders have strong emotional attachments to their work. No builder is going to be swayed by technical interpretations of the law. So explain the intent of the code. Explain what could happen if the violation were allowed to stand. To be a good inspector, *lead* a builder to code compliance. "Because it says so" is never a good argument.

■ Be cordial and professional. Consider how your actions may affect a builder. His financial well-being may be in jeopardy. Listen to his problems. Try to understand and help when you can. Be a professional friend, not a policeman, jury, judge and executioner.

Working with an Unreasonable Builder

There will be times when you reach an impasse with a builder. Different personalities, backgrounds and experience levels can set the stage for conflict. Again, you're a government official and should try to reach an amicable resolution. Keep in mind that you'll be inspecting his work again in the future.

■ Be calm and polite. Consider the consequences of your actions. Many disagreements show a lack of respect and are an exercise in futility. You'll prevail by keeping a cool head.

■ Try to reach the builder objectively. Use reason and facts to support your position.

■ Find points of agreement. There's always *something* you can agree on. Ask what specific items present a problem. Concentrate on those points. Explain your stand. Listen to the builder's response. He may have a point you didn't consider.

■ Document everything that happens. This assures that any later arguments are based on the initial problems. You'll be discussing the situation with your supervisor or the building official. It's easier to remember all issues when you have notes.

■ If you can't resolve some problem to mutual satisfaction, consult your supervisor or the building official. Try not to use this option too often. You might give the impression that you can't handle your job. Get the support of the builder with a request like, "I know that you agree with me that my boss has the final word, so let's get his opinion."

■ If you can't reach a resolution with the building official, the last informal step is the Board of Appeals. This group of technical experts listens to complaints and either supports or denies the position of the building official. It's the builder's last option before seeking justice in the courts.

Building inspectors and builders are partners with a common goal: Building safety. Your job is to find safety flaws; the builder's job is to provide a safe structure. You both want the same thing. How each of you approaches that common goal will define your relationship. Keep your eye on the big picture. Ask yourself, "Why am I really here?" You can explain your role to others when you understand it yourself.

The Mechanics of an Inspection

As mentioned earlier, I recommend that building inspectors follow regular procedures when doing inspections. It helps to have a checklist in your head. But I'll admit there are probably as many good ways to approach an inspection as there are good inspectors. Even so, I'll offer some general rules that apply to all. If you're an inspector, consider the following points as a guide:

■ Did I park where I should? Am I blocking an exit or parking on a flower garden?

■ Am I at the right site? Is there an address posted? Check the inspection request.

■ Did I get permission to enter the property? Is there a "No Trespassing" sign posted? Does this apply to me?

■ Does the project look ready for inspection?

■ Does the project look safe to enter and inspect?

■ Are the approved plans and permit paperwork available on site?

■ What's the history of the project? Did another inspector set up some conditions or inspect some other part of the project? What's the status of that inspection?

■ Am I approaching the job with the right attitude and perspective?

Finally, remember the limits of your authority. Gain voluntary compliance whenever possible. Be driven by a passion for excellence.

The Most Common Code Violations

This chapter is about code violations. Violating the building code isn't the same as committing a crime. Criminal statutes are adopted by our elected representatives (either state or federal). The building code doesn't qualify as a criminal statute. Instead, it's a *regulation.* I explained the difference in Chapter 2, using Minnesota as an example. By statute, Minnesota gave authority to the Commissioner of the Department of Labor and Industry to adopt a building code. With that authority, the Commissioner adopted the *IRC* as a regulation. After that, anyone who didn't follow the *IRC* was violating a state regulation.

A violation of the building code is considered harmful to society and a detriment to building safety. The penalty for each violation is set by the adopting authority. But here's where the building code is different from other regu-

lations. If you violate the motor vehicle code and get cited, you've going to pay a fine or end up in traffic school. Violations of the building code come with a big advantage. *You get to try it again.* Do it right the second time and there's no penalty. Suggest that to the arresting officer the next time you get cited for running through a red light: Offer to try it again. Unfortunately, that's not how it works with traffic violations. But it's exactly what happens with violations of the building code. You get a second chance.

Building inspectors have good enforcement tools, just like traffic cops. An inspector can deny an inspection request, write a notice of violation, issue a stop work order or withhold a certificate of occupancy. But the entire focus is on compliance. Once your work is in compliance, the case is closed. You're done. There's no fine and no penalty.

All of this is spelled out in the first chapter of a code (usually called the *administration* chapter). That's where you'll find details about enforcing the code:

- Definitions of terms
- Requirements for permits
- Plan review and inspection specifications
- Civil prosecutions and injunctive relief
- Powers and duties of the building official

Violations of the building code are also defined in the administration chapter.

Unlawful Acts, Notices, Prosecution and Penalties

Building code enforcement is far more forgiving than motor vehicle code enforcement. Still, the building code shouldn't be taken lightly. Code officials and the building departments have good enforcement tools. Here are some quotes from the administrative provisions of the *IRC*.

R113.1 Unlawful acts.

"It shall be unlawful for any person, firm or corporation to erect, construct, alter, extend, repair, move, remove, demolish or occupy any building, structure or equipment regulated by this code, or cause same to be done, in conflict with or in violation of any of the provisions of this code."

R113.2 Notice of violation.

"The building official is authorized to serve a notice of violation or order on the person responsible for the erection, construction, alteration, extension, repair, moving, removal, demolition or occupancy

of a building or structure in violation of the provisions of this code, or in violation of a detail statement or a plan approved thereunder, or in violation of a permit or certificate issued under the provisions of this code. Such order shall direct the discontinuance of the illegal action or condition and the abatement of the violation."

R113.3 Prosecution of violation.

"If the notice of violation is not complied with in the time prescribed by such notice, the building official is authorized to request the legal counsel of the jurisdiction to institute the appropriate proceeding at law or in equity to restrain, correct or abate such violation, or to require the removal or termination of the unlawful occupancy of the building or structure in violation of the provisions of this code or of the order or direction made pursuant thereto."

R113.4 Violation penalties.

"Any person who violates a provision of this code or fails to comply with any of the requirements thereof or who erects, constructs, alters or repairs a building or structure in violation of the approved construction documents or directive of the building official, or of a permit or certificate issued under the provisions of this code, shall be subject to penalties as prescribed by law."

Sanctions available to the building inspector aren't the only consequences. If you build in Kentucky, for example, failure to follow the code has repercussions that extend far beyond the next inspection.

Kentucky Revised Statutes § 198B.130(1)

"Notwithstanding any other remedies available, any person or party, in an individual capacity or on behalf of a class of

persons or parties, damaged as a result of a violation of ... the State Building Code, has a cause of action in any court of competent jurisdiction against the person or party who committed the violation. An award may include damages and the cost of litigation, including reasonable attorney's fees."

In Kentucky, among other states, an owner who suffers a loss due to a violation of the building code can sue to collect damages — plus attorney fees! Obviously, the inspector is on your side, trying to keep you out of court. Anything the inspector *doesn't* catch could cost you plenty.

Common Violations

Any construction work that doesn't follow the building code is a violation. Some violations are the result of poor construction technique. Others are due to poor selection of materials. Let's look at some examples.

"Both the builder and building official have an interest in the inspector's decision. Citing a code violation is an art, not an exacting science."

Suppose the wall frame isn't nailed correctly where studs join the plates. The wall could collapse under load. Or suppose an undersized sewage pipe is attached to a water closet. Waste is likely to back up, even under normal conditions. The pipe has to be replaced. Or suppose a 20-amp electrical circuit to the kitchen uses 14-gauge, 2-conductor (14/2) wire. That's a fire hazard. The 14/2 wire has to be replaced with a 12/2 wire. These are all clear-cut issues. Any inspector can deal with them.

Now, let's compare some technical violations. None of these are likely to compromise building safety. For example, on wood stud framing, drywall fasteners have to be at 6 inches center to

center (oc). Suppose some are spaced at 5 or 7 inches. Technically, if there's even one fastener that exceeds 6-inch spacing, it's a violation. But I give my inspectors discretion to approve a job if a few fasteners are spaced at 5 or 7 inches. Drywall hangers can't be expected to measure precisely before driving every fastener. Many situations fall into this category. Judgment is important.

Another example: Should the inspector require that a builder remove and replace poorly-installed flashing around a window. Or is it enough to let the builder install another weatherproofing material? Is it acceptable to use a strap to connect opposing joists that don't lap far enough over a bearing wall or beam? Suppose an exhaust vent from a gas appliance is too close to a required 8-inch wood beam. If the beam is cut, it won't be as strong. Re-routing the vent will void the manufacturer's product listing. Will the builder have to take out the appliance? These are cases that require an inspector with experience and good judgment. Both the builder and building official have an interest in the inspector's decision. Citing a code violation is an art, not an exacting science.

Top Ten Building Code Violations

Here's my list of the top 10 *IRC* violations. Even though violations like these are common, none are necessarily open-and-shut cases. Judgment is always required.

1

Failure to follow the approved plans

I don't meet a lot of builders who willfully disregard their plans. But I *do* see a lot of builders — or, more often, subcontractors — who don't realize they're working with an outdated set of plans.

To avoid delays at the beginning of a project, architects often ask contractors to submit bids based on preliminary drawings. Those drawings are usually revised either before or after being submitted to the building department for review.

Once approved, all subcontractors should get copies of the final plans. But (of course!) that doesn't always happen.

Everyone on the job should be building the same house. As a contractor, it's good practice to call in all copies of preliminary drawings before work begins. And, of course, a copy of the approved plan set has to be kept on site.

Field changes are another problem. Builders often have to make changes on the job site. That's just the nature of construction. When changes are necessary, drawings have to reflect these changes. As-built drawings have to be routed through the building department for review, analysis and approval. Then someone has to make sure all subs are notified of the change and receive a copy of the revised plans.

Failure to follow approved plans may sound like a simple technical violation. But on a complicated construction job, even a minor alteration can affect the reliability of a building, and the safety of the occupants.

2

Inadequate soil preparation

IRC Section R401.2 states, in part:

"Foundation construction shall be capable of accommodating all loads according to Section R301 and of transmitting the resulting loads to the supporting soil. Fill soils that support footings and foundations shall be designed, installed and tested in accordance with accepted engineering practice."

A building foundation is only as sound as the soil it rests on. If the soil shifts, collapses, or expands, the foundation will fail. Walls, floor, and roof may be damaged when the foundation settles. Obviously, every foundation has to rest on a solid soil base. Compaction is required when building on filled ground. To test compaction in the surface, just dig your heel into the top layer. If your heel makes an impression, the soil hasn't been compacted.

To check on what lies deeper, a geotechnical engineer will have to evaluate the soil. Contractors and owners who don't invest in a soil evalua-

tion can end up with a building that settles or even collapses. Also, soil under the foundation has to be free of organic material such as vegetation, roots, or branches. These will decay, leaving empty places in compacted fill. Also, organic matter is food for vermin or insects.

> *"Contractors and owners who don't invest in a soil evaluation can end up with a building that settles or even collapses."*

Footing and foundation preparation is the next important step. Make sure the tops of all footings are level. Any sloped footings have to be properly stepped. See that the required reinforcing steel is installed. Any electrical service ground must be connected to footing steel unless other grounding means are provided. And be sure drainage is provided for any basement foundation.

3

Inadequate flood-resistant construction

Flood damage is common in many communities. There's a common lament: Man and beavers are the only mammals who build their homes within a flood plain. And between the two, the beavers are better able to deal with the consequences of a flood. The *Federal Emergency Management Administration (FEMA)* has enacted guidelines and published maps intended to reduce flood damage. Every building department has access to these maps.

Building departments have responsibility for evaluating flood-resistant construction. If no FEMA flood map is available in your community, the building department is going to make a judgment call based on historical data. The *IRC* requires that construction in flood zones be elevated to a height necessary to prevent damage.

Generally, the most effective way to prevent flood damage is to raise the foundation above the assumed 100-year flood level. But as we saw in the Ohio floods of 2008, that may not be enough. Another way to minimize damage is to install openings in foundation walls that allow for drainage. Foundations installed in coastal or high hazard areas must include pilings, or columns anchored to pilings. Any wood used in a foundation must be properly treated to resist decay. Mechanical, plumbing, and electrical runs must be protected to prevent damage. For more on flood protection and flood maps, see *FEMA's* website at www.fema.gov.

4

Inadequate or poorly-installed reinforcing steel in masonry or concrete walls

The code permits use of non-reinforced concrete and masonry walls outside of zones prone to earthquake damage. Most masonry walls use steel reinforcement tied to the foundation and run through grouted block cavities. This makes a composite wall that will resist forces both wind and earthquake. The size, spacing and location of reinforcement must comply exactly with what's specified by the designer.

If the plans call for a #5 grade 60 deformed bar every 24 inches oc, the mason can't install a #4 grade 40 deformed bar every 16 inches oc. The change in center spacing doesn't compensate for the change in design size and strength.

The design of a reinforced wall assumes precise location of reinforcement. For example, the plans probably call for steel placed at the center of each cavity. A section of reinforcement touching the inside face shell will be weaker, even when completely encased in grout. Unfortunately, in this situation, the only solution may be to tear the wall down and start over.

The condition of the steel is also important. Rust, mud, or other debris on reinforcing bars will reduce the ability of a deformed bar to hold grout properly. Use only clean rebar in walls. If block cavities are dirty or have excessive fins from mortar joints, the cavities should be cleaned out before being grouted.

You may notice that the plans call for grout consolidation with a mechanical vibrator. If the mason doesn't have one on site, I recommend stopping the job. Using rebar tampers isn't the same. Grout consolidation is important to the design strength of the assembly. Hand tamping will result in a wall that's weaker than intended.

Any solid grouted wall sections will be particularly important to the strength of the wall assembly. As the blocks are being laid up, watch the mason's treatment of the interior portion of the mortar joint. The interior joint may not be visible when the job is complete. But interior joints are just as important to wall strength as exterior joints.

5

Improper stud wall framing methods

This is a broad category. Some building inspectors who see many framing violations on a job won't list each separately. That doesn't make it easy for the framer. Here are some common framing code violations:

- Inferior lumber grade. Utility grade studs shouldn't be used as structural members. Lumber that's weathered or damaged in shipping or storage shouldn't be used for framing.

- Size, height and spacing of wood studs should comply with *IRC* Table R602.3(5). Don't let a framer increase the center spacing just to save lumber or to accommodate more insulation without a change in plans.

- Second top plate not installed or not offset at least 24 inches. A single top plate may be used only under very specific conditions. A second top plate adds a lot to rigidity of a stud wall.

- Inadequate header for span and bearing condition.

- Inadequate corner framing. Three studs are required, per *IRC* Table R602.10.4.4(1) and Section 602.10.5.3, when using the continuous-sheathing method.

- Untreated sole plate installed on concrete.

- Missing structural blocking.

- Inadequate or missing anchor bolts.

- Inadequate shear walls (braced wall panels).

- Emergency exit bedroom windows are too small.

IRC section R602 covers wood wall framing. Wall corners have to be braced at least 4 feet in each direction. A braced wall panel is required every 25 feet along each wall. Conventional framing methods impose limits on wall heights and the width of openings for windows and doors.

If a design varies from what's required by R602, a registered engineer may have to draw the plan. The framer should follow the plans exactly. Anchors, hold-downs, drag struts, structural connections and nailing patterns must be as specified. Any changes made in the field will have to be reviewed by both the engineer and the plans examiner.

- Truss bracing, as specified in the layout and design, is missing or installed improperly.

- Hold-down clips missing for floor joists, rafters, or trusses.

- Floor or roof decking not properly nailed. I've seen cases where a fast-nail-gun carpenter missed an entire framing member.

- Floor or attic access is missing. In some cases, attic access is required. If attic height is less than 30 inches, no access is required.

6

Inadequate floor or roof framing methods

This isn't a place for creativity and improvisation. Some of the most common errors in floor and roof framing are:

- Floor joists not installed true and plumb. If floor joists are installed at an angle, the joists will tend to twist and lose effectiveness. Structural blocking helps keep joists in place.

- Missing structural blocking at points of support. Besides providing a brace to maintain a vertical position, structural blocking keeps connections between members rigid.

- Improper lap or connection in joists. Floor joists over a bearing partition must be lapped at least 3 inches and nailed with three 10d face nails.

- Improper ridge board construction for rafter framing. Notice the limitations and installation methods for steel roof construction in *IRC* Figure R804.3.

- Improper or misplaced trusses according to engineer's design layout and manufacturer's installation instructions. Damaged trusses have to be analyzed by the engineer who designed them. Fixes must be prescribed by the engineer. In some cases, repairs will have to be made by the factory.

7

Inadequate connections between materials

Proper connection is required to resist earthquakes, wind and gravity.

Builders can follow either conventional or design standards for connections. The code shows what I'll call *conventional connection standards*. You'll see connection standards for various sizes and spacing of materials. For example, you'll see the connections required to join wood plates and studs. Design connection standards are specified by a design professional based on engineering calculations: the forces expected, the size, strength, and member spacing. Either conventional or design standard are acceptable under the code. Ignoring connection details specified on the plan can lead to structural failure.

8

Too much cutting and notching of wood structural members

Holes, notches and cuts weaken wood framing members. The code specifies how much a wood member can be cut, bored or notched.

The maximum allowable hole that can be drilled in a floor or roof joist is one-third of the joist depth. A 2 x 10 floor joist is only about 9½ inches in overall depth. The maximum size hole that can be drilled is just a little over 3 inches in diameter. See *IRC* Figure R602.6(1) for frame walls.

Notches in floor or roof joists are prohibited in the middle third of the joist span. Notches, where permitted, are limited to one-sixth of the depth of the joist. So the same 2 x 10 floor joist can be notched no more than about 1½ inches. If a joist must be cut at the end to accommodate framing, it can only be cut to one-fourth of its depth. That's 2⅜ inches in a 2 x 10.

For manufactured I-joists, the manufacturer's product listing will show what cutting and notching are permitted.

The code also sets limits for holes cut through wall studs. Each stud within an exterior or bearing wall frame may have a hole that's up to 40 percent of the stud depth. A 2 x 6 stud (really 5½ inches in depth) may have a hole a little over 2 inches in diameter. The hole can't be closer than ⅝ inches to either edge of the stud. The edge of any stud can only be notched to 25 percent of its width. That's 1⅜ inches in a 2 x 6. Bored holes may not be in the same section as a cut or notch in a stud.

9

Improper stairway or handrail construction

IRC Section R311.7 sets standards for stairways and handrails:

- Maximum rise on a tread is 7¾ inches.

- Minimum run is 10 inches.

- Maximum variation among riser heights is ⅜ inch.

- Section R311.7.7 identifies two types of handrails, Type I and Type II. A

Type I Handrail must have a profile with an outside diameter between 1¼ and 2 inches. Type II requires a graspable finger recess area on both side of the handrail. The width of the handrail above a recess must be between 1¼ and 2¾ inches for Type II handrails. Additional options and limitations for each type are included in this section.

- Handrail must be installed not less than 34 inches and not more than 38 inches above the nosing of the tread.

- Headroom must be at least 6 feet 8 inches above the nosing of the tread.

10

Missing fireblocking

Fireblocking is required in a wall frame every 10 feet horizontally and vertically at floor and ceiling level. The fireblocking can be pieces of wood blocking equal to the size of the wall frame, installed tightly to each stud. Check to be sure fireblocking is installed around a fireplace chimney.

What's Next?

We've hit just the high points in this chapter — things that most frequently go wrong. In the next chapter we begin our in-depth study of the code, starting with a broad perspective — organization, intent and scope.

C H A P T E R   1 2

Code Organization & Scope

This chapter is a survey of the code. We'll begin with the source of the code: the International Code Council. Then we'll explore provisions that apply to all code sections — mostly information about the approval of alternative materials and methods.

The ICC has a wide range of professional and technical programs designed to promote code compliance and enforcement in the construction industry. These include:

- Code development, printing, and distribution
- Member actions during hearings or meetings on code development
- Chapter associations sponsorship and support
- Written or oral code opinions

- Periodicals like *Building Safety Journal* and *Building Safety Bulletin*
- Manufactured products listing, testing, evaluation, and certification
- Building code education and training
- Offering advice on complex code questions
- Testing and certification exams
- Building safety awareness events such as Building Safety Week
- Books, commentaries, guide tools, and instruction manuals
- Video material for the media to promote building safety
- Employment opportunity directory

The vision, mission, and values of the ICC are:

Vision: Protecting the health, safety, and welfare of the public by promoting safer buildings and communities.

Mission: Providing the highest quality codes, standards, products, and services to the community of construction professionals.

Values:

- Customer value
- Integrity and trust
- Member-focus
- Professionalism
- Public service
- Quality

How Each I-Code is Organized and Arranged

All construction standards, including all building codes, can be placed in one of two categories, either *prescriptive* or *performance*. Most of the *IRC* is prescriptive. The *IBC*, *IPC* and *IFGC* are both prescriptive *and* performance-based.

A prescriptive code identifies how the work should be done. A framing detail is a prescriptive standard. It identifies the materials to be used and how those materials should be assembled or installed. Prescriptive codes deal with the size, shape, length, height, and conditions of use for a specific material.

For example, *IRC* Table R602.3(4) requires that particleboard wall sheathing at least ⅜-inch thick be nailed to studs spaced no further than 16 inches o.c. apart. That's a *prescription* for compliance. Prescriptive standards make it easy to understand what meets code standards, but leave little room for creativity.

A performance standard requires that an assembly be designed and constructed to meet a specific safety standard — usually strength under load. A performance code permits use of alternative materials or methods of construction as long as the finished product meets objective performance criteria. That can lower construction costs but usually requires work by a design professional such as an engineer or architect.

A performance code encourages innovation. For example, approval of both the *Insulated Concrete Form (ICF)* wall system and the *Structural Insulated Panel (SIP)* wall system was based on performance standards. The regional acceptance of straw bale, adobe and rammed earth buildings were a direct result of adopting performance standards.

Performance standards are often developed by comparison with prescriptive standards. We learn a lot about the safety characteristics of a particular structure when we've had the opportunity to observe that structure in normal use for many years. Most prescriptive standards are based on materials, dimensions and construction methods that have been used successfully for many years. New alternative standards gain acceptance when they compare favorably with older standards generally recognized as good practice.

The IRC

The *IRC* is a comprehensive, stand-alone, residential construction code, and has nine parts and 17 appendices. Most of the nine parts include more than one chapter.

Part I covers the administration of code enforcement, including:

- Title, Scope and Purpose
- Department of Building Safety
- Duties and Powers of the Building Official
- Plans, Specifications, Permits, and Inspections
- Fees
- Certificate of Occupancy (C of O)
- Service Utilities
- Board of Appeals
- Right of Entry for Inspectors
- Record Keeping Requirements
- Violations and Prosecution
- Stop Work Orders

Part II defines terms in the code that are subject to interpretation. These definitions are very important. The difference between "accessible" and "readily accessible" may be thousands of dollars and an access panel that's an eyesore on a wall. Anyone new to the *IRC* needs a basic understanding of these definitions. The people who developed the code considered every part of these definitions very carefully. Even punctuation marks and spelling are questioned and debated before a particular definition is adopted. Throughout the code, defined words appear in italics. That's your clue that the word is being used in a sense that may not be consistent with the dictionary definition.

Part III (Chapters 3 to 10) deals with the standards for specific topics and phases of residential construction:

- basic design criteria
- illumination, ventilation, heating, sanitation
- means of egress (exits)
- structural design for most common materials and methods of construction
- concrete and masonry foundations
- wall systems built of wood frame, steel frame, masonry, concrete, structural insulated panels, and insulated concrete forms
- approved materials and application for all types of wall coverings
- roof and floor systems
- roof coverings and fireplace construction

Parts IV through *IX* cover mechanical and electrical work:

- *Part IV* — energy efficiency for residential buildings
- *Part V* — HVAC installations and venting; solar energy system installations
- *Part VI* — residential fuel gas system installation
- *Part VII* — plumbing installations
- *Part VIII* — electrical installations within a residence and a swimming pool

- *Part IX* — standards referenced in the code, including agency name, effective date and title, and code sections that refer to the standards

IRC Appendices

Appendices A-Q must be specifically adopted by a jurisdiction to be enforceable. *IRC* Section R102.5 states:

"Provisions in the appendices shall not apply unless specifically referenced in the adopting ordinance."

Many of these appendices offer building standards that are an alternative to what appears in the first eight parts of the *IRC*. Most of these are based on practices recognized as acceptable in a specific region of the country. Many of these regional practices are based on performance standards.

Subjects in the *IRC* Appendices include:

Appendix	Subject
A	Sizing of gas piping
B	Sizing of venting system
C	Exit terminals of mechanical draft and direct venting requirements
D	Recommended procedure for appliance safety inspection
E	Design criteria for manufactured housing used as dwellings
F	Radon control methods
G	Installation standards for swimming pools, spas, and hot tubs
H	Patio covers for residential structures
I	Private sewage disposal
J	Existing buildings and structures
K	Sound transmission standards
L	Permit fees
M	Home day care — R-3 occupancy
N	Venting methods
O	Gray water recycling systems
P	Water piping system sizing
Q	ICC *IRC* electrical provisions/ *NEC* cross-reference

Unlike all previous model codes (including the *CABO One- and Two-Family Dwelling Code*), the *IRC* includes *all* code requirements that apply to home building — structural, architectural, plumbing, electrical, mechanical, and energy. That's a major advantage when you're trying to comply with the code.

For example, legacy codes specified the locations for smoke detectors. But in order to find out how those smoke detectors should be connected to the electrical source, you had to refer to the electrical code. Requirements for sinks, showers and water closets were in all building codes; *how* to plumb those fixtures was in the plumbing code. The requirements for heating a dwelling were in the building code; details about HVAC installation were in the mechanical code. The *IRC* is the first comprehensive stand-alone document that covers all code requirements for one- and two-family dwellings.

The *IRC* is a minimum standard intended to be enforced. That's the way it has to be. It isn't a "how-to" guide to residential construction; you'll have to look elsewhere for that information. But the *IRC* does include many detailed drawings, charts, graphs, and descriptive tables that explain code requirements. Another advantage: The *IRC* is considerably less expensive than its predecessors. It replaces other codes that cost hundreds of dollars.

The *IRC* simplifies both code enforcement *and* compliance, thus providing the first complete and consistent set of rules for residential construction.

The IBC

The *IBC* is the parent document in the family of I-Codes®, regulating architectural, fire and life safety, and structural design of nearly all types of building construction. Thus the *IBC* sets a standard for design, approval and inspection of residential buildings as well as commercial and industrial buildings. If the proposed design of a house isn't covered in the *IRC*, the designer has the option of complying instead with the *IBC*. Registered design professionals (architects and engineers) use structural engineering principles to create designs that comply with performance standards in the *IBC*.

Any section in the *IBC* that begins with a letter designation in brackets is a section that's maintained by another code development organization. For example, an [F] means the section is maintained by the *IFC*, while a [P] means it's maintained by the *IPC*.

The *IBC* has 35 chapters and 11 appendices. Here's a list of topics by *IBC* chapter:

Chapter	Subject
1	Administrative provisions such as scope, purpose, applicability, duties and powers of building officials, permits, inspections, certificate of occupancy, board of appeals, violations, and stop work orders.
2	Definitions
3-6	Use, occupancy-related requirements, general building limitations, areas, heights, and types of construction
7, 9	Fire protection requirements, interior finishes, rated construction
10	Means of egress (exits)
11	Accessibility
12	Interior environment
13	Energy efficiency
14	Exterior walls
15	Roof assemblies and rooftop structures
16	Structural design regulations and loads
17	Structural tests and special inspections
18	Soils and foundations
19	Concrete
20	Aluminum
21	Masonry
22	Steel
23	Wood
24	Glass
25	Gypsum board and plaster
26	Plastic
27	Electrical
28	Mechanical
29	Plumbing
30	Elevators
31	Special construction
32	Right-of-way
33	Construction safety
34	Existing structures
35	References and standards

The IPC

The *International Plumbing Code (IPC)* is intended to give broad latitude to anyone designing a plumbing system. It uses both prescriptive and performance standards to set code requirements. The *IPC* regulates the installation and quality of materials for plumbing systems in both new and existing buildings.

Subjects covered in the *IPC*:

Chapter	Subject
1	Administration
2	Plumbing terms definitions
3	General regulations for piping, trenching, excavation, etc.
4	Fixtures
5	Water heaters
6	Water supply
7	Sanitary drainage
8	Indirect waste drainage
9	Vents
10	Traps
11	Storm water drainage
12	Special piping systems
13	Standards and references

Appendices in the *IPC* show alternative design methods for special systems.

The IMC

The *International Mechanical Code (IMC)* regulates the installation and quality of materials in mechanical systems.

Subjects covered in the *IMC* by chapter:

Chapter	Subject
1	Administration
2	Mechanical terms definitions
3	General regulations
4	Ventilation
5	Exhaust systems
6	Duct systems
7	Combustion air
8	Chimneys and vents
9	Special appliance installation, fireplaces
10	Boilers, water heaters, other pressure vessels
11	Storm water drainage
12	Refrigeration

Chapter	Subject
13	Fuel oil piping
14	Solar systems
15	Referenced standards

Two appendices in the *IMC* show alternative design methods for special systems.

The IFGC

The *International Fuel Gas Code (IFGC)* regulates installation and quality of materials for fuel gas systems.

Here's a list of the subjects covered in the *IFGC* by chapter:

Chapter	Subject
1	Administration
2	Fuel gas terms definitions
3	General regulations
4	Gas pipe installation
5	Chimneys and vents
6	Specific appliances
7	Gaseous hydrogen systems
8	Referenced standards

Four appendices in the *IFGC* show alternative sizing and capacity calculations, venting systems, exit terminals, and safety inspection procedures.

The IFC

The *International Fire Code (IFC)* establishes minimum fire safety and property protection standards for both new and existing buildings.

Here's a list of some of the subjects covered in the *IFC* by chapter:

Chapter	Subject
1	Administration
2	Definitions
3	General fire precautions
4	Emergency preparedness
5	Fire service features
6	Emergency building services
7	Fire-resistance-rated construction
8	Interior finish requirements
9	Sprinklers, standpipes, smoke control systems, heat vents

Chapter	Subject
10	Egress requirements
11	Aviation precautions
12	Dry cleaning businesses
13	Combustible dust regulations
14	Construction safety regulations
15	Flammable finishes
22	Fuel dispensing and repair garages
27	Hazardous materials
33	Explosives and fireworks
34	Flammable and combustible liquids
45	Referenced standards

Seven appendices in the *IFC* cover optional designs.

What Requires a Permit and What Doesn't?

Every builder (and every inspector) needs to know:

"Do I need a permit for _____?"

Back in Chapter 6, I listed three good reasons to get a permit when a permit is required:

- Working without a permit is like skating on thin ice.
- Starting work without a permit will double the cost of the permit.
- Every home built or remodeled without a permit is a lemon.

Applying for a permit begins the process of review and inspection which ends in approval of the work by the building department. Final approval is verification that the work complies with the building code. That helps protect every builder. Approval of work that doesn't comply with the code could make a jurisdiction liable for defects in the work. Your permit fee covers the cost of this protection.

IRC Section R105.1 says that permits are required for work regulated by the code.

"Any owner or authorized agent who intends to construct, enlarge, alter, repair, move, demolish or change the occupancy of a building or structure, or to erect, install, enlarge, alter, repair, remove, convert or replace any electrical, gas, mechanical or plumbing system, the installation of which is regulated by this code, or to cause any such work to be done, shall first make application to the *building official and obtain the required* permit."

Certain construction work is exempt from a building permit. *IRC* Section R105.2 says, in part:

"Permits *shall not be required for the following. Exemption from* permit *requirements of this code shall not be deemed to grant authorization for any work to be done in any manner in violation of the provisions of this code or any other laws or ordinances of this* jurisdiction."

Building:

1. One-story detached accessory structures used as tool and storage sheds, playhouses and similar uses, provided the floor area doesn't exceed 200 square feet (18.29m²)

2. Fences not over 6 feet (1829 mm) high

3. Retaining walls that are not over 4 feet (1219 mm) in height measured from bottom of footing to top of wall, unless supporting a surcharge

4. Water tanks supported directly upon grade if the capacity doesn't exceed 5,000 gallons (18927 L) and the ratio of height to diameter or width doesn't exceed 2 to 1

5. Sidewalks and driveways

6. Painting, papering, tiling, carpeting, cabinets, countertops and similar finish work

7. Prefabricated swimming pools that are less than 24 inches (610 mm) deep

8. Swings and other playground equipment

9. Window awnings supported by an exterior wall which do not project more than 54 inches (1372 mm) from the exterior wall and do not require additional support

10. Decks not exceeding 200 square feet (18.58 m²) in area, that are not more than 30 inches (762 mm) above *grade* at any point, are not attached to a *dwelling* and do not serve the exit door required by Section R311.4

Electrical:

1. Listed cord-and-plug connected temporary decorative lighting

2. Reinstallation of attachment plug receptacles but not the outlets therefor

3. Replacement of branch circuit over-current devices of the required capacity in the same location

4. Electrical wiring, devices, appliances, apparatus or equipment operating at less than 25 volts and not capable of supplying more than 50 watts of energy

5. Minor repair work, including the replacement of lamps or the connection of approved portable electrical equipment to approved permanently installed receptacles

Gas:

1. Portable heating, cooking or clothes drying appliances

2. Replacement of any minor part that does not alter approval of equipment or make such equipment unsafe

3. Portable-fuel-cell appliances that are not connected to a fixed piping system and are not interconnected to a power grid

Mechanical:

1. Portable heating appliances

2. Portable ventilation appliances

3. Portable cooling units

4. Steam, hot or chilled water piping within any heating or cooling equipment regulated by this code

5. Replacement of any minor part that does not alter approval of equipment or make such equipment unsafe

6. Portable evaporative coolers

7. Self-contained refrigeration systems containing 10 pounds (4.54 kg) or less of refrigerant or that are actuated by motors of 1 horsepower (746 W) or less

8. Portable-fuel-cell appliances that are not connected to a fixed piping system and are not interconnected to a power grid

9. The stopping of leaks in drains, water, soil, waste or vent pipe; provided, however, that if any concealed trap, drainpipe, water, soil, waste or vent pipe becomes defective and it becomes necessary to remove and replace the same with new material, such work shall be considered as new work and a permit shall be obtained and inspection made as provided in this code

10. The clearing of stoppages or the repairing of leaks in pipes, valves or fixtures, and the removal and reinstallation of water closets, provided such repairs do not involve or require the replacement or rearrangement of valves, pipes or fixtures

It's legitimate to ask the building department for guidance even if a permit isn't required. For example, you might want suggestions when pouring a driveway slab or trenching for the footing on a garden wall. Most building departments will respond favorably to requests like that. Of course, the building department will try to avoid designing what you're planning to build. And even if what you're building doesn't require a permit, the structure itself must comply with the code.

"Shall" vs. "Permitted": Mandatory vs. Permissible

Those new to the code are sometimes confused by the code's use of two words: *Shall* and *permitted*. It's quite simple... *shall* means the requirement is mandatory — it has to be done that way, whether you like it or not. But *permitted* means the installation is optional. An inspector might recommend it. But it's only a recommendation. The builder doesn't *have* to do it.

The term "shall" is defined in *IRC* Section R202 as:

"The term, when used in the code, is construed as mandatory."

As an example, *IRC* Section R602.8 states:

"Fireblocking shall be provided in accordance with Section R302.11."

Section R302.11 establishes specific requirements for the installation, location, and type of materials allowed for fireblocks. This means that fireblocking *must* be installed as specified.

The term "permitted" means that you have the ability, permission or freedom to make a decision on your own. In the code, "permitted" means you have permission. As an example, *IRC* Section R301.1.3 states, in part:

"Engineered design in accordance with the International Building Code *is permitted for all buildings and structures, and parts thereof, included in the scope of this code."*

That means you have the option of following performance standards in the *IBC* if prescriptive standards in the *IRC* don't meet your needs. The term "shall" is used throughout the code, many more times than the term "permitted."

If code provisions are in conflict with each other, the most strict code provision will apply. *IRC* Section R102.1 states:

"Where there is a conflict between a general requirement and a specific requirement, the specific requirement shall be applicable. Where, in any specific case, different sections of this code specify different materials, methods of construction or other requirements, the most restrictive shall govern."

Special Inspections

Design for a residential building can follow either the prescriptive standards set by the *IRC* or the performance standards which appear in the *IBC*. A designer who elects to comply with the *IRC* will follow conventional designs outlined in the code, use code-approved materials and observe code criteria specific to the weather conditions and seismic zone at the building site. No engineered design is needed when following prescriptive sections of the *IRC*.

If a designer needs to go beyond this standard, *IRC* Section R104.11 gives a designer authority to substitute a different standard:

"...Compliance with the specific performance-based provisions of the International Codes in lieu of specific requirements of this code shall also be permitted as an alternate."

This means that performance-based provisions published in other ICC codes can be substituted for standards which appear in the *IRC*. This includes both provisions in the *IBC* and performance provisions in other ICC codes. Sometimes use of this approach will trigger requirements such as in Chapter 17 of the *IBC* — special inspections and the use of specialized materials.

For example, substituting *IBC* standards in a residential project many affect the inspections required. *IBC* Section 1704.1, states, in part:

"Where application is made for construction as described in this section, the owner or the registered design professional in responsible charge *acting as the owner's agent shall employ one or more* approved agencies *to perform inspections during construction on the types of work listed under Section 1704."*

The next sentence in *IBC* Section 1704.1 defines the special inspector:

"The special inspector shall be a qualified person who shall demonstrate competence, to the satisfaction of the building official, *for the inspection of the particular type of construction or operation requiring* special inspection."

A special inspector has usually qualified as an expert in the type of work involved. Many of the following will require special inspections:

- certain types of steel structures, including high-strength bolt connections, welding, designed high-strength concrete, masonry that's not empirically designed, and structural load-bearing wood assemblies fabricated in a shop

- certain soil conditions
- fill dirt placement and compaction over 12 inches
- pile and pier foundations
- architectural wall panels
- some types of adhered veneers in certain seismic zones
- sprayed fire-resistant materials
- exterior insulation and finish systems
- smoke control systems

IBC Section 1704.15 gives a building official broad authority to require special inspection for situations that aren't covered in the code:

"Special inspections shall be required for proposed work that is, in the opinion of the building official, *unusual in its nature..."*

These special inspections are in addition to the regular inspections required by the code.

Results of any special inspections will be reviewed by inspection staff in the office of the building official. And, of course, final authority to approve the work rests with the building official.

Abatement of Unsafe Structures

IBC Section 116 "Unsafe Structures and Equipment" regulates existing residential and commercial structures for safety. *IBC* Section 116.1 states, in part:

"Structures or existing equipment that are or hereafter become unsafe, insanitary or deficient because of inadequate means of egress facilities, inadequate light and ventilation, or which constitute a fire hazard, or are otherwise dangerous to human life or the public welfare, or that involve illegal or improper occupancy or inade-

quate maintenance, shall be deemed an unsafe condition."

Getting a Modification Accepted by the Building Code

Sections 104 in both the *IBC* and the *IRC* authorize the building official to "render interpretations of this code and to adopt policies and procedures in order to clarify the application of its provisions."

This doesn't mean that the building official can ignore the intent of the code. It merely places responsibility on the building official for evaluating construction that isn't covered in the code. If convinced it's safe, the building official has authority to approve any alternate construction not covered by the code.

The early building codes allowed "accepted good practice" to satisfy safety concerns. That resulted in more than a few heated discussions beginning with, "I've always done it that way and you've never objected before!" Later editions offered detailed criteria for determining what constituted "accepted good practice." More than a few building officials had trouble identifying exactly what qualified as "accepted good practice." The current standard requires the approval of alternate construction only when the building official is convinced that the proposed design and construction are safe.

The building official (the inspector's boss), has authority to accept any alternative method presented that meets safety criteria similar to what the code requires. Usually, the inspector will recommend either for or against the alternative.

If rejected, the builder carries the burden of proof — to demonstrate that what's proposed is equivalent to what the code requires. How do you do that? A statement from a registered engineer or architect can make your case. If the problem involves structural design, a stamp by a structural engineer should settle the matter. Submit engineering calculations and a sealed design with your request for a modification. Of course, the best time to request an alternate is well before the first spade of earth is turned.

Using Alternative Materials

Strictly speaking, there are no installation standards for materials not listed in the code. An inspector who is uncomfortable with the use of some particular material has authority to reject installation. For example, if a builder plans to erect an igloo in Tucson in July, I would hope that the building official would have the good common sense to question construction materials. But be careful; any new or different building material (even straw bales) may be practical everywhere, even if none has ever been used in your area.

An inspector has authority to accept or reject materials not specifically listed in the code. Normally, decisions about building materials will be made by the plans examiner and the building official at the design stage, long before construction begins. Discussion of alternate materials usually begins with a builder or owner visiting the building department with a proposal. The department will look for:

1. design criteria from the manufacturer
2. third party testing
3. independent evaluation of the proposed material.

If the builder has done his homework, then approval should be routine. Few builders and even fewer owners are willing to risk money on materials that may not pass inspection. So they check before making a purchase.

"It's not easy to get alternative materials or construction methods approved."

But every seasoned inspector has seen "alternate" materials show up on a job site: lumber without a grade mark, shingles not properly identified as code-compliant, drywall of indeterminate origin. That's when the inspector is called on to make a decision.

Experienced builders recognize advantages of alternative materials. Many are widely accepted because they're cheaper, stronger, easier to use or longer lasting than conventional materials. *IRC* Section 104.11 gives every building official the authority to accept an alternative material or method of construction that is:

"...for the purpose intended, at least the equivalent of that prescribed in this code in quality, strength, effectiveness, fire resistance, durability and safety..."

This language is slightly different from similar provisions in earlier codes. Formerly, a building official could accept or deny alternate materials and methods based on a subjective personal evaluation. For example, before the first I-Codes in 2000, Insulated Concrete Forms *(ICF)* required an engineered design. Now they're considered "conventional" and are referenced in *IRC* Sections R611 and R404 (foundations and walls). ICC codes require building officials to accept new products and methods if the proposed design "is satisfactory and complies with the intent of the provisions of this code." (*IRC* Section R104.11)

Don't read too much into a building official's authority to interpret the *IRC*. Building officials and inspectors still have to enforce the code and decide which code sections apply to a particular situation.

IRC Section R104.11.1 covers testing of alternate materials. A building official has to determine whether evidence offered by the manufacturer demonstrates compliance with the code. The best evidence will be valid research reports conducted by approved sources. Tests of new materials are normally conducted by the manufacturer and certified by an independent testing service. If no accepted test methods exist, the building official will want to approve the testing procedure.

Tests must be performed by an approved agency. The term, "approved agency" is defined by *IRC* Section R202 as "An established and recognized agency regularly engaged in conducting tests or furnishing inspection services, when such agency has been *approved* by the *building official.*" After performing the tests, the accepted agency will analyze the resulting data and issue a report citing the methods and procedures used, and the results. The product in question may then be listed as approved for certain use within the parameters of the testing criteria. Any conditions or design requirements will also be noted in the test summary.

It's not easy to get alternative materials or construction methods approved. As explained in Chapter 5, there are a number of organizations that perform these evaluations on behalf of manufacturers and building officials. One of the most sophisticated and well-known of these services is ICC Evaluation Service, Inc. ICC-ES reviews thousands of products and materials annually. It also evaluates testing methods and procedures and certifies labs to ensure their accuracy and independence. The ICC-ES website is http://www.icc-es.org/.

That completes our introductory survey of the code. Next, we'll get down to business — the business of passing foundation and footing inspections.

Foundations & Footings Inspection

Most states now require that builders respond to construction defect claims made during the first few years after any residential building is completed. That's called an *implied warranty* and is entirely separate from any written warranty a residential builder offers. Most builders are prepared to handle minor warranty claims that require no more than cosmetic patching or sealing. But no builder wants to deal with a major structural failure, such as a foundation that's subsiding. In extreme cases, a settling foundation can make a home both unsafe and uninhabitable. In nearly every case, repairing a defective foundation will be expensive; more than any builder wants to contemplate. Obviously, foundations should be built right the first time.

Whether you're preparing for a footing and foundation inspection or conducting that inspection, I recommend using the checklist in this chapter. I've brought together in a single package nearly all the code references you'll need to identify potential foundation problems.

Fortunately for both inspectors and contractors, most of the basic rules are obvious:

- a level surface
- adequate depth, width and thickness of the foundation system
- correct reinforcing steel placement
- adequate connection to other structural members

Something else that should be obvious: Concrete pours can't begin until the job passes foundation inspection. Defects have to be repaired before the cavity is filled with concrete.

☐ **Does footing width and depth comply with *IRC* Section R403.1.4 and Table R403.1?**

The code specifies footing widths based on soil bearing value measured in pounds per square foot. This bearing value will be determined by a soils engineer and should appear on the approved plans. Table R403.1 shows the proper footing width based on the number of stories and the type of wall assembly, either light frame, brick veneer or fully grouted masonry. Both footing width and depth will be shown on the approved plans. Verify that work done complies with what the approved plans show.

☐ **Is the cavity where the footing or slab will be poured clean and clear of debris, per *IRC* Section R403.1?**

IRC Section R403.1 requires that footings be supported on undisturbed soil or engineered fill. This means there shouldn't be any loose soil, debris or organic material (such as roots) in the cavity prepared for the footing or slab. Any loose soil or extra material will weaken the concrete or make it thinner than required. The result will be a footing with less than the required loadbearing capacity. It's OK if the cavity is a little wider or deeper than required. But the width and depth can't be *less* than shown on the approved plans.

☐ **Could the loadbearing value of the soil be considered *poor* or *expansive*?**

Footing width is based on the loadbearing capacity of soil in *IRC* Table R403.1. But none of the soil types in this table consider either *poor* or *expansive* soil. A soil map for your area will identify any unsuitable soil conditions likely to be present. If you suspect poor or expansive soil, consider a geotechnical study to determine the soil condition.

☐ **Is seismic reinforcing (horizontal and vertical) installed correctly, per *IRC* Section R403.1.3? Will any steel be in direct contact with the soil?**

Steel reinforcing bars will be required in seismic regions. Figure 13-1 shows an example. While concrete can take a lot of compressive stress,

Figure 13-1   Steel installed to reinforce concrete sits above the soil to prevent rust.

it doesn't resist tension (pulling apart) forces very well. Steel reinforcing helps resist tension in concrete.

The type and placement of reinforcement has to conform with the plans. *IRC* Tables R404.1.1(2) through (4) and the accompanying text identify correct bar diameters and bar spacing in foundation walls. The tables also identify correct installation methods and other requirements.

Reinforcing steel can't be in direct contact with the ground or affected by rust. Oxidation can destroy unprotected steel, leaving the concrete with rust cavities where there used to be steel bars. Notice that reinforcing steel in Figure 13-1 is supported above the soil level.

☐ **Does the foundation wall thickness comply with *IRC* Section R404.1.5?**

The thickness of foundation walls is based on material used, foundation type, wall height and the load imposed. Compare the plans with the actual cavity width.

☐ **Are concrete forms installed in proper position to define the future foundation wall, per *IRC* Section R404.1.2.3.6?**

Check installation of the forms and steel, as in Figure 13-2. Be sure the form cavity will support poured concrete at the width shown on the plans.

Figure 13-2 Check the forms and steel before the concrete is poured.

Figure 13-3 An electrical ground connection is made to the reinforcement inside a footing.

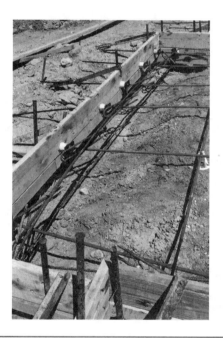

Figure 13-4 A continuous footing without interruptions.

□ **Are electric grounding conductors connected to 20-foot lengths of reinforcing steel in footings, per *IRC* Section E3608.1.2?**

The electrical system in every building has to be grounded to operate properly and safely. The most common method is to tie an electrical grounding conductor to the rebar reinforcement

in a concrete footing. See Figure 13-3. An acceptable alternative is to embed at least 20 feet of bare No. 4 copper wire in the concrete.

□ **In seismic regions, is the footing used to support a braced wall panel continuous, per *IRC* Section R403.1.2?**

A braced wall panel absorbs energy from wind or earthquakes and transfers those forces through the foundation to the footing. A monolithic (one piece) footing is required under a braced wall panel. Figure 13-4 shows forms prepared for a monolithic pour.

□ **Will the top of the footing be level, per *IRC* Section R403.1.5?**

To build a level wall frame, the supporting surface must be level. The top of a footing will normally be set by a survey instrument and marked on the form. The concrete finisher will use this mark as a limit line for the concrete pour. Look for this mark to be sure the finisher has a guide. In Figure 13-5, the inspector is checking forms to make sure the top of the footing will be level.

□ **Are bottom surfaces of footings level, per *IRC* Section R403.1.5?**

IRC Section R403.1.5 permits a slope of up to 10 percent under a footing. A concrete footing will tend to slide along any surface that slopes

Figure 13-5 Inspector checks that forms for top of footing will be level.

Figure 13-6 The bottom of the footing is level without swales or valleys.

Figure 13-7 Anchor bolts embedded in concrete after the pour.

□ **Will compressive strength of concrete in the footings meet or exceed the design strength, per *IRC* Table R402.2?**

The strength of concrete is measured in pounds per square inch (psi) of resistance to compression. *IRC* Table R402.2 requires 2,500 to 3,500 psi concrete in footings, depending on the weathering potential and intended use. There's no need to measure the actual psi rating of concrete in a poured footing. Concrete strength will be calculated at the concrete batch plant and recorded on the shop ticket. This shop ticket should be available to the inspector at final inspection.

□ **Are required anchor bolts ready to be placed at locations, per *IRC* Section R403.1.6?**

Before the pour begins, anchor bolts should be laid out next to the trench every 6 feet. After the pour, anchor bolts must be embedded in fresh concrete to a depth of at least 7 inches. See Figure 13-7. Determine the embedded depth by subtracting the bolt projection above the foundation from the overall bolt length.

more than about 10 percent. To prevent subsidence, be sure the bottom of the footing is nearly level and free of swales or valleys, as shown in Figure 13-6. You can measure the slope using a line level. If the slope of any section of a footing is more than 1:10, the footing must be "stepped" so no section exceeds the maximum slope.

Figure 13-9 A hand-held line level could be used to measure the elevation between the finished floor and the street gutter.

Figure 13-8 A footing that's very close to the edge of the slope.

☐ **Does the distance from footings to any ascending or descending slope comply with *IRC* Section R403.1.7.1?**

The footing above a descending slope and below an ascending slope must meet setback requirements. Figure 13-8 shows a footing that may be too close to the edge of a descending slope. There's danger the building could subside. Setback from an ascending slope keeps runoff and silt away from the foundation.

☐ **Do setbacks from the property line comply with *IRC* Section R302.1?**

If the exterior walls don't have at least a 1-hour fire-resistive rating, the foundation should be at least 5 feet from the property line. Check the approved plan.

☐ **Is the foundation height at least 12 inches plus 2 percent above the elevation of the gutter, per *IRC* Section R403.1.7.3?**

To protect the building from rising water, the foundation must be higher than the street gutter by 12 inches plus 2 percent. Use a line level or survey instrument to check the required height. To calculate the 2 percent incline, measure the distance from the gutter to the foundation and divide by 50. For example, if the foundation is 50 feet from the gutter, a 2 percent rise is 1 foot (50 feet divided by 50). So the foundation must be 12 inches plus another 12 inches above the level of the gutter. Figure 13-9 shows a foundation height that's 24¼ inches above the level of the street gutter.

☐ **Are foundation walls at the required height above the adjoining grade, per *IRC* Section R404.1.6?**

To prevent flood damage, foundation walls must be higher than the adjacent grade. Use a tape measure to check for 6-inch height above the adjacent grade. If the exterior wall finish is masonry veneer, the foundation wall has to extend only 4 inches above grade.

☐ **Do interior bearing walls have footings that comply with *IRC* Table R403.1?**

Footings for interior foundation walls have to comply with requirements for exterior wall footings. The width of the footing is based on the type of construction, soil bearing capacity and the number of stories supported.

Figure 13-10 Perimeter insulation installed to retard heat flow.

Figure 13-11 Part of an ICF wall system.

☐ **Are concrete block walls properly prepared for grout placement, per *IRC* Section R609?**

Are cleanouts provided in the base course of the wall? After inspection, these cleanouts will be closed. Is the grout cell free of debris? Has reinforcing steel been installed? *IRC* Section R609.1.4 identifies placement procedures for grout.

☐ **Does the fireplace footing comply with *IRC* Section R1001.2?**

A masonry fireplace places a significant load on a foundation. To resist this load, the footing has to be at least 12 inches thick and should extend beyond the face of the fireplace walls at least 6 inches on all sides. When inspecting the foundation, look for a 12-inch-thick trench with seismic reinforcing in place around the perimeter where the fireplace will be located.

☐ **Is perimeter insulation installed as required by *IRC* Section R403.3 and Figure R403.3(1)?**

Frost protection is required for shallow foundations in many areas. Figure 13-10 shows perimeter insulation installed to help retard heat loss during cold weather.

☐ **If Insulated Concrete Form *(ICF)* foundation walls are used, make sure the building is within the width and length limits for ICF wall systems, per *IRC* Section R611.2.**

Figure 13-11 shows an ICF wall system under construction. Buildings with exterior concrete or ICF wall systems have a limited roof span, floor span, overall length and width. Without an engineered design, building width can't exceed 32 feet and building length can't exceed 60 feet. Generally, building height is limited to two stories and 35 feet in overall height.

ICF foundations walls that intersect have to be connected with reinforcing steel that complies with the manufacturer's specifications. Figure 13-12 shows an example. Reinforcing steel placed inside ICF walls can't be closer to the outside face of the wall than one-half the ICF wall thickness.

Figure 13-12   Reinforcing steel connects ICF walls at the intersection.

☐ Does the foundation have adequate drainage?

Water that collects in pools near a foundation is likely to damage the building. Unless the soil is well-drained gravel or a sand-and-gravel mix, *IRC* Section R405.1 requires a 12-inch-wide drainage system around the perimeter of the foundation. The drainage system can be made from drain tile, gravel, perforated pipe or crushed stone.

☐ Is the crawl space ventilated per *IRC* Section R408.1? Is access provided per *IRC* Section R408.4?

A crawl space under a floor that collects moisture can cause damage to supporting wood floor joists and beams. Foundation vents promote free passage of air, which removes excess moisture. Both vent size and location are regulated by *IRC* Section R408.1. Generally, one square foot of free vent area is required for each 150 square feet of enclosed area. The vent area can be smaller if the ground is covered with a vapor retarder. Access to the crawl space must meet requirements in *IRC* Section R408.4.

☐ Does the plan for termite treatment comply with *IRC* Section R318?

Termites are a problem nearly everywhere in the U.S. The map in *IRC* Figure R301.2(6) shows the risk of termite damage by state. Methods of treatment must comply with *IRC* Section R318.1. Termite shields on top of the foundation are approved by the code, but only in combination with other methods of treatment. In areas with heavy infestation (nearly all of California, states bordering the Gulf of Mexico, Georgia and South Carolina) foam plastic insulation is permitted below grade on foundation walls only when the foam is protected from termite damage.

☐ Is the property address legible from the street or road, per *IRC* Section R319.1?

Since this is probably the first time an inspector will be on the site, this is the first time you'll encounter this requirement. Nothing fancy is required. But lettering has to be 4 inches high and each stroke has to be at least ½ inch thick. Posting the site address isn't simply a convenience for delivery drivers. Emergency vehicles may have to find the site too.

☐ Are approved plans available on-site, per *IRC* Section R106.3?

The plans have to be available on-site during inspections.

Once you've passed the foundation and footing inspection, pouring and finishing can begin. The inspector won't be back on-site until groundwork plumbing is ready for inspection. So that's the subject of our next chapter.

Groundwork Plumbing Inspection

As mentioned back in Chapter 12, plumbing is covered in *IRC* Part VII, Chapters 25 to 33. That's toward the back of the *IRC*. But plumbing groundwork will be among the first inspections on most jobs. Groundwork plumbing may be inspected at the same time footings and foundations are inspected (Chapter 13) and at the same time the slab base is inspected (Chapter 15). On other jobs, groundwork plumbing inspection may be a separate visit by the inspector.

Not every inspector assigned to a residential job will qualify as a true expert on the plumbing code. Not many are eager to go head-to-head with a master plumber over some complex section of the plumbing code, such as venting. If your background isn't in plumbing, you probably feel a little uncomfortable with highly technical sections of the plumbing code. That's probably true whether you're on the contractor's side of the counter or the inspector's side of the counter. But I'm not sure you need the savvy of a plumbing code expert to inspect most residential plumbing systems. Here's why: Mastering a few dozen points in the plumbing chapters of the *IRC* will take you a long way, whether you're an inspector or a general contractor. About 90 percent of the most common plumbing mistakes can be summarized in a few pages. And that's what you'll find in the remainder of this chapter.

The value of these pages will be in the selection of topics. I've identified the most common plumbing mistakes. Of course, there's a lot more to learn. And I hope you find the time to become an expert on the plumbing code. Until that happens, you'll get along just fine simply by applying the information found in the rest of this chapter.

Figure 14-1   This pipe is rated to be a DWV pipe and is Schedule 40 in grade.

Figure 14-2   The vent is larger than the minimum.

☐ **Do DWV piping materials, size, and placement comply with *IRC* Section P3002?**

Much of the groundwork plumbing inspection is simply a matter of checking to be sure the materials installed are appropriate for the intended service. To make your task easier, piping materials are clearly identified by the manufacturer. For example, Figure 14-1 shows Schedule 40 DWV pipe designed for use as part of the drain, waste and vent system. You wouldn't want to see DWV pipe used in supply lines. *IRC* Tables P3002.1(1) and P3002.1(2) list pipe designations appropriate for either underground or above ground drainage and vent pipe. The ABS pipe in Figure 14-1 meets standards set by ASTM F-628 and could be used either underground or above ground, as shown in *IRC* Tables P3002.1(1) and P3002.1(2). Many types of DWV pipe can be used either above ground or underground. But some can be used only above ground or only underground. It's easy to make a mistake, so keep these tables handy.

☐ **Are piping materials identified by the manufacturer as either third-party certified or third-party tested?**

IRC Section P2608 identifies which plumbing products need to be either third-party certified or third-party tested. Third-party testing is required for the subsoil piping. An inscription on the pipe will identify the organization that did the certification or the testing.

☐ **Do plumbing vents meet minimum size requirements in *IRC* Section P3113.1?**

The minimum vent size for each fixture depends on the diameter of the drain line. The diameter of the vent has to be *at least* one-half the diameter of the drain line. So if the drain pipe diameter has to be 4 inches, the vent diameter should be at least 2 inches. The approved plan should show proper vent pipe sizes. Note that the vent extending up from the drain line in Figure 14-2 is larger than the minimum.

☐ **Is piping properly supported, per *IRC* Table P2605.1?**

Pipe that isn't supported can sag, crack and eventually break. Support requirements are based on the type of pipe and whether installed horizontally or vertically. Pipe supports probably aren't shown on the plans. So you'll need to refer to *IRC* Table P2605.1 to be sure supports are correct.

☐ **Is DWV pipe installed in trenches backfilled with compacted earth, sand, fine gravel or similar granular material to protect it from damage, per *IRC* Section P2604?**

DWV pipe can be damaged if the loads aren't distributed evenly. For example, DWV pipe compressed against buried rock is likely to crack and leak. To prevent damage, the trench should be backfilled with a bed of compacted earth, sand, fine gravel or granular material, as in Figure 14-3.

Figure 14-3 Pipe bedding and backfill.

Figure 14-4 The inspector shakes the pipe, checking for water to spill over.

☐ **Do vent pipe and vent fittings, installations and usage comply with *IRC* Chapter 31?**

Vent design is covered in both *IPC* Chapter 9 and *IRC* Chapter 31. This is one of the more complex areas of the code. There are too many possibilities to cover here. Your best guide will be the approved plans. Industry and manufacturers' guides to vent and waste systems are available from plumbing manufacturers. Craftsman sells two plumbing manuals, *Plumber's Handbook* and *Planning Drain, Waste & Vent Systems*. An order form is at the back of this book.

☐ **Does the horizontal piping slope the required amount for the pipe size, per *IRC* Section P3005.3?**

Drain and vent pipe must slope enough to prevent an accumulation of condensation and waste. An experienced plumber can spot DWV pipe with less than the required slope. The rest of us need to use a bubble level. The minimum slope is ¼ inch per foot on pipe less than 3 inches in diameter and ⅛ inch per foot for pipe 3 inches and larger.

☐ **Do DWV fittings and connections comply with *IRC* Table P3002.3?**

Fittings are marked with designations similar to what you find on pipe. But the marking will be more abbreviated because pipe fittings are much smaller than pipe. Make *IRC* Table P3002.3 your guide to the correct fittings. While this table refers to a standard for each material, the standard should be part of your library since it identifies proper use. Also note that many underground fittings have an arrow to indicate the direction of flow. Sometimes a tradesman will install a fitting with the wrong direction of flow. Keep an eye out for this simple mistake.

☐ **Are there any leaks at pipe joints, per *IRC* Section P3003.1?**

IRC Section P2503.5.1 describes the test procedure for DWV pipe. Plug the pipe ends and extend a test pipe 10 feet vertically to create head pressure. Fill the system with water to the 10-foot level. Then allow 15 minutes for seepage to develop. If there's a leak, you'll probably see a small puddle. If the ground is wet from rain, you may not be able to spot any sign of leakage. In that case, check the water level in the 10-foot test pipe. Figure 14-4 shows an inspector shaking the 10-foot section for spillover. If the DWV system is tight, giving the test section a good jolt will spill water over the top of the pipe.

Figure 14-5 Stub up for a cleanout.

Figure 14-6 A fixture trap and trap arm.

☐ **Are cleanouts located per plans and *IRC* Section P3005.2?**

Cleanouts in a DWV system must be installed at each fitting where there are changes in direction of 45 degrees or more. But only one cleanout is required in each 40 feet of run, regardless of how many changes in direction. Figure 14-5 shows a cleanout extending 3 feet beyond the foundation form.

☐ **Are traps and trap arms the required size for the fixtures they serve, per *IRC* Table P3201.7?**

A trap that meets code requirements ensures that the fixture will drain properly. The drain-pipe connected to the trap must be the same size or larger than the trap. *IRC* Table P3201.7 shows minimum trap sizes for fixtures.

☐ **Are fixture traps within the prescribed maximum distance from the vent, and do traps have the required slope, per *IRC* Table P3105.1?**

Each trap connects to a trap arm, the pipe between the trap and a vent. See Figure 14-6. *IRC* Table P3105.1 limits the maximum length of trap arms. For a 1¼-inch trap, the maximum arm length is 5 feet and the required slope is ¼ inch per foot.

☐ **Are backwater valves, if required, installed according to *IRC* Section P3008?**

Fixtures that have flood rim levels below the next manhole cover upstream on the public sewer are considered subject to a backflow of sewage. If there's an elevation change in adjacent lots, check if any fixtures in the lower lot are below the level of the manhole cover upstream. If so, a backwater valve will be required to keep sewage from entering fixtures in the lower building.

Figure 14-7 Building sewer cleanout.

☐ **Is there a building cleanout fitting installed in the building sewer, near the building line, per *IRC* Section P3005.2.7?**

Every building must be provided with a standard building cleanout fitting. The cleanout fitting has to be near the building so mechanical equipment can be used to remove obstructions. Cleanout fittings have to rise to the surface, as in Figure 14-7.

☐ **Will the water supply system pass the required pressure test?**

IRC Section P2503.7 requires that supply pipe be pressurized with system pressure or an air test pressure of at least 50 psi for at least 15 minutes. The water used to perform the tests must be from a potable water source. The plumber will have installed a pressure gauge somewhere on the supply line. Check for leaks in the system and check for the required pressure.

☐ **Will a pressure-reducing valve be required, per *IRC* Section P2903.3.1?**

If the water district supplies water at more than 80 psi, a pressure-reducing valve will be required. A pressure-reducing valve isn't required to pass the groundwork plumbing inspection. But the valve will have to be installed before calling for final inspection.

☐ **Was primer used on plastic pipe glue joints, per *IRC* Section P2905.9.1?**

With a few exceptions, ABS, CPVC and PVC pipe have to be brushed with primer before the joints are cemented with solvent. You should see traces of the primer at each joint.

☐ **Are DWV drainpipe sizes appropriate for the drainage fixture unit (d.f.u.) load, per *IRC* Section P3005.4 and Table P3004.1?**

IRC Table P3004.1 assigns unit values to residential plumbing fixtures. For example, a kitchen sink rates a value of 2 and a low-flow water closet rates a value of 3. When you know the fixture load, turn to *IRC* Section P3005.4 to figure the minimum drain pipe size.

Ready for the Pre-Slab Inspection

If the home will be built on a concrete slab, inspection will be required before that slab is poured. In most cases, the inspector will check preparation for the concrete slab on the same visit as when plumbing groundwork is inspected. So the inspection checklist in Chapter 15 will cover preparation for the concrete slab.

Pre-Slab Work Inspection

If you're a residential builder in Maine or Minnesota or if you're an inspector in either of those states, you won't have many jobs with a concrete slab. But in more moderate climates, most homes are built, at least partially, on a concrete slab. Slab construction costs less than a conventional foundation and results in a home that's both durable and free of floor squeaks — at least on the ground floor.

But slabs come with the risk of uneven settling if the slab base isn't compacted and built-up correctly. Obviously, that's a primary focus on any pre-slab inspection. But the inspector will also be interested in placement of the vapor retarder. Code requirements for the pre-slab inspection aren't complex. A few simple rules will cover most of the significant points. That's what you'll find on the pages that follow.

☐ **If a monolithic footing/slab is intended, is the ground under the slab adequately compacted and level, per *IRC* Section R506.2?**

Concrete slabs must be at least 3½ inches thick. If the soil and pre-slab material aren't prepared properly, the slab is going to crack and settle.

Walk on the compacted earth. Dig the heel of your boot into the soil. If you feel the surface compact under your weight, the weight of the concrete will have the same result.

The fill should include no organic material such as vegetation, roots or limbs, and should be free of trash, broken tools and debris.

Figure 15-1 shows the three materials permitted for any slab. The bottom layer is

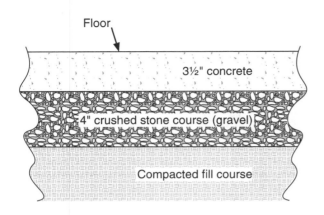

Figure 15-1 The three layers of material that make up the slab.

Figure 15-2 Measuring the distance between the base and the rebar.

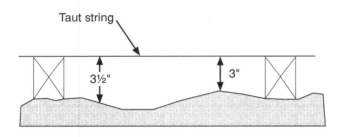

Figure 15-3 Cross-section illustration of stringline across form tops shown in Figure 15-4.

Figure 15-4 The base is at least 3½ inches thick; the drainage (DWV) pipe extends above the height of the slab.

compacted fill. On top of that, the builder will spread 4 inches of sand, crushed stone or gravel. The top layer is 3½ inches of concrete.

☐ **Is there a 4-inch base course, per *IRC* Section R506.2.2?**

Unless you're building on soil classified as Group I in *IRC* Table R405.1, the builder will have to import and spread a base course. This is usually crushed stone, but could be sand or gravel. Base depth has to be no less than 4 inches in any spot. Measure the thickness of the layer in several spots. The builder in Figure 15-2 is checking both the thickness of the base and the distance between the base and the rebar.

☐ **Are there any shallow spots under the slab?** *IRC* Section R506.1 requires at least 3½ inches of concrete for floor slabs.

Before the pour, stretch a taut stringline across the top of the forms at building corners. See Figure 15-3. You need at least 3½ inches between the stringline and the top of the base. Look for any shallow spots. While you've got the stringline stretched taught, check to be sure DWV piping extends above the slab level. Notice in Figure 15-4 that the DWV pipe is above the line of the future slab.

Figure 15-5 A pipe wrapped with protective foam material.

Figure 15-6 The anchor bolts and straps meet specifications.

☐ **Are pipes that pass through the concrete protected with sheathing, wrapping or by other means, per *IRC* Section P2603.3?**

Look for some type of sheathing or wrap around any pipe that extends through the slab, as in Figure 15-5. This pipe wrap offers protection from abrasive action caused by expansion and contraction in the concrete. Sheathing or wrap will also offer protection against chemical reaction caused by lime and acid in the concrete. Similar protection is required when pipe passes through cinders or steel. The wrap or sheathing material must be at least 0.025 inch (0.64 mm) thick.

☐ **Do pipes that pass under a footing or through a foundation wall have a protective sleeve or relieving arch, per *IRC* Section P2603.5?**

A pipe sleeve should be two pipe sizes larger than the pipe passing through the wall. This offers a margin which can prevent damage if the wall settles or shifts. When a pipe passes under a footing, a relieving arch is required to ensure that foundation loads aren't transferred to the pipe.

☐ **Are anchor bolt locations marked, and do the bolts conform to *IRC* Section R403.1.6?**

It's easy to forget about required anchor bolts. Many inspectors have saved as many builders from making this embarrassing mistake. Look for marks on the forms where anchor bolts will be installed. Note that anchor bolts may be required in both the foundation wall and in the slab, depending on the application. Figure 15-6 shows anchor bolts and straps extending from the slab after forms have been stripped. The requirements in *IRC* Section R403.1.6 are very detailed. I won't try to paraphrase that section. Have a copy of the *IRC* handy when installing or checking anchor bolt locations.

☐ **Is vapor retarder installed with joints lapped not less than 6 inches, per *IRC* Section R506.2.3?**

Vapor retarder serves two purposes. When the home is occupied, the vapor barrier prevents passage of moisture from the ground to the building interior. But a vapor retarder also prevents excessive loss of moisture while the concrete is curing. Concrete that dries out too fast will be weak. To ensure adequate curing time, the code requires an approved vapor barrier (retarder), such as 6 mil polyethylene, on top of the concrete base. Figure 15-7 shows welded wire mesh and steel rebars on top of the vapor retarder. Joints of this vapor retarder must overlap at least 6 inches.

Figure 15-7 Vapor barrier (retarder) with joints overlapping 6 inches.

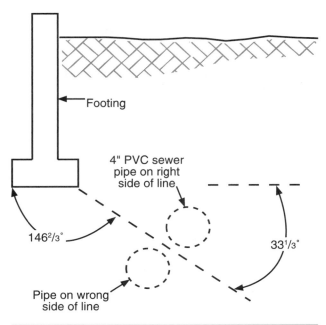

Figure 15-8 One pipe was installed below the 33⅓rd-degree requirement.

☐ **Check that pier footing sizes comply with *IRC* Section R403.1.1.**

Concentrated loads like posts and piers need more support than offered by a 3½-inch slab. Footing widths are based on the load-bearing value of the soil and the type of structure. To calculate the required bearing surface area of pier footings, divide the load by the allowable soil-bearing pressure. For example, if the load is 10,000 pounds and the soil load-bearing value is 1,500 psf, the pier footing has to be 6⅔ square feet. (10,000 divided by 1,500 is 6.666.) A footing 32 inches square will have 6⅔ square feet of bearing surface.

☐ **Does the depth of the footing comply with *IRC* Section R403.1.4?**

Exterior footings must extend at least 12 inches into natural undisturbed soil where frost depth and earthquakes aren't a consideration. The code lists several methods and depths to ensure that foundations are protected from frost. Some seismic conditions may require a depth of 18 inches or more.

☐ **Are footing bottoms either close to level or stepped, per *IRC* Section R403.1.5?**

The footing bottoms may not slope more than 1:10. Otherwise, a stepped footing is required.

☐ **Is any soil excavated within a 33⅓ percent slope extending down from the footing, per *IRC* Section R403.1.7?**

Footings must be supported by firm earth. Excavation within a 33⅓ percent slope under a footing jeopardizes this support. As you see in Figure 15-8, one of the pipe trenches is too close to the footing.

☐ **Is all electrical wiring under the slab protected, per *IRC* Section E3803.3?**

Underground cables or conductors (wiring) that extend above the surface must be protected against damage from stones and rocks. A bed of sand may be necessary to prevent damage. *IRC* Section E3803.3 specifies the required protection.

With groundwork plumbing inspected and concrete poured, it's time to begin framing. That's our next inspection.

C H A P T E R   1 6

Wood Wall Framing Inspection

Walls can be framed with light-gauge steel, masonry, ICFs, SIPs, concrete, or even straw bales. But wood is still the most common framing material used in residential construction. That's probably because it's fairly easy to get wood framing right. Chapter 6 of the *IRC* lays out framing requirements in considerable detail. Slight variations are acceptable, of course. But significant deviations will require the stamp of a registered engineer or architect.

The inspector will be interested in both how the framing is assembled and the materials that have been used. This chapter will help you spot deviations from what the code requires.

☐ **Are studs identified by a grade stamp from an approved grading agency? Does the grade meet requirements in *IRC* Section R602.1?**

Figure 16-1 A typical lumber grade stamp.

The code is very strict about the type and size of lumber that is acceptable. The stamp in Figure 16-1 identifies the lumber grade and its strength. Number 3 Standard or Stud Grade is the *minimum* acceptable grade for studs. Number 2 or Select Grade is better for studs.

Figure 16-2 Shear wall holddowns anchored and nailed to the manufacturer's specifications.

☐ **Do any framing members have notches or bored holes larger than allowed by the code? Are any of these notches located where they will weaken the member more than allowed? See *IRC* Section R602.6 and Figure R602.6(1).**

Allowable loads for framing members are based on their full dimensional size. But many studs and plates will be notched or bored out for electrical wiring and plumbing runs. The code regulates the size, number and placement of these cuts and holes. For example, no stud in a bearing wall may be notched more than 25 percent of its width; this increases to 40 percent in a nonbearing wall. No hole in any stud may have a diameter exceeding 60 percent of its width nor be located within ⅝ inch from the edge. There can't be more than one hole or notch in the same cross section.

☐ **Are wall intersections and corners connected correctly, as shown in *IRC* Figure R602.10.4.4(1)?**

The parts of a wall frame must join each other by attaching two studs on one wall to one stud on the other wall. The nails must be 16d, driven at prescribed intervals. *IRC* Figure R602.10.4.4(1) details the requirements.

☐ **Is lateral bracing (such as shear walls) installed where required and nailed correctly, per *IRC* Section R602.10 and Tables R602.3(1) and (2)?**

Holddowns for shear walls must be anchored and nailed per the manufacturer's specifications. See Figure 16-2.

A shear wall must have a brace panel at particular locations, usually at each end and at 25-foot intervals along the wall. The nailing for shear wall brace panels is detailed in *IRC* Tables R602.3(1) and (2).

☐ **Are brace panels installed according to seismic design category, condition, type of brace and amount of bracing, per *IRC* Table R602.10.1.1?**

IRC Table R602.10.1.2(1), (2) and (3) details the type of bracing material. Installation varies with seismic design category.

☐ **Verify that framing members are properly connected and that approved fasteners are used, per *IRC* Tables R602.3(1), (2), and (3).**

All framing members must be connected with screws or nails according to the standards in these tables. To withstand wind and seismic loads, each joist must be nailed to the sill plate or girder with three 8d nails driven as toe nail.

☐ **Verify that top plates in bearing walls are doubled, as required by *IRC* Section R602.3.2.**

Top plates must be doubled to adequately support vertical loads. Joints in doubled top plates must be offset at least 24 inches. The exception in *IRC* Section R602.3.2 allows a single top plate if the plate is either (1) galvanized steel, or (2) installed over a lintel that complies with *IRC* Section R602.3.2.

Figure 16-3   Is the total window area large enough to admit the required natural light?

Figure 16-4   Hallways must be at least 3 feet wide to comply with emergency exit standards.

☐ **Do wall openings, such as doors and windows, provide adequate natural light and ventilation, per *IRC* Section R303.1?**

With a few exceptions, the code requires natural lighting in all habitable rooms. See Figure 16-3. Any habitable room, such as a living room, must have windows whose total area is no less than 8 percent of its floor area. For example, if a room measures 20 x 20 feet, the floor area is 400 square feet. Window area must total not less than 8 percent of 400 square feet. That's 32 square feet. One 4- x 8-foot window or two 4- x 4-foot windows would meet code requirements. The window opening requirement doesn't apply if the room has adequate artificial lighting and ventilation no less than specified in the exception.

☐ **Do hallways and stairways meet minimum width and height requirements? *IRC* Section R311.6 requires that hallways be no less than 3 feet wide. *IRC* Section R311.7 sets standards for stairways.**

Hallway and stairway dimensions are part of emergency exit (egress) standards in the code. Both must be at least 36 inches wide. Figure 16-4 is a framed hallway ready for inspection. Stairways must have headroom of at least 6 feet 8 inches of above each stair tread. Stair tread width and riser height are identified in *IRC* Section R311.7. Handrails must be installed between 34 and 38 inches above the nosing of the tread.

☐ **Are support columns and posts installed per plans and properly anchored to the foundation and beams, per *IRC* Section R407.3?**

Support columns have to be sturdy enough to prevent collapse. Figure 16-5 shows steel post columns 3 inches in diameter. That's the minimum for steel columns. Wood posts must measure at least 4 x 4 inches. All columns must be anchored well enough to resist lateral displacement.

Figure 16-5 Steel post columns must be at least 3 inches in diameter.

Figure 16-6 Make sure the header above the windows is the correct size.

Figure 16-7 Uniform stud spacing.

Figure 16-8 An example of 16-inch center-to-center stud spacing.

☐ **Do dimensions of girders, headers, lintels and beams comply with the plans and *IRC* Tables 502.5(1) and (2)?**

Notice the header above the windows in Figure 16-6. Header and lintel sizes in the *IRC* Tables 502.5(1) and (2) vary with the load and span. The loading conditions include ground snow load, building width, tributary width for the load, number of floors and span of the header.

☐ **Does stud spacing comply with the plans and *IRC* Table R602.3(5)?**

Check the layout and stud spacing shown in Figure 16-7. This is a good example of uniform spacing. Maximum center-to-center spacing is based on the load and size of the stud. Note that *IRC* Table R602.3(5) refers to *loading conditions*, not just loads. A load is a weight, such as pounds. Loading condition refers to all framing elements above the wall. For most exterior walls, stud center-to-center spacing will be 16 inches, as shown in Figure 16-8.

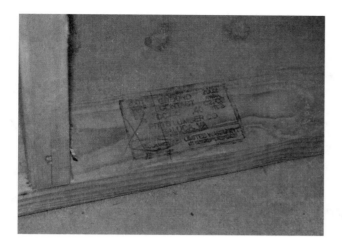

Figure 16-9 Note the required label for lumber in contact with concrete or ground.

Figure 16-10 The treated bottom plate being installed by the framer complies with the *IRC*.

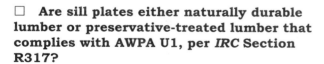

Figure 16-11 Checking anchor bolt spacing.

resistant to decay. Look for a stamp indicating that the plate is either treated or cut from a decay-resistant species. Figure 16-10 shows a framer nailing a treated bottom plate.

☐ **Are anchor bolts or the appropriate anchor straps installed on sill plates? Are they properly installed, spaced, and embedded to the right depth, per *IRC* Section R403.1.6?**

Anchor bolts and straps must be embedded in fresh, wet concrete. The code is very specific on the size, number, and placement. Spacing can't be more than 6 feet. Anchor bolts and straps probably aren't shown on the plans. So they have to be checked during the framing inspection. See Figure 16-11.

☐ **Are sill plates either naturally durable lumber or preservative-treated lumber that complies with AWPA U1, per *IRC* Section R317?**

Figure 16-9 shows a grade stamp for lumber intended to be in contact with concrete or the ground. Lumber that isn't allowed to dry out completely is vulnerable to decay. The bottom plate has to be either treated lumber or cut from a wood species with natural resistance to decay and termites. Heartwood redwood, black locust and some types of cedar qualify as naturally

☐ **Does each individual sill plate section have at least two bolts the required distance from the end of the section, per *IRC* Section R403.1.6?**

Figure 16-12 shows a properly-placed anchor bolt. Note that it's about 9 inches from the end of the plate. If a wall section is short or an odd size, the framer may use a single anchor bolt. Since the code requires only one anchor bolt every 6 feet, the framer may argue that only one bolt is required. Not true. Any wall section with fewer than two anchor bolts will be unstable.

Figure 16-12 Anchor bolt placement is critical for the builder who wants his job to pass inspection.

Figure 16-13 Properly-installed fireblocking slows the spread of fire into the attic.

An anchor bolt must be placed within 12 inches of the end of each plate, but no closer than seven bolt diameters from the end of the plate. So, if the plate is 24 inches long, and if ½-inch anchor bolts are used, both bolts must be at least 3½ inches from the end of the plate. In seismic regions, more stringent requirements apply. See *IRC* Section R403.1.6.1.

☐ **Is there fireblocking in every wood wall frame, including in concealed spaces, interconnections and in openings for vents, ducts, cables and wires, per *IRC* Sections R602.8 and R302.11?**

The code requires wood blocking in every frame wall. Fireblocks slow the spread of smoke and fire upward through the wall into the attic. See Figure 16-13. Imagine a snake in a wall frame. Blocking should keep that snake from getting into the attic. Fireblocking is also required between stories and between the top story and the roof space.

☐ **Is every wood member that will support drywall at least 2 inches in nominal thickness, per *IRC* Section R702.3.2?**

Drywall is heavy and must be supported adequately. A 2 x 2 is the minimum size support permitted for drywall.

☐ **Is wood framing that will support gypsum board spaced no more than 24 inches oc, per *IRC* Section R702.3.2 and Table R702.3.5?**

Gypsum board snaps under pressure if not supported adequately. Whether the board is ½ inch thick or ⅝ inch thick, support in both walls and ceilings must be spaced no more than every 24 inches.

When Framing Fails Inspection

Chapters 13, 14 and 15 covered getting ready for concrete pours. Most of the common code violations in those chapters are an easy fix. That simplifies an inspector's task. There's seldom any negotiation required when the inspector cites a violation in form layout or placement of reinforcing. With framing, it's different. Working off code violations in this chapter and the following chapter (floor and roof framing) can be anything but easy and cheap. That complicates an inspector's task considerably.

Figure 16-14 illustrates the point. Notice the header in the wall over the windows. The two windows are separated by a narrow vertical support and include only a single jack stud on

Figure 16-14 A framing mistake.

each side of the span. The header was made from two 2 x 12s. Total span of the two windows was 6 feet. Let's use *IRC* Table R502.5(1) to identify what header is required.

This wall had to support the roof, ceiling and one clear span floor. If the building is 34 feet wide and has a ground snow load of 30 pounds per square foot, *IRC* Table R502.5(1) tells us that two 2 x 12s will span up to 5 feet 5 inches. To span up to 6 feet 6 inches, the header must be made of at least three 2 x 12s and include two jack studs.

> *"Fixing a framing mistake like this won't be either easy or cheap."*

Next, we have to decide if this is a 6-foot span or two 3-foot spans. To comply with the code, framing of window openings has to match *IRC* Figure R602.3(2). Any support between the two windows in Figure 16-14 that's not a structural part of the framing system cannot be considered when identifying the span. With a *cripple* between the two windows, the span would be considered a full 6 feet. Note in *IRC* Figure R602.3(2) that location of the jack studs or trimmers identify the span. Here there are only two jack studs, one at each side of the

6-foot span. So we have to conclude that the effective span is 6 feet.

Two 2 x 12s won't do when three 2 x 12s are required. The inspector was justified in citing a violation of *IRC* Table R502.5(1). That creates an obvious problem for the builder.

The wall in Figure 16-14 was framed with 2 x 4 lumber and measured 3½ inches thick. The 2 x 12 headers we found in *IRC* Table R502.5(1) are 1½ inches thick. Two headers sandwiched around a ½ inch thickness of plywood comes to 3½ inches, perfect for a 3½-inch-thick wall. But a third 2 x 12 would make the header 4½ inches thick, too wide for a 3½-inch-thick wall. The builder has a huge hurdle to jump. Fixing a framing mistake like this won't be either easy or cheap.

The builder has three options. First, he could tear out what's there and re-frame the opening. That's going to require an investment of time and money. Second, he could get an independent engineering analysis to show that the wall as built meets strength requirements in the code. That could delay the job several weeks. Finally, the builder could appeal the inspector's decision to the Building Official. The Building Official has authority to accept variations from code requirements when following the strict letter of the code would be impractical. Of course, any modification must be consistent with the intent and purpose of the code.

Inspectors I know have little trouble responding with a simple "No" when it appears the builder made a conscious decision to ignore code requirements. You'll see examples of that in the next chapter. But a simple "No" isn't enough when a builder shows good intent and gets tripped up by a subtle point in the *IRC*. In a case like Figure 16-14, I feel the inspector has an obligation to identify perfectly good options when those options exist. When you have the opportunity, opt for flexibility and consideration — without compromising strict safety standards.

In this case, the inspector suggested the builder prepare an appeal form. That leaves a record of both the failure to pass inspection and an effort to find an alternate solution. It also limits wholesale requests in the future for similar exceptions. On this job, the Building Official considered the appeal and found good reason to approve the work with only a minor change. What could have become a bitter and expensive dispute turned into a win-win situation for all. I like that. You should too, whether you're a builder or an inspector. It reaffirms a point I've made more than once on these pages. Think of the inspector as a key member on every construction team.

More Framing Ahead

So far, I've discussed only wall and ceiling framing. We haven't talked about floor and roof framing yet. Even though I've covered wall framing as a separate topic, your wall, floor and roof framing inspections will usually be completed at the same time. In the next chapter, we'll inspect both floor and roof framing.

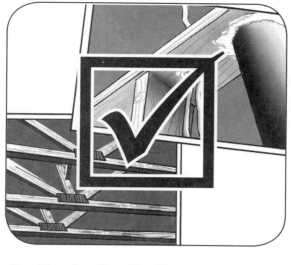

C H A P T E R   1 7

Floor & Roof Framing Inspection

This chapter will cover the most common violations cited during floor and roof framing inspection. If your job fails a floor and roof framing inspection, about 90 percent of the time the cause will be one of the 15 points made in this chapter. Expressed another way, if your job doesn't include any of the potential violations cited below, you can be 90-percent sure of passing a floor and roof framing inspection the first time.

Every floor frame is designed to accommodate a certain live load. Generally, the 2009 *IRC* requires that floor joists in habitable rooms be designed to support at least 40 psf. The approved plans will identify the size, grade and spacing for each framing component based on the design load.

☐ **Does floor joist layout, selection and installation follow the approved plans, per *IRC* Section R106.3.1?**

The first issue will always be compliance with the approved plans. Most of the time, when a job fails flooring inspection, it's because the framer made changes in the field without consulting the architect, engineer, or designer. All builders are tempted to do the fastest, most economical job possible using the materials on hand. Sometimes that's not what the designer had in mind. Review the plans to be sure what you see and what the plans show are the same. Consider carefully any deviation. Sometimes the result of improvisation will be an improvement. Sometimes the result will be a code violation.

Figure 17-1 Looking up at floor joists that met code requirements but didn't follow the approved plans.

Figure 17-2 2 x 10 joists set 24 inches on center.

Figure 17-1 shows floor joists viewed from below. When inspecting this job, I discovered the framer had used a grade of lumber different from what appeared on the approved plans. When I failed the job, the framer insisted I was wrong. The grade used met code requirements, he claimed. He was right about that. But I was also right to fail the job. If the plans show one grade and the framer uses a different (but acceptable) grade, the plans have to be approved once again, based on the lumber grade actually used. *IRC* Section R106.4 allows a revision of plans. And that's exactly what this job required.

If the approved plans call for more than what the code requires, the inspector is entitled to insist on what the plans show, not merely what the code requires. If a builder wants only the minimum required by the code, the approved plans need to show that.

☐ Do floor joists comply with the span and loading conditions in *IRC* Table R502.3.1(1)?

Joist size and spacing in *IRC* Table R502.3.1(1) are based on span, tributary load, live load, etc. Figure 17-2 shows a job I inspected several years ago. The 2 x 10 joists are set 24 inches on center (oc). The approved plans for the job assumed a 10-pound dead load and called for 2 x 10s set 16 inches on center. Why the change? It seems the plumber wanted more space between

joists to run his DWV piping. And the framer just wanted to be helpful. My task was to see if 24-inch spacing complied with the code.

IRC Table R502.3.1(1) shows an allowable span of 17 feet 2 inches for joists made from 2 x 10 Douglas fir-larch #2. The actual span in this case was 16 feet. But increasing the center-to-center spacing to 24 inches reduced the allowable span to 14 feet 1 inch. If the builder had used 2 x 12s, 24 inches on center or even increased the quality of the 2 x 10 lumber to select structural, there wouldn't have been a problem. A careless "field change" like this makes it easy for an inspector to give a flat answer of "No way!" In this case, the contractor had to double the 2 x 10s to pass inspection.

☐ Is the proper grade of lumber used per the plans and *IRC* Section R502.1?

Most lumber is graded under standards that consider visible flaws such as knots, checks and splits. Imperfections such as these help predict the strength of each piece of lumber. If the species, grade or size of a wood member is different from what the plans show, the strength won't be what the designer expected.

Lumber arrives at the job site with grade stamps, even though they sometimes can't be

Figure 17-3 Typical illegible grade stamp.

Figure 17-4 Solid blocking between joists.

read, like the fuzzy example in Figure 17-3. On this job, the plans called for floor joists made of select structural grade Douglas fir-larch. Reading *IRC* Table R502.3.1(1), I discovered that 2 x 12 select structural Douglas fir-larch floor joists supporting a 20-pound dead load could span exactly 23 feet, if on center spacing is 16 inches. But, to save money, the builder substituted hemlock fir — with an illegible grade stamp. Unfortunately, hemlock fir has an allowable span of only 21 feet 11 inches. So this lumber wasn't appropriate for a span of 23 feet. You get to decide if this was an innocent mistake or an effort to confuse the inspector. In either case, this code violation resulted in a serious delay, costing the builder much more than what he saved by using inferior grade lumber.

☐ **Make sure there's at least 1½ inches of bearing support at the end of each floor joist, per *IRC* Section R502.6.**

Floor joists must have at least a 1½-inch edge support on a wood-frame bearing wall or a wood beam. The minimum support on a masonry or concrete wall is 3 inches. If support is less than the code requires, the framer needs to install either a ledger support at the top of the wall or joist hangers.

☐ **Is blocking installed at points of support to keep joists from rotating or falling over (per *IRC* Section R502.7), and are the blocks utility grade or better (per *IRC* Section R502.1.2)?**

Blocking between joists is required at points of support, such as at bearing walls and beams. Solid blocking, as in Figure 17-4, meets the code requirement. There are alternatives, such as attaching joists to a full-depth header, a band or rim joist, or to an adjoining stud. Anything that keeps the joist from rolling off vertical alignment is acceptable. Lateral restraint is also required in the span, depending on the size and shape of the floor joists. See *IRC* Section R502.7. Bridging or mid-span blocking every 8 feet usually meets this code requirement. See *IRC* Section R502.7.1. For example, a joist larger than 2 x 12 must be braced with solid blocking or other approved bracing every 8 feet.

☐ **Are joists under bearing partitions doubled where required, and of the right size, per *IRC* Section R502.4?**

Many floor joists support a bearing wall that supports the roof or another floor. Floor joists that run parallel to and support a bearing wall may have to be doubled to provide adequate support. It's a code violation if that supporting joist isn't adequate. Another option is to provide a beam under the bearing wall. If floor joists in a bearing wall run perpendicular to the wall being supported, no additional support may be required, assuming the bearing wall isn't offset more than the depth of the joist, per *IRC* Section R502.4.

☐ **Where joists join a header or girder, are approved framing anchors or ledger strips installed, per *IRC* Section R502.6.2?**

Floor joists that frame into the side of a wood girder or header must be supported by approved framing anchors. Ledger strips measuring at least a nominal 2 x 2 inches are also permitted by the code. It's a code violation if the framer merely toe-nails floor joists to a header or girder. Fortunately for builders, this code violation is easy to fix. Just install joist hangers.

☐ **Where joists from opposite sides of a span lap over a support, such as a wall or beam, do the joists lap at least 3 inches? And are the joists nailed together, per *IRC* Section R502.6.1?**

Lapped joists are inherently weak, if not lapped properly and tied together securely. The minimum lap is 3 inches. Lapped joists must be nailed together with at least three 10d nails. A wood or metal splice is an acceptable alternative, if the splice is as strong as a nailed lap.

☐ **Have floor joists been cut or notched more than the limits in *IRC* Section and Figure R502.8?**

Any time a hole or notch is cut in a joist, the section is weakened. Electricians and plumbers can get a little trigger-happy when boring and notching framing members. *IRC* Figure R502.8 shows the cutting and notching allowed under the code. If a notch or hole exceeds what the code allows, the framer may be able to solve the problem with metal strap reinforcement. Cuts, notches and holes bored in engineered wood products are permitted only when part of the engineered design.

☐ **Do all fabricated wood I-joists have designations that comply with what's in the approved plans and specs, per *IRC* Section R502.1.4?**

Figure 17-5 shows engineered I-joists. An I-joist is a manufactured product designed for use under very specific conditions. I-joists that look the same can have very different ratings. It's easy to make a mistake. The *exact* I-joist must be installed, not one from the same fabricator with the same size and shape. Even experienced framers can make a mistake — installing a substitute without checking plan details. The

Figure 17-5 Engineered I-joists that didn't comply with the plans.

plans or specifications will show exactly what's needed. Be sure every I-joist installed carries the appropriate designation.

The framer who installed the I-joists in Figure 17-5 probably saved a few dollars by installing I-joists slightly different from what was specified. But cheaper usually means weaker. The inspector had no trouble explaining why this floor framing didn't pass inspection. It was an open and shut case. To pass inspection and still use the inferior I-joists, the framer had to install extra beams, columns and footings. I expect that framer was much more careful about substituting I-joists on later jobs.

☐ **Are there any cuts, notches or holes in engineered wood products, such as glu-lam beams, laminated veneer lumber or I-joists?**

Cuts, notches and holes in engineered wood products are prohibited unless specifically allowed by the fabricator. If you see holes cut or bored in an I-joist, read the fabricator's product description to be sure the cuts comply with what the manufacturer permits, according to *IRC* Section R502.8.2.

☐ **Is engineered framing material installed as specified by the fabricator and per *IRC* Section R502.8.2?**

All engineered wood products are designed for a specific use and condition. I-joists are like floor trusses, designed to be used as horizontal floor

Figure 17-6 Braced roof truss ready to install.

Figure 17-7 Roof truss without bracing.

or roof supports and nothing else. For example, I-joists can't be used as posts or columns. Refer to *IRC* Section R502.11.

☐ **Are floor joists connected to other framing members per *IRC* Section R502.9 and fastened according to *IRC* Table and Figure R602.3(1)?**

Friction and gravity aren't going to hold floor joists in place. Metal framing anchors and hangers are needed to secure floor joists. See *IRC* Table R602.3(1) for the correct quantity and size of nails or staples.

☐ **Are trusses installed per the truss layout on the plans, and with proper bracing? Is the correct truss design used in each situation, per *IRC* Section R502.11? Check for alterations, such as cuts or splices, or additional loads, such as HVAC equipment.**

A truss is an engineered product, like an I-joist. As with all engineered structural materials, use of trusses is limited to a particular design purpose. For example, the code doesn't allow a roof truss designed for a live load of 20 psf to be used as a floor truss with a live load of 40 psf. The truss fabricator will provide a layout and instructions that must be followed *exactly*. Any other use is likely to both violate the building code and nullify the warranty.

Be sure the required truss bracing is installed. Figure 17-6 shows appropriate bracing

installed by a framer who played by the rules. Figure 17-7 shows what the inspector saw when he arrived to check roof framing on a different job. The trusses weren't braced as required by the fabricator's instructions. Fortunately for this builder, installing braces was an easy fix. But failing any inspection will usually delay the job for at least a day or so.

☐ **Has draftstopping been installed in the floor-ceiling assembly? Is it installed correctly and with the correct materials, per *IRC* Sections R502.12 and R302.12? Is fireblocking installed properly and with the correct materials, per *IRC* Section R302.11?**

Figure 17-8 shows fireblocking created by doubling the top plate. Fireblocks help control the spread of fire. Draftstops serve the same purpose. Fire spreads very quickly through large concealed spaces. To help control the spread of fire, the code puts limits on the area of uninterrupted concealed space allowed in a floor-ceiling assembly.

If a building has concealed space over 1,000 square feet, a draftstop is required for each 1,000 square feet of space. If the concealed space is up to 2,000 square feet, a single draftstop is required, breaking the space into two separate fire-control areas of approximately equal size. Draftstops can be made of drywall, wood structural panels and several other approved materials.

Figure 17-8 A double top plate serves as a fireblock.

Figure 17-9 Draftstopping is provided by sealing holes with an approved material.

Figure 17-9 shows holes in framing members that have been sealed with material approved for draftstopping.

More Framing Ahead

The walls are up and the roof is framed. Sheathing will be the next inspection. So that's where we're headed in Chapter 18.

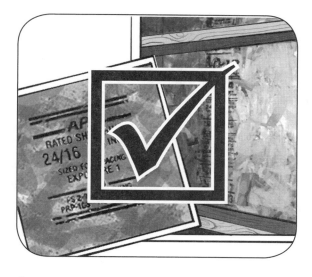

C H A P T E R   1 8

Floor & Roof
Decking Inspection

Roof and floor sheathing add rigidity to the building frame. Securely nailed panels transfer lateral forces (such as from wind or earthquake) to the adjacent walls. That's why nailing of these panels is so important.

We'll cover panel fasteners in more detail later. But the first topic in this chapter will be the panels themselves.

☐ **Are sheathing panels the correct grade, per *IRC* Sections R503.2.1 and R803.2.1?**

Wood structural panels used in modern construction are an engineered product. Like all engineered products, specifications are important. Panel specs are summarized in the grade stamp you'll see on each panel. Figure 18-1 shows an example. Notice that the grade stamp includes a span rating. That makes it easy for an inspector to verify code compliance.

Figure 18-1   Wood structural sheathing panel with grade stamp.

Unfortunately, most panels have only a single stamp on one side of the sheet. The stamped side may not be exposed when the panel is installed. That makes an inspector's task a little more difficult. And panels that have been cut may not show a grade stamp on either side. In my opinion, if most panels on a job show the correct grade stamp, I consider all panels to be in compliance. Nothing in the code requires that a grade stamp be visible on every panel. In practice, substituting inferior grade cut panels isn't worth a builder's time. A builder who isn't aware of code requirements will install bad panels throughout the job. The issue will be obvious.

☐ **Is the center-to-center spacing of supporting joists or rafters within the allowable span for the panels being used, per *IRC* Table R503.2.1.1(1)?**

IRC Table R503.2.1.1(1) sets allowable spans for panel products, whether for roof, floor or subfloor. First, check the span rating stamped on the sheathing — two numbers separated by a forward slash, such as 24/16. Read down the left column of *IRC* Table R503.2.1.1(1) until you find those numbers. Then read across the row to find allowable live loads. For panels stamped 24/16, the allowable live load is 100 pounds for supports 16 inches on center, and 40 pounds for supports 24 inches on center. A panel stamped 24/16 would be a good choice over roof joists set on 24-inch centers where the code requires 40 pounds per square foot live load. For subflooring, notice that the last column of *IRC* Table R503.2.1.1(1) restricts 24/16 panels to spans of 16 inches on center.

☐ **Are roof or floor particleboard panels installed per the manufacturer's specifications and *IRC* Section R503.3.3?**

Particleboard is a manufactured product and must be installed according to the manufacturer's instructions. Installation any other way is a code violation and has to be redone. Most inspectors verify installation of every panel.

☐ **Do panels meet exposure standards in *IRC* Section R803.2.1.1?**

Figure 18-2 shows the exposure rating as part of a grade stamp. There are four exposure ratings for engineered panel products. It's important to select a rating appropriate for the expected severity and duration of weather and moisture exposure.

Figure 18-2 Panel with grade stamp showing exposure rating.

■ *Exterior* panels can be used when exposure to moisture will be constant, such as a panel in contact with the soil. Usually, a pressure-treated panel will be a better choice. CDX plywood is *not* the same as Exterior Classification. CDX panels aren't rated for Exterior exposure.

■ *Exposure 1* panels aren't intended for permanent exposure to moisture. Use Exposure 1 panels, for example, on a porch where the underside of panels will be exposed. Exposure 1 is also a good choice when panels will be open to the elements for some time before being protected by other material.

■ *Exposure 2* panels are intended for protected construction applications where high humidity or short term water leakage are expected.

■ *Interior* panels are intended for interior applications only.

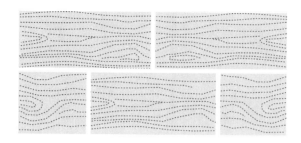

Figure 18-4   Staggered roof sheathing joints.

Figure 18-3   The inspector is pointing to the embedded holddowns.

□ **Are wood structural panels connected to framing according to *IRC* Table R602.3(1)?**

Every panel has to be secured to a rafter or joist. The nails to use and the spacing of those nails varies with panel thickness. For panels up to ¾ inch thick, use 6d deformed or 8d common nails spaced not more than 6 inches along the edges and 12 inches at intermediate supports. For ⅞- to 1-inch-thick panels, use 8d common or deformed nails. Figure 18-3 shows embedded holddowns connected to framing and panels.

□ **Do blocking and panel edge clips comply with *IRC* Sections R503.2.3 and R503.3.3 and Table 503.2.1(1)?**

The maximum span for structural panels varies with support provided at panel ends. Notice the *Maximum Span (inches)* column in the center of *IRC* Table 503.2.1(1). The sub-column on the left assumes edge support. The sub-column on the right assumes no edge support. Footnote d for the sub-column on the left identifies the correct location for blocking or panel edge clips.

□ **Do end joints in lumber used in subflooring occur over support, per *IRC* Section R503.1.1?**

Unless you're using end-matched lumber, such as tongue and groove, end joints must be supported by framing members. Even with end-matched lumber, at least two joists must support each panel.

□ **Are wood structural panels used as roof sheathing installed with joints staggered, per *IRC* Section R803.2.3?**

Joints in structural panels have to be staggered, as in Figure 18-4. Staggered joints help transfer loads across roof diaphragm.

Up Next: The Last of the Framing Inspections

The roof and floor deck inspection may be completed at the same time as the *exterior cover* inspection. *Exterior cover* is the term used by the *IRC* to describe exterior wall sheathing. Many of the panel materials and principles discussed in this chapter will appear again in Chapter 19. If you've mastered the basics of code compliance for roof and floor decks, you'll feel right at home in Chapter 19.

Exterior Covering Inspection

Exterior wall cover includes two broad categories of material. The first is structural panel sheathing such as plywood and particleboard. The second is structural siding installed over wall studs without a sheathing substrate. We'll cover both types of exterior wall cover in this chapter.

Plywood and particleboard are the two most common types of exterior wall sheathing. But many other products are available, including exterior wall covers that add insulation value. No matter the type, structural exterior sheathing serves three purposes. First, and most obvious, sheathing panels act like a skin to keep wind and weather out of the building interior. Second, structural exterior sheathing forms a rigid diaphragm that resists lateral loads such as wind and earthquake. Finally, exterior wall sheathing provides a sturdy substrate for non-

structural finish materials such as brick, stone, stucco or even decorative wood siding.

☐ **Are wall panels installed in compliance with the manufacturer's instructions and per *IRC* Tables R602.3(3) or R602.3(4)?**

Exterior wall panels are a manufactured product. Like all manufactured building materials, installation has to comply with the manufacturer's instructions. Any other installation is likely to void the warranty. Both the manufacturer's installation instructions and the manufacturer's listing requirements should be available on site for verification by the inspector. These instructions vary from manufacturer to manufacturer, even for similar products. It's good practice to review installation instructions and listing requirements as part of every inspection.

STRUCTURAL GRADE

Figure 19-1 Structural exterior wall panel.

Of course, installation also has to meet code requirements. Figure 19-1 shows insulated exterior wall cover. Look closely and you'll see the designation "Structural Grade." As with floor deck and roof panels, structural wall panels carry a rating, such as 24/16. *IRC* Table R602.3(3) shows minimum ratings for 16-inch and 24-inch stud spacing for plywood wall panels. Table R602.3(4) shows allowable spans for particleboard wall sheathing.

☐ **Do fasteners comply with *IRC* Section R703.4 and Table R703.4?**

Exterior wall cover will be exposed to weather and moisture. The code requires corrosion-resistant fasteners to prevent oxidation and ensure a durable attachment to the wood frame. Corrosion can destroy fasteners that aren't protected against oxidation. Staining around fasteners is a good clue that corrosion has started and that the fasteners may not meet code standards. Approved

Figure 19-2 Structural blocking for exterior wall panels.

fasteners are listed in *IRC* Table R703.4. These include aluminum, galvanized steel, stainless steel and zinc-coated fasteners.

☐ **Are the fasteners the correct size and are they spaced according to *IRC* Tables R703.4 and R602.3(3)?**

Exterior wall panel connections have to comply with *IRC* Table R703.4. This table shows fastener requirements for every common type of exterior wall panel. The inspector will check the size, type and spacing of fasteners.

☐ **Where studs are longer than 8-foot panels, is blocking installed at all panel edges, per *IRC* Section R703.3.1? Are panels properly nailed to blocking, per *IRC* Table R703.4?**

Exterior wall panels have to be supported on all edges. Wall siding panels are normally 8 feet long. When stud walls are more than 8 feet high, structural blocking will be required on at least one panel edge, as in Figure 19-2.

☐ **Has siding been damaged by nailing? Is the damage serious enough to void the manufacturer's warranty or product listing?**

Figure 19-3 Don't expect work like this to pass inspection.

Figure 19-4 Verify stud spacing for siding by inspecting from the inside.

Any panel edge that shows significant damage from handling or poor nailing should be replaced. Nothing in the code says how much damage is acceptable. The manufacturer's specifications or warranty may offer guidance. But usually this will be a judgment call. In my opinion, any panel with edge damage that prevents secure connection to the framing should be replaced. Patching is allowed only if all panel edges are supported by framing members. Don't call for inspection while any section of exterior wall panel looks like Figure 19-3.

☐ **Has weather-resistant sheathing paper been installed under the wall panels, per** *IRC* **Section R703.2?**

To keep weather out of the stud cavity and to preserve the wall veneer, a weather-resistant sheathing paper must be installed over studs (when there's no sheathing) or over the sheathing itself. There are a few exceptions, such as detached accessory buildings. Asphalt-saturated felt is one recommended weather-resistant sheathing paper. Rips aren't permitted in the felt. Ripped sheathing paper must be replaced. It can't be patched. All sheathing paper must be applied with the proper lap, which varies with the manufacturer's specifications.

☐ **Do all joints in panel siding fall on framing members? Are siding joints lapped properly, per** *IRC* **Section R703.3.1?**

Although it's normally a workmanship issue, not a code compliance issue, *IRC* Section

R703.3.1 does set minimum standards for joints and laps in structural exterior wood siding. A proper connection is important for structural integrity and weather protection. Requirements for laps and joints depend on whether the siding joint is vertical or horizontal. Joints may have to be shiplapped, covered with a batten, or flashed.

☐ **Does the stud spacing match the manufacturer's specifications for siding support, per** *IRC* **Table R703.4 — footnote (a)?**

Verify stud spacing by checking the wall interior, as in Figure 19-4. Normal stud spacing for siding is 16 inches on center. Studs spaced 24 inches on enter are acceptable only if in compliance with the manufacturer's specifications.

☐ **Do construction joints between dissimilar building materials fit tightly to prevent leakage, per** *IRC* **Section N1102.4.1?**

All joints, seams and penetrations in wall assemblies must be made weathertight. That's especially important where dissimilar materials join. Each material will have distinct expansion and contraction characteristics. The joint will tend to open and close with changes in temperature and humidity. That makes proper sealing very important. Figure 19-5 shows the sealed joint between two dissimilar building materials (wood and steel). Windows and doors must have gaskets and weatherstripping that maintain a

good seal as weather conditions change. Exterior wall siding must be caulked and wrapped with weather-resistant sheathing paper.

Done with Framing

When the exterior wall cover inspection is complete, you're done with rough carpentry. The plumbing contractor will go to work running interior supply and DWV lines. So that's our next inspection.

Figure 19-5 Tight joints are required where dissimilar materials meet.

Intermediate Plumbing Inspection

Chapter 14 covered the first plumbing inspection, the portion of the piping system that is run in trenches below the building. The last plumbing inspection will focus on plumbing fixtures. That's the topic for Chapter 25. The subject of this chapter is the portion of the plumbing system that will be concealed when wall and ceiling finish have been applied. This includes nearly all drain, waste, vent and supply lines.

This inspection is usually referred to as the *intermediate* plumbing inspection because it comes after the first plumbing inspection and before the last plumbing inspection.

IRC Section P2503.1 makes it clear that the entire plumbing system is subject to inspection.

> *"New plumbing work and parts of existing systems affected by new work or alterations shall be inspected by the building official to ensure compliance with the requirements of this code."*

IRC Section P2503.2 requires inspection before work is covered by finish materials:

> *"A plumbing or drainage system, or part thereof, shall not be covered, concealed or put into use until it has been tested, inspected and approved by the building official."*

What if the inspector arrives for the intermediate plumbing inspection and finds that drywall is already up? It happens. What should the inspector do? I would do my best to check what I can see, perhaps from the other side of the wall. However, it's not enough to see both ends of a length of pipe if everything between those ends has been covered with drywall. A plumbing

Figure 20-1 An approved pipe hanging method.

inspector needs to see the entire length of every pipe run. If that's not possible, walls have to be opened up. That won't make any inspector popular with a builder. But it's what the code requires and most builders understand that — without being reminded.

☐ Are supports for drain, waste and vent lines in compliance with *IRC* Table 2605.1?

DWV lines that aren't supported adequately will crack and break. *IRC* Table 2605.1 sets the maximum vertical and horizontal spacing allowed for pipe supports. Notice in the table that plastic DWV (the most common pipe in residences) must be supported at least every 4 feet horizontally and at 10 feet vertically. The pipe support in Figure 20-1 will pass inspection.

☐ Does DWV pipe comply with standards in *IRC* Section P3002 and *IRC* Table P3002.1(1)?

The *IRC* requires that all pipe used in residential construction comply with approved standards. Drain, waste and vent pipe has to comply with ASTM standards. Every type of pipe approved for use in residential construction has a specific ASTM standard. The most common plastic pipe is either ABS or PVC. This pipe is normally Schedule 40 and will be labeled to simplify an inspector's task. *IRC* Table P3002.1(1) lists all ASTM or CSA standards for aboveground drain and vent lines. For example, PVC pipe labeled *ASTM 2665* is acceptable for drain and vent lines run aboveground or underground. You don't need to understand what these standards

mean. You just need to read the label on the pipe and be sure that specification appears in *IRC* Table P3002.1(1).

Pipe sizes should appear on the plans. The rules for installation of DWV pipe can be complex. All the basics are covered in the *IRC*. Even experienced plumbing inspectors have to refer to Chapters 30, 31 and 32 regularly.

☐ Do vent pipe fittings comply with the standards in *IRC* Section P3002.3?

IRC Table P3002.3(1) lists ASTM or other designations for pipe fittings. Every drain, waste and vent fitting used in residential construction should be identified with one of these standards.

☐ Do plumbing vents comply with the minimum sizes in *IRC* Section P3113.1?

Vents let air into a drain system to prevent siphoning. Each trap or trapped fixture has to be vented using one of the methods permitted by the *IRC*. Every building must have a main vent that extends to open air above the roof. Vent lines must be at least half the *required* diameter of the drain served, but never less than 1¼ inches. If the drain diameter is larger than required by the code, the vent diameter can be based on the minimum drain diameter allowed. For example, if a 3-inch drain is required, vent size has to be 1½ inches, even if the actual drain pipe diameter is 4 inches. Chapter 30 of the *IRC* lists approved pipe diameters for sanitary drain lines.

☐ Are drainage fittings and connections appropriate for changes in direction of flow, per *IRC* Section P3005.1?

Every fitting is designed for a specific application. With so many choices, it's easy to make a mistake. For example, a sanitary tee may look like it could be installed on its back, changing a vertical flow into a horizontal flow. Unfortunately, that's not acceptable. If installed on its back, the change in direction from vertical to horizontal is too abrupt. Waste is likely to accumulate at the bend, creating a blockage. Note in *IRC* Table P3005.1 that sanitary tees can't be used to turn a vertical flow into a horizontal flow. Figure 20-2 shows a sanitary tee installed correctly.

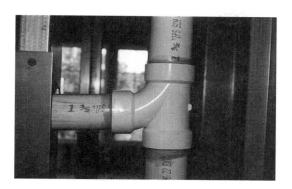

Figure 20-2 A sanitary tee installed to provide venting.

Figure 20-3 A vent fitting complying with the requirement of an upward slope.

The rules for installation of DWV systems can be complex. If you need more information on the fine points, the order form at the back of this manual lists how-to manuals written by a plumbing inspector.

☐ Does the slope of horizontal drainage pipe comply with *IRC* Section P3005.4.2?

Unless there's a pump in the system, sewage lines rely on gravity flow. The required slope for a drain pipe can be as much as ½ inch per foot to as little as ⅛ inch per foot. Minimum slope depends on the pipe diameter and the number of fixture units connected. A 3-inch pipe serving as a branch drain carrying waste from a group of bathroom fixtures rated at five fixture units can slope as little as ⅛ inch per foot. All drain lines have to meet code standards for slope in the direction of flow. Vent lines have to slope up in the direction of air flow, as in Figure 20-3. The upward slope promotes good ventilation and prevents accumulation of condensation in the line.

☐ Are there any leaks in the sanitary pipe joints, per *IRC* Section P3003.1?

Sanitary drain pipe isn't sanitary if it leaks. To test for leaks using water, cap all ends of the pipe. Erect a riser 10 feet above the highest fitting and fill the system to the height of the riser with clean water. The inspector will check to be sure there aren't any leaks. Details are in Chapter 14.

☐ Are all required cleanouts installed properly? Are they located per the plans? Do they meet the requirements of *IRC* Section P3005.2?

Nearly every drain line will get clogged eventually. Cleanouts installed at strategic locations should make it possible to clear a blockage anywhere in the system. Some cleanouts will be set into building walls. Others will be outside the building walls. Normally, the location of cleanouts will be selected during the design stage and will appear on the plans. But more than one plumbing inspector has been called on to cite the location for a cleanout. Figure 20-4 shows a cleanout fitting rising to grade at the base of a vertical waste or soil stack. Note that this cleanout is within 3 feet of the building foundation.

Figure 20-4 Cleanout fittings correctly installed on the jobsite.

IRC Sections P3005.2.1 through P3005.2.11 cover requirements for cleanouts. Here's a short summary of the most-common code violations:

1. Cleanouts must be accessible.

2. Cleanouts must be located near the base of each vertical waste or soil stack.

3. There must be a cleanout at the junction of the building drain and the building sewer, either inside or outside the building.

4. A cleanout is required any time a drain line changes direction more than 45 degrees. Where there's more than one change of direction, only one cleanout is required in each 40 feet of developed length in a drain line.

5. Cleanouts must be installed so their opening allows cleaning in the direction of flow.

6. Cleanouts must be the same nominal size as the pipe served, up to 4 inches. For drain pipe larger than 4 inches, the minimum cleanout size is 4 inches.

7. Cleanouts may not be more than 100 feet apart in horizontal drain lines.

8. Cleanouts must be liquid- and gas-tight. Plugs must be brass or plastic.

9. Some fixtures or fixture traps may serve as a cleanout if they're readily removable.

10. Cleanouts may not be used for anything other than cleanouts. They can't serve a double purpose, such as an additional drain or vent.

The drainage piping isn't complete until every foot of pipe is accessible from a cleanout. Ask yourself, will a plumbing snake be able to access every section of this sanitary system? If not, at least one more cleanout is required.

Figure 20-5 Slope of drain line and trap arm length are regulated by the *IRC*.

☐ **Are trap arms the proper size and length, per *IRC* Tables P3105.1 and P3201.7?**

Every fixture must have a trap. The function of a trap is to provide a water seal that keeps sewer gas out of the building. Some plumbing fixtures have an integral trap. Toilets are an example. In other types of fixtures, the trap is a separate fitting installed during the rough-in or when setting the fixture. The size of each trap is regulated by the code and has to be appropriate for the type of fixture. For example, a clothes washer stand must have a 2-inch trap. A trap arm connects the trap to both the fitting that transfers waste to the drain line and the vent that allows outside air to enter the plumbing system. The length of this trap arm is also regulated by the *IRC*. The maximum length of a trap arm varies with the size of the trap. For example, the 2-inch trap required for a clothes washer cannot be more than 8 feet from a vent.

IRC Section P3002.3.1 requires that drainage fittings slope down at least one-fourth unit measured vertically for each 12 units measured horizontally. That's a two-percent slope and is enough for good drainage. Figure 20-5 shows just about the minimum slope and the maximum trap arm length for a 2-inch pipe. *IRC* Table P3105.1 shows both the maximum distance between the fixture trap and the vent and the minimum slope required. The minimum slope is ⅛ inch per foot for 3-inch and 4-inch pipe and ¼ inch per foot for smaller pipe diameters.

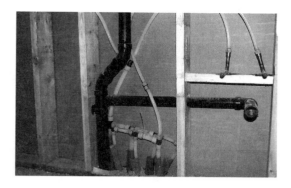

Figure 20-6 A trap arm located 6 inches above the fixture flood rim.

☐ **Are all required backwater valves installed correctly, per *IRC* Section P3008?**

Backwater valves prevent backflow of sewage and are required when the manhole cover of the public sewer is above the elevation of a fixture (or even an entire house). The backwater valve keeps sewage from the public sewer system out of the DWV system in the residence. For more information, review the section on backwater valves in Chapter 14.

☐ **Are required sump pumps or ejectors installed properly, per *IRC* Section P3007?**

If a plumbing fixture is below the sewer tap in the street (or the septic tank inlet), an ejector or sump pump will be required to lift sewage to the public system. Basements with plumbing fixtures will usually need an ejector. The minimum discharge pipe size is 2 inches, but high-capacity pumps or ejectors require 2½- or 3-inch pipe. *IRC* Section P3007 has complete details.

☐ **Has a water test been made on DWV piping on the upper story, per *IRC* Section P2503.5.1?**

DWV piping on a lower story is usually installed and tested before DWV piping is installed and tested on the upper story. When ready for testing the upper story, the plumber will cap all fixtures and fill drain and vent pipes to a height of 10 feet above the *highest fitting*.

☐ **Are vent connections at least 6 inches above the fixture flood rim, per *IRC* Section P3104.5?**

The connection of any vent pipe and vent stack (or stack vent) must be at least 6 inches above the flood level rim of the highest fixture served by the vent. Horizontal vent pipes that form branch vents must also be at least 6 inches above the flood level rim of the highest fixture served. Notice in Figure 20-6 that the trap arm (running diagonally) connects to the vent stack (running vertically) 6 inches above the rim of the fixture to be installed at the right. The flood rim is the highest level that water can reach within the fixture without overflowing.

☐ **Are plumbing vents kept the required distance from doors, operable windows and air intake openings, per *IRC* Section P3103.5?**

Vents must extend to open air. To keep sewer gas out of the building, vents may not end closer than 4 feet beneath or 10 feet from the side of any door, openable window or air intake. However, there's an exception. Vents can terminate closer than 10 feet from a door, window or air intake if the termination is at least 2 feet above the top of the door, window or air intake.

☐ **Do plumbing vents that extend through a wall meet the requirements of *IRC* Section P3103.6?**

Vents may extend through the wall as well as the roof. They must terminate at least 10 feet from the lot line and at least 10 feet above any adjacent grade within 10 feet horizontally. Vent terminals must not end under an overhang that has soffit vents. That helps keep sewer gas out of the attic. The termination of any side wall vent should be protected from nesting birds and rodents.

☐ **Does the required plumbing vent extend at least 6 inches above the roof plus the average snow-accumulation depth, per *IRC* Section P3103.1?**

Vents that extend through the roof system must rise at least 6 inches above the finish roof surface (and higher in areas with heavy snow

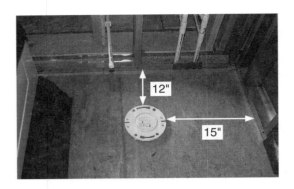

Figure 20-7   A closet flange located 15 inches from side walls and 12 inches from the rear wall.

accumulation). That helps ensure free movement of air through the vent system and protects water seals in fixture traps.

☐ **Are toilet rooms properly ventilated, per *IRC* Section R303.3?**

This isn't exactly a plumbing inspection item. But now is a good time to check for ventilation in bathrooms. A bathroom without at least a 3-square-foot window, half is of which can be opened, needs an exhaust fan. If a fan is installed, it must be rated at no less than 50 cubic feet per minute and must exhaust directly to the exterior, not to the attic.

☐ **Does the location of the water closet flange comply with *IRC* Section P2705.1 (item 5) and *IRC* Figure R307.1?**

The centerline of each water closet and bidet flange has to be at least 15 inches from *adjacent* walls or partitions and at least 30 inches (measured center to center) from any adjacent fixture. Clearance in front of the water closet, bidet or lavatory, to any wall, fixture or door must be at least 21 inches. The flange in Figure 20-7 meets code requirements.

☐ **Do water supply pipe materials, sizes and supports comply with *IRC* Section P2608 and *IRC* Table P2608.4?**

Normally, the plans will identify exactly the type of water supply pipe required. The inspector's task is to verify that the pipe used is the same

as what the plans show. Any change from the approved plans will require a new approval from the plans examiner. Getting a change like this approved is a risky proposition.

Inspectors usually develop an instinct for what is and what isn't an acceptable alternative. Most seasoned inspectors have seen "fixes" to code problems and understand what's likely to be acceptable. Every building official retains authority to apply the code as conditions require. When in doubt, ask at your local building department — before doing the installation and before calling for inspection. Note that *IRC* Table P2608.4 requires third-party testing and certification for certain uses of plumbing products and materials.

☐ **Does installation of water supply pipe comply with *IRC* Section P2903?**

The type and size of water supply pipe will normally be approved when the plans are approved. But routing of water supply pipe is usually left to the discretion of the plumber. That raises a potential problem. Routing can affect flow rates and thus the pipe size. Minimum pipe size is set by demand from fixtures on each branch and the total developed length of any branch. So the route selected may require a change in pipe size. Sizing of supply pipe can be a complex issue. Get expert advice if you suspect that pipe routing choices will affect flow rates.

☐ **Has the water supply system been tested, per *IRC* Section P2503.7?**

The water supply system must be tested under pressure, either with the working pressure of the system or, for metal pipe, with a 50-psi air test. The inspector has to observe that the system is holding pressure for at least 15 minutes. Figure 20-8 shows a pressure test in progress.

☐ **Are shield plates installed on stud walls to protect plumbing pipes, per *IRC* Section P2603.2.1?**

Water supply pipe passing through wood studs or joists must be protected with shield plates. That prevents damage from nails and screws driven to secure drywall, sheathing or even picture hangers. A shield plate is required any time a hole for a pipe is within 1½ inches of the edge

Figure 20-8   A water pressure test gauge.

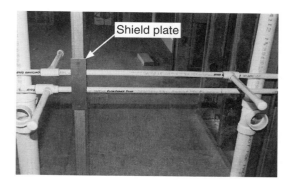

Figure 20-9   Shield plate installed to protect pipe from nails driven through the drywall.

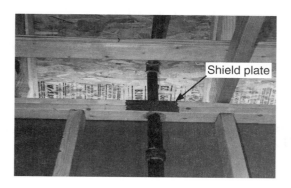

Figure 20-10   Protective shield plate.

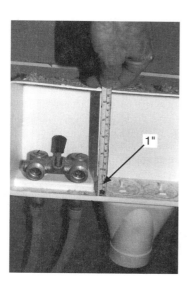

Figure 20-11   A 1-inch air gap to prevent cross-connection.

of a stud or joist. See Figure 20-9. Protective shield plates must be at least 0.0575-inch-thick (#16 gauge) steel, must cover the pipe area where framing is notched or bored, and must extend at least 2 inches above a sole plate and 2 inches below a top plate, as in Figure 20-10.

☐ **Does any part of the system offer an opportunity for cross-connection between the water supply and a source of contamination? Cross-connection is prohibited by *IRC* Section P2902.1.**

Cross-connection refers to a union of the water supply system with the waste disposal system. The normal flow of water is from a supply line to the point of use and then to a waste disposal line. A cross-connection makes reverse flow possible, from a waste line or point of use back into a supply line. If the water pressure fails for any reason, a cross-connection could result in waste water getting sucked back into a supply line. When supply pressure is restored, waste water could be distributed through the water supply system.

The code requires that every water supply system be designed and installed to prevent cross-connection. That keeps waste water out of supply lines. Figure 20-11 shows an example. If the faucet spout is below the rim of the basin, any loss in water pressure could cause water from the basin to be sucked back into the supply line.

Hose-connection vacuum breakers and other backflow prevention devices help protect against cross-connection. In Figure 20-11, a 1-inch air gap between the bottom of the faucet and the top of the basin rim will prevent cross-connection.

☐ Are all plumbing fixtures installed as required by *IRC* Section P2705.1?

Here are the most common problems with plumbing fixture installation:

1. Have corrosion-resistant fasteners been used to secure each floor-outlet or floor-mounted fixture to the drainage connection?

2. Are wall-hung fixtures mounted so none of the fixture weight falls on the plumbing line?

3. Are joints (contact area) sealed where plumbing fixtures contact the wall or floor?

4. Are all plumbing fixtures usable?

5. Are water closets and bidets the correct distance from walls and other fixtures?

6. Is any piping or plumbing fixture located where it will interfere with the operation of a window or door?

7. In areas where flooding is likely, installation of plumbing fixtures has to comply with *IRC* Section 322.1.7.

☐ Is there a separate pressure-relief valve on the water heater, per *IRC* Section P2803?

A separate pressure-relief valve or a combination pressure- and temperature-relief valve is required on water heaters. If pipe is routed through a wall, the inspector will want to check the route, materials used, pipe size and pipe termination.

So far in this chapter, the only supply lines we've discussed have been water supply lines. But fuel gas supply is considered plumbing in the *IRC* and appears in Part VI of the code. For the remainder of this chapter, I'll cover the most common errors in gas supply systems.

☐ Is gas piping sized according to *IRC* Section G2413.1?

Plans examiners use tables in *IRC* Section G2413 to determine the correct pipe diameter at any point along the system. These tables consider total gas demand, the developed length of the pipe, and gas pressure. The approved plans will show the correct size. An inspector's task is to verify that completed work is consistent with the plans.

☐ Is gas piping made of approved materials, per *IRC* Section G2414?

Both metal and non-metallic pipe is approved for gas systems in residences. Steel, wrought iron, seamless copper, aluminum alloy and steel tubing are all approved for gas piping under specific conditions. Many types of plastic pipe are also approved for gas. But plastic pipe must comply with restrictions in *IRC* Section G2414.6.

☐ Is gas piping clearly identified, per *IRC* Section G2412.5?

For other than black steel pipe, all exposed gas pipe has to be identified with a yellow label and has to be marked "Gas" in black letters. These labels must be spaced no more than 5 feet apart. The purpose of this marking is to alert workers that there's gas under pressure in the pipe. Marking isn't necessary when gas pipe is located in the same room as the appliance served.

☐ Is gas pipe protected from physical damage, per *IRC* Section G2415.5?

Just like DWV and water supply pipe, non-metallic gas pipe must be shielded from accidental damage. However, the requirements are different for gas pipe. If the gas pipe is other than steel, a shield plate must be installed when any edge of the hole in a stud or joist is closer than 1½ inches from the edge. Refer back to Figure 20-10 for an example of a protective steel shield installed on a top plate.

☐ **Has the gas piping system been pressure-tested for leaks, per *IRC* Section G2417?**

All portions of a gas piping system must withstand a test pressure of 1½ times the working pressure, but not less than 3 psig. The pressure test must be performed for at least 10 minutes, using air or an inert gas, but never oxygen. A manometer or pressure-measuring device will be required to read and record pressures. *IRC* Section G2417.3 identifies the test procedure and safety precautions to observe while testing.

☐ **Is gas piping properly supported, per *IRC* Section G2418 and IRC Table G2424.1?**

Gas pipe must be supported at intervals specified in the *IRC*. Pipe hooks, metal pipe straps, bands, brackets and hangers for gas pipe must meet code requirements for size, strength and quality.

On to the Mechanical Inspection

Of course, there's a lot more to learn about what the *IRC* requires in plumbing systems. But I've covered all the common code compliance issues inspectors encounter during intermediate plumbing inspections.

Assuming the residence includes heating, ventilating or air conditioning equipment, inspection of the mechanical work comes next. I'm going to call this next inspection "intermediate" because that's the common designation among code enforcement personnel. It makes sense in a way because the "intermediate" mechanical inspection is usually done when the intermediate plumbing inspection is done. But in another sense, the term *intermediate mechanical inspection* is misleading. It's not really *intermediate* at all. This will be the first time any inspector has checked the mechanical work.

But if you want to call this an *intermediate* inspection, you won't hear any objection from inspectors.

With that qualification, we'll proceed to HVAC work and the intermediate mechanical inspection.

Intermediate Mechanical Inspection

The intermediate mechanical inspection has to cover all HVAC equipment to be concealed by wall and ceiling finish materials. This inspection won't usually include HVAC equipment that will be readily accessible after finish materials have been installed. For example, heat pumps, blowers, condensers and furnaces usually won't be onsite when the intermediate mechanical inspection is performed. Mechanical equipment like that will be checked during final inspection.

The *IRC* sets rules for installation of HVAC materials. But in many cases, *IRC* rules take a back seat to what each material manufacturer requires. The best source of guidance on installation requirements for HVAC materials will usually be installation, operation and maintenance (IOM) manuals published by manufacturers. Of course, the installer should have an IOM manual available for each major component of the HVAC system. If the installer's

collection of manuals isn't complete, every major manufacturer offers IOM manuals on the Web. For example, suppose you need installation standards for a Trane 3-ton heat pump, model WSC036E. A search on the Web for "WSC036E heat pump" will probably access exactly the information you need.

☐ **Are approved exhaust vents installed per the manufacturer's specifications? Are these vents approved for the type of fuel to be used, per *IRC* Section M1804?**

Most gas appliances require a particular type of exhaust vent. For example, use an approved Type-B exhaust vent with gas appliances and a Type-L exhaust vent with oil-burning appliances. Regardless of the type of vent, separation between the vent and combustible materials must comply with the manufacturer's instructions.

☐ **Is enough combustion air provided for each appliance, per *IRC* Chapter 17 and Chapter 24?**

For safe, efficient operation, gas and oil appliances must have enough air to support the combustion process. The plans should specify the size of duct required for combustion air. An inspector's task is to verify that the duct shown on the plans is the same as the duct installed.

☐ **Do supply ducts and return ducts comply with the approved plans? Do locations selected for supply and return ducts comply with *IRC* Section M1601.3?**

The supply duct delivers conditioned air (heated or cooled) to the living space. In a closed system, the return air duct recycles that same air back to the mechanical equipment. Installation details should be resolved during plan review. Both supply and return duct should conform with what appears on the approved plans. But site conditions may require changes in duct materials and duct routing. Materials approved on the plan may not be readily available when installation begins. Framing materials may obstruct the route planned for duct. So be alert for substitutions and improvisation.

Check the label on factory-made duct and on connections to supply boots. The label should list an approved use, such as *air duct*. You'll also see the name of the listing agency, such as UL.

☐ **Does ductwork support comply with the manufacturer's specifications and *IRC* Section M1601.4?**

Duct must be supported to prevent sagging. With some exceptions, metal ducts must be supported by ½-inch-wide, 18-gauge metal straps or 12-gauge galvanized wire at least every 10 feet. Non-metallic duct must be supported as required by the manufacturer's specifications.

Both metal and non-metallic duct can be supported by the bottom chord of a truss. That's OK. But flexible duct inadequately suspended on wire or twine doesn't comply with the code. Over time, duct not properly supported will collapse or get pinched, restricting airflow. One good support material is woven polypropylene

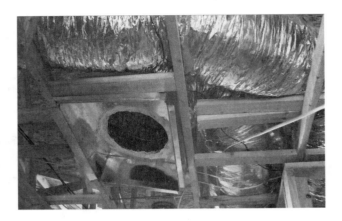

Figure 21-1 Distribution box supported between trusses.

strap, available in various widths. But the best support system is the one recommended by the duct manufacturer. Review the manufacturer's installation instructions. The installer should have a product brochure on hand. If not, the manufacturer's recommendation will be available on the Web.

Figure 21-1 shows a distribution box supported between trusses and blocks. The code doesn't specify how distribution boxes should be supported. Your best guide will be the manufacturer's instructions. In any case, nothing in the box should obstruct the flow of conditioned air.

☐ **Does flexible ductwork have any bends or kinks that could restrict air flow?**

IRC Section M1601.2 requires only that manufactured duct be installed in compliance with the manufacturer's instructions. Nothing in the *IRC* requires that ductwork be installed without kinks and bends. The manufacturer's instructions may not even mention the subject. But when I see duct that looks like Figure 21-2, I'm going to mention it to someone. This is more of a workmanship issue than a code compliance issue. The duct in Figure 21-2 is bent too tight for unobstructed passage of air. Over time, the bend is going to turn into a kink and further reduce capacity. Most cases aren't this clear. The inspector is going to make a judgment call. But if significant loss of airflow is likely, I would ask the installer to make a correction.

Figure 21-2 This duct is blocked by excessive bends that restrict airflow.

☐ **Does the size and material used for return duct comply with the approved plans? Does return air duct routing comply with *IRC* Section M1602.2?**

Return air duct must be large enough to relieve pressure that results when supply air is forced into conditioned space. Sizing of return air duct was part of the design process and should have been considered during plan review. An inspector is responsible for making sure work was completed in compliance with approved plans.

The *IRC* lists six sources from which return air may not be collected. For example, return air sources can't include garages, bathrooms, kitchens or certain configurations of the crawlspace under a residence. Dilution with outdoor air is OK if the inlet is covered with screen wire with openings between ¼ inch and ½ inch. It's good practice, though not required by the code, to include at least some outside air in the return air system. Modern homes are built much tighter than older homes. There's much less natural air flow from the exterior to the interior. Providing a source of outside air helps control humidity and odors on the interior.

☐ **Are duct joints and distribution boxes airtight, per *IRC* Sections M1601.4.1 and M1103.2?**

Duct joints and seams should be sealed with tape, mastic, gaskets or some other approved closure system. These seals have to be checked

visually. In addition, the *IRC* requires a pressure test of ductwork in unconditioned spaces such as an attic or crawlspace. It's hard to tell if a joint is really airtight without pressurizing the system, checking the tightness and listening or feeling around each joint. The test for leakage can be during the rough-in or at the final inspection. So if you see an obvious gap in a joint during intermediate inspection, ask for repairs.

☐ **If HVAC equipment is in the garage, ductwork that goes through the firewall between the dwelling and the garage must be made of at least 26-gauge (0.48 mm) material, as required by *IRC* Section R302.5.2.**

A firewall is required between the house and the garage to slow the spread of a fire between the two areas. Any ductwork passing through a firewall must be of no less than 26-gauge material. There shouldn't be any openings into the garage from a system supplying conditioned air to the house. If the garage air is conditioned (heated or cooled), it has to be with a system that serves the garage exclusively.

☐ **HVAC equipment installed in a garage has to be protected from damage by vehicles with an approved barrier, per *IRC* Section M1307.3.1.**

The *IRC* requires some type of barrier if HVAC equipment in a garage is exposed to vehicle damage. A raised ledge makes a good tire-stop. The post in Figure 21-3 is protecting a water heater from damage by vehicles. The same post would meet the requirement in *IRC* Section M1307.3.1.

☐ **Does the condensate drain comply with *IRC* Section M1411.3?**

Condensate from cooling equipment has to be piped to an approved place for disposal — either a fixture drain or to the building exterior. Pipe must be at least ¾ inch in diameter and has to slope at least ⅛ inch per foot to the point of disposal. A secondary drain is required for equipment in an attic or equipment installed where overflow from the equipment could cause damage.

Figure 21-3 The post that protects this water heater could be used to protect a furnace.

Figure 21-4 This is the rough frame for the attic access door.

☐ **Is there adequate access to remove, replace or work on mechanical equipment, per *IRC* Section M1305?**

If HVAC equipment is installed in an attic or in a crawlspace under a building, the minimum access opening is 22 x 30 inches. Figure 21-4 shows the rough-in for an attic crawlspace. There are other minimums, including passageway width and length. For example, a central furnace in a compartment or alcove must have a working space clearance of at least 3 inches along the sides, back and top. The total enclosed width must be at least 12 inches more than the furnace.

☐ **Does the passageway and working platform provided for HVAC equipment in an attic comply with *IRC* Section M1305.1.3?**

A passageway leading to mechanical equipment in an attic must be at least 22 inches wide, 30 inches high and no more than 20 feet long, measured along the centerline from the passageway opening to the appliance. The platform to service that equipment must be level and 24 inches in width.

☐ **Does the attic have a switched light and an electrical service outlet, per *IRC* Sections M1305.1.3.1?**

If mechanical equipment is installed in the attic, a light switch must be located at the normal entry point to the attic. A receptacle outlet is also required at or near the appliance location. Of course, the light, switch and outlet have to comply with requirements in *IRC* Chapter 39, Power and Lighting Distribution.

☐ **Is the length of the clothes dryer vent duct within the maximum permitted by *IRC* Section M1502.4.4?**

Unless the duct manufacturer offers some other standard, exhaust duct for a dryer must be no more than 25 feet long. With each bend of 45 degrees or more, that 25-foot maximum is reduced according to length reductions in *IRC* Table M1502.4.4.1. However, if the manufacturer offers some other standard for computing maximum duct length, that standard applies. For example, a clothes dryer vent with a booster fan can be any length allowed by the manufacturer.

You're probably thinking, "What happens when the owner replaces the dryer with another brand with different requirements?" This is one of those areas the code hasn't yet addressed. The intent of the code is to relax requirements for an owner who wants to add specific equipment. The assumption is that the owner will replace vent components with like components or will replace the entire vent system.

☐ Is all HVAC equipment installed at the time of this inspection labeled and listed, per *IRC* Section M1303?

All HVAC equipment will have a permanent factory-applied nameplate affixed to the appliance. The label will show the manufacturer's name or trademark, model and serial number, and the seal or mark of the testing agency. Check the nameplate on any appliances that have been installed prior to intermediate inspection. Equipment installed later will be checked at final inspection.

☐ Do appliances installed to this point meet the manufacturer's requirements for clearance from combustibles (*IRC* Section M1306) and installation details (*IRC* Section M1307)?

You'll need a copy of the manufacturer's installation instructions to verify code compliance. Clearance between an appliance and any combustibles, such as wood framing, is particularly important. Check anchorage to the framing, elevation of the ignition source, protection from impact, ventilation, and electrical restrictions. Fuel gas equipment can't be installed in rooms used for sleeping, bathrooms, toilet rooms or storage closets. If equipment is located outdoors, it must either be listed for outdoor installation or adequately protected. A mechanical contractor should be aware of these limitations. But anyone can make a mistake.

☐ Is mechanical equipment properly sized for the intended use, per *IRC* Section M1401.3?

Equipment for heating and cooling a house (or any building) should be the right size for the intended use. *IRC* Section M1401.3 approves

ACCA Manual S for sizing equipment based on building loads calculated using ACCA Manual J. These ACCA manuals are published by the Air Conditioning Contractor's Association (ACCA).

The size of mechanical equipment is normally worked out during the design process and approved in plan review. However, to cut costs, or simply by mistake, a contractor may install equipment that's either too small or too large for the residence. Equipment that's too small (not enough capacity) will be overworked, may overheat and has a shortened life expectancy. Equipment that's too large (too much capacity) will cycle on and off more than necessary. That wastes fuel because heating and cooling equipment reach peak efficiency after running for a while. Make sure the equipment installed is the same as the equipment identified on the plans.

Another Intermediate Inspection

The next inspection I cover will be the intermediate electrical inspection. Like the intermediate plumbing inspection and intermediate mechanical inspection, the intermediate electrical inspection has to be performed before work is covered with wall and ceiling finish materials.

I'm covering electrical work last among plumbing, mechanical and electrical. But there's no logical reason why, among the three, the electrical inspection has to come last. Intermediate plumbing, mechanical and electrical work can be completed in any order. What gets finished first will probably be the first to be inspected. And order of completion usually depends on the schedule of installing subcontractors.

Intermediate Electrical Inspection

Our focus in the last two chapters was on plumbing and HVAC materials installed in wall and ceiling cavities. This chapter will focus on the same wall cavities. But this time we'll be checking electrical materials. The job is ready for this electrical inspection when all wiring is complete (boxes worked up and wiring tied off), but *before* insulation or drywall are installed.

If the drywall has already been installed when the inspector arrives, the inspector has a perfect right to reject the electrical inspection. In fact, that's what I recommend in the case of any electrical subcontractor whose work is unknown or has been found to be questionable in the past. I'll consider making an exception for work done by an electrical sub I know and trust. And even in that case, I'll insist that random drywall panels be removed to check samples of completed work. Making a one-time only accommodation like this can help preserve

good working relations with both the builder and the electrician.

☐ If there's an overhead service drop, do clearances comply with *IRC* Section E3604?

Three-foot clearance is required between electrical wires running to the residence and any door, porch, deck, stair, ladder, fire escape or balcony. The same 3-foot rule applies to the sides and bottom of a window that opens. Clearance above the roof is based on slope. The service drop height above grade depends on whether it's above a residential property, driveway, street, alley or road. Service drop conductors must be 10 feet above any sidewalk accessed by pedestrians only. Service drops must be at least 12 feet above residential property and driveways and 18 feet above public streets, roads, parking areas and alleys subject to truck traffic.

ESSEX 14-26 NON-METALLIC SHEATHED CABLE TYPE NM-B

Figure 22-1 Type NM-B Romex cable.

□ **Does the electrical layout follow the approved plans, per *IRC* Sections R106 and E3404?**

Check for significant changes in the electrical layout. As with plumbing and mechanical work, site conditions sometimes force an electrical contractor to improvise. That raises the questions: Is this a change that requires a new approval? Does the change comply with both the letter and the spirit of the code?

Approved plans should be available onsite. Many jurisdictions provide the inspector with a set of approved plans. The file copy of the permit and the results of previous electrical inspections will be available at the building department office, if needed.

□ **Are electrical outlets located as required by *IRC* Section E3901 and Figure E3901.2?**

The *IRC* identifies where outlets have to be located. There should be little or no deviation. Circuits should match the approved plan and deviations should be corrected. If a small field change is essential, weigh the advantages and disadvantages. If the change is significant, the electrical contractor should run the plans back through plan review.

□ **Are boxes, wiring, and conduit identified with the manufacturer's name, per *IRC* Sections E3403.3 and E3905?**

Outlet boxes are manufactured to comply with an approved product listing. For example, listed outlet box sizes have wire-fill limitations. Non-listed box sizes don't. Look for a product evaluation listing like the UL label to make sure outlet boxes are an approved type. Wiring and conduit also carry a product listing and must be installed in compliance with that listing. Figure 22-1 shows the designation on Type NM-B cable.

Figure 22-2 A panelboard being wired.

Wire that carries current warms any space the wire occupies. Conduit and boxes too full of conductors can overheat when under load. That's why the *IRC* limits wire sizes and the number of conductors permitted in conduit, whether encased in concrete, buried underground or pulled through framing materials. Wiring limits in the *IRC* are based on standards published in the *National Electrical Code (NEC)*.

Conduit isn't required for most residential buildings. Type NM Cable, known by the trade name *Romex*, can be used for power and lighting circuits in one- and two-family residences.

□ **Has any panelboard been installed in a prohibited location, such as a clothes closet, bathroom, or where not readily accessible or where subject to physical damage, per *IRC* Section E3705.7?**

Panelboards, such as in Figure 22-2, aren't particularly attractive. Designers try to locate them out of sight. But the code prohibits locating a panelboard anywhere it would increase the risk of fire, such as in a clothes closet. And because of the electrocution hazard, a panelboard can't be installed where occupants may be wet, such as in a bathroom. Panelboards are permitted in habitable rooms or even in a storage room, so long as the room isn't designed for storage of clothes. A large pantry, basement or garage will usually be a good choice.

Figure 22-3 The cutout holds the ceiling box for the luminaire.

☐ Do lights in clothes closets comply with *IRC* Section E4003.12?

A hot lightbulb and clothes should never come into contact. A light can't be so close to a shelf that items on the shelf could ignite if the light is left on. The box in Figure 22-3 will pass inspection. If a light (a *luminaire* in code-speak) is too close to a shelf, someone stacking bulky items on the top shelf could break the fixture. Incandescent and LED lamps suspended from the ceiling need at least 12 inches of clearance from storage on any shelf. Surface-mounted fluorescent fixtures need at least 6 inches of clearance.

☐ Are kitchen and dining area outlets fed with two 20-amp circuits using 12-gauge wire, per *IRC* Section E3703.2?

Kitchens and dining areas must have at least two 20-amp appliance circuits served with at least 12-gauge wire. Look for two homeruns (circuits) to the breaker panel from the kitchen and dining area, indicating that at least two circuits are provided. Verify that the breaker panel is able to accommodate at least two 20-amp circuits using 12-gauge wire. Some manufacturers now color code their cable sheathing. That makes it easy to identify kitchen circuits.

Receptacles over a kitchen counter must be arranged so that no point along the wall line is more than 2 feet from an electrical plug, one

exception being granted for where it's behind a range or a sink. The same is true of any island or peninsula counter.

☐ If there's a laundry room, does it have a separate 20-amp branch circuit, per *IRC* Section E3703.3?

Clothes washing machines require a dedicated circuit serving that appliance only. Every clothes washer has a high-amperage motor that draws a heavy electrical load on startup. The circuit breaker would probably trip if any other appliances were on that line during startup. Regular tripping of a breaker during startup could damage the motor of the clothes washer.

☐ Is there a separate 20-amp branch circuit for every bathroom, per *IRC* Section E3703.4?

Appliances such as hair dryers and curling irons demand a lot of electrical current. So the *IRC* requires a dedicated 20-amp circuit using 12-gauge wire in each bathroom. The general rule is that no other outlets are permitted on this dedicated circuit. But when a single bathroom is served by a single circuit, bathroom lighting, vent fan or similar equipment may be on this circuit.

☐ Are any pendant fixtures installed too near to, or too low over, a bathtub or shower stall, in violation of *IRC* Section E4003.11?

The *IRC* prohibits any cord-connected, chain-, cable-, or cord-suspended light, track light, pendant light, or ceiling-suspended paddle fan within 3 feet horizontally or 8 feet vertically of the top of a bathtub rim or shower stall threshold. The idea is that no bather standing in the tub or shower should be able to reach any electrical fixture. Look for a light fixture wiring box that isn't a recessed fixture. If the inspector sees a potential problem, expect a warning notice on the inspection ticket.

☐ Do you see at least 6 inches of free conductor wire at outlet boxes, per *IRC* Section E3406.10.3?

Wire to an outlet box must extend out of the box by at least 6 inches. That makes it easy to pull a receptacle out of the box while still connected to

Figure 22-4 Conductor wire extending from an outlet box.

the wire. The wire extending from the outlet box in Figure 22-4 is clearly within regulation.

☐ Are there boxes for exterior lighting at residence exits, per *IRC* Section E3903.3?

Grade level exterior exits (doors) must have at least one lighting outlet to illuminate the path for safe egress. This outlet must have at least one wall switch control.

☐ Are there ground-level receptacle outlets at the front and back of each dwelling unit, per *IRC* Section E3901.7?

Every grade-level access door should have an outdoor receptacle outlet nearby. The outlet must be installed not more than 6 feet 6 inches above grade. This outlet must be protected with a GFCI (Ground Fault Circuit Interrupter).

☐ Are ceiling fan boxes an approved type, per *IRC* Section E3905.9?

A ceiling fan with a light can be heavy. And movement of the fan blades can affect the security of the mounting box. Any box intended for mounting a ceiling fan has to be marked as suitable for that purpose. Maximum support weight is 75 pounds. A box designed to support more than 35 pounds has to be marked with the maximum design weight.

☐ Are fixtures such as heavy lights supported properly, per *IRC* Section E3905.7?

Even with an approved box, proper support for the box is also essential. The weight can cause nail connections to the rafter to work loose. Any mounting box intended to support more than 50 pounds has to comply with *IRC* Section E3905.7. The box must be supported with framing members or mechanically connected to framing.

☐ Will a listed IBTB be installed, per *IRC* Section E3609.3?

Beginning in 2008, residential electrical systems were required to have an intersystem bonding termination block, or IBTB. That's a big name for small device that permits joining ground wires from all grounded systems in the home, including electric power service, telephone, cable TV, TV antenna, data network wiring, solar systems, etc. A common ground reduces damage if there's a power surge, such as from a lightning strike. The IBTB should be mounted near the meter and can be grounded in any of several ways. Because the IBTB is readily accessible, every grounded system in the home, including systems added after completion, can be connected. Figure 22-5 shows a typical installation.

☐ Is there a receptacle on an adjacent wall within 36 inches of the outside edge of each lavatory basin, per *IRC* Section E3901.6?

At least one wall receptacle outlet is required within 36 inches of the outside edge of each lavatory basin. The outlet must be beside the lavatory basin so there's no need to stretch an electrical cord across the basin. Face-up receptacle outlets are prohibited on bathroom work surfaces and countertops. That helps keeps standing water out of the receptacle.

☐ Is there enough working space around panelboards? Is this space easily accessible and provided with lighting, per *IRC* Section E3405?

All energized electrical equipment that may require servicing, examination or maintenance needs a clearance at least 30 inches wide by 36 inches deep by 6 feet 6 inches high. The door

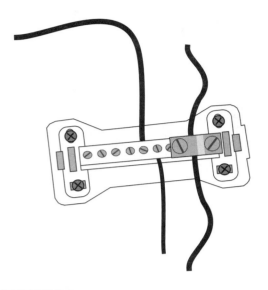

Figure 22-5 Intersystem bonding termination block (IBTB).

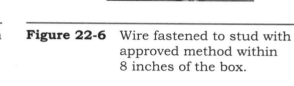

Figure 22-6 Wire fastened to stud with approved method within 8 inches of the box.

enclosing any electrical equipment needs enough space to swing open at least 90 degrees. A switched light is required to provide illumination for repair work.

☐ **Is wire entering each outlet or switch box fastened to the box, per *IRC* Section E3905.3.2?**

The type of fastener used is important. Neither a bent-over nail nor duct tape is acceptable. The connection between the wire and the box cannot damage the wiring and has to be secure. But there is an exception. Nonmetallic-sheathed cable doesn't have to be fastened to boxes up to 2¼ inches by 4 inches if cable enters the box through a knockout not over ¼ inch and if the cable is fastened to framing within 8 inches of the box. Figure 22-6 shows the exception.

☐ **Are approved conductor crimp rings and compression fittings installed properly, per *IRC* Sections E3406.9 and E3406.10?**

Wire must be connected to an outlet, a switch, an approved device, or to another wire using an approved connector. Splices must be made using approved devices only. Crimp rings and compression fittings use pressure to make a mechanical connection. Avoid damaging the wire when making any mechanical connection. The compression fittings (wire nuts) in Figure 22-7 are fastened correctly and will pass inspection. The crimp ring connecting bare ground wire in Figure 22-8 has also been attached according to code.

☐ **Does the number of wires entering any outlet box comply with the limit in *IRC* Section E3905.13 and *IRC* Tables E3905.13.1 and E3905.13.2.1?**

Every box has a cubic-inch-capacity rating which identifies how many conductors can enter the box. The *IRC* uses the term *conductor* to refer to any wire that transfers electricity. The cubic-inch rating of any box is usually stamped on the side of the box. If you see a metal box without a capacity rating, use the cubic-inch rating in *IRC* Table E3905.13.1. The same table lists the maximum number of conductors permitted in a metal box. For other boxes, divide the free space required in *IRC* Table E3905.13.2.1 into the cubic-inch rating of the box and round down to the nearest whole number. That's how many conductors are permitted.

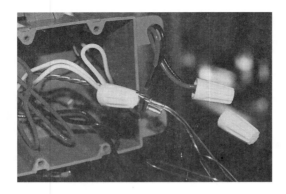

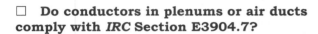

Figure 22-7 Compression fittings (wire nuts) correctly fastened to pass inspection.

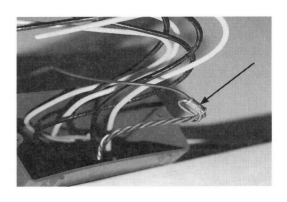

Figure 22-8 A crimp ring attached according to code.

☐ **Do conductors in plenums or air ducts comply with *IRC* Section E3904.7?**

Non-metallic cable may be run through stud cavities and joist spaces that also include supply or return-air plenum. But the electrical wire must be protected from decay. The code says that the method of protecting wire in contact with a plenum is to align the wire with the long dimension of the stud. That way, only a short length of cable is in contact with the plenum.

☐ **Is any NM or NMS cable run through concrete, adobe, or cinder block in violation of *NEC* Article 334.12(B)?**

Cable Types NM and NMS must not be embedded in masonry, concrete, adobe, fill, or plaster. Also, NM and NMS cable can't be exposed to fumes or vapor. Wiring used in these areas must be run through conduit. If NM cable is within air voids of masonry, the installation is acceptable.

☐ **Are all motors ventilated and accessible, per *NEC* Article 430.14(A)?**

Motors in equipment such as a hydro-massage tub must be well ventilated and accessible for service. Submersible motors don't require ventilation.

☐ **Are branch circuits rated according to the maximum allowable amperage setting of any breaker or overcurrent device, per *IRC* Section E3702.2?**

A circuit breaker (overcurrent device) limits the maximum amperage permitted for the size of wire supplying a circuit. Most common circuits in a residence are 15- or 20-amp circuits. Normally, a 15-amp circuit may feed #14 (AWG) conductors and a 20-amp circuit may feed #12 (AWG) conductors.

☐ **Is a steel plate used to protect any hole bored for electric cable that's within 1¼ inches of the edge of a stud or joist, per *IRC* Table E3802.1?**

A steel plate will protect wiring against penetration by a nail or screw used to fasten drywall. A 2 x 4 stud is only 3½ inches wide. So a ½-inch hole bored in the exact center of a stud is within 1¼ inches of both sides of the stud. Obviously, the electrician has to be precise when boring out studs.

☐ **Is the grounding conductor joined to the grounding electrode using an approved connector, per *IRC* Section E3611.1?**

An approved pressure connector is required when joining a grounding electrode to the grounding conductor. Figure 22-9 shows a single clamp connected to a grounding connector. This connection will pass inspection.

Figure 22-9   A single clamp connected to a grounding connector.

Figure 22-10   Grounded metal light base box.

Figure 22-11   Outlets spaced along a wall.

□ **Are metal boxes grounded, per *IRC* Section E3905.2?**

Every metallic part of a building that has the possibility of becoming energized must be connected to the electrical ground. A metal outlet or lighting box is certainly likely to become energized. To prevent accidental electrocution, the metal box must be grounded with a mechanical connection (green ground screw). In Figure 22-10, the metal light base is grounded by the screw which secures the grounding conductor.

□ **Is each circuit run to the service panel clearly identified as to purpose or use, per *IRC* Section E3706.2?**

Each run to the service panel has to be identified on the panel. For example, the label "Kitchen

outlets" would meet code requirements. Although this is a point for final inspection, it's a good idea to identify each homerun when making up the service panel.

□ **Does outlet spacing around rooms comply with *IRC* Section E3901.2.1?**

Receptacles must be spaced so that no point along the floor line of any wall is more than 6 feet, measured horizontally, from an outlet. See Figure 22-11. That means at least one outlet is required in every wall that's 12-feet long or more. As far as practical, outlets should be spaced at equal intervals. An outlet is required within 6 feet of any door frame, per *IRC* Figure E3901.2.

□ **Is at least one wall-switch-controlled lighting outlet provided in habitable rooms and bathrooms, per *IRC* Section E3903.2?**

For safety reasons, every habitable room needs a switch-operated light. This light can be either a ceiling light fixture or a switched outlet for use with a lamp, in rooms other than bathrooms and kitchens.

□ **Are smoke alarm outlets installed as required by *IRC* Sections R314.2, R314.3 and R314.4?**

The *IRC* requires smoke alarms in each sleeping room and immediately outside each group of sleeping rooms in adjacent hallways. Smoke alarms are also required on each story of a home, including the basement. They must be connected to the building power supply in new construction. Also, smoke alarms should be interconnected. Activation of one alarm should activate all alarms. This interconnection wiring may not be obvious. Look for a separate low-voltage wire running between the alarms. This guarantees that all residents in a dwelling will be alerted if fire breaks out anywhere in the building. A battery backup is required so smoke detectors will operate even if the power fails. Most smoke detectors have this capability. Where a building is not provided with power, or for additions not requiring the removal of interior finishes, battery-only units are permitted.

A Final Word about Electrical Inspections

The *IRC* is intended to be consistent with the *National Electrical Code*. But, obviously, the *IRC* doesn't include the entire *National Electrical Code*. It doesn't have to. One- and two-family dwellings don't involve most of what's in the *NEC*.

But if you see an electrical issue that's not covered in the *IRC*, it's perfectly acceptable to reference the *NEC*. You'll note that I've done that a few times in this chapter. Section E3401.1 makes that clear. What's allowed (and prohibited) by the *NEC* is also allowed (and prohibited) by the *IRC*.

"E3401.1 Applicability. The provisions of Chapters 34 through 43 shall establish the general scope of the electrical system and equipment requirements of this code. Chapters 34 through 43 cover those wiring methods and materials most commonly encountered in the construction of one- and two-family dwellings and structures regulated by this code. Other wiring methods, materials and subject matter covered in the NFPA 70 are also allowed by this code."

Once all work in wall and ceiling cavities has been approved, it's time to start filling those cavities with insulation. And that's where we're going in Chapter 23.

C H A P T E R   2 3

Energy Efficiency Inspection

IRC Chapter 11, Energy Efficiency, has probably changed more than any other chapter in the *IRC* over the last few years. That's probably because our concept of what constitutes energy efficiency has changed so fundamentally over the last decade. Nearly one-third of all energy consumed in the U.S. is used to heat and cool buildings. So it makes sense to have building codes that require energy efficiency. Over the lifetime of a building, the cost of energy consumed to heat and cool it may total nearly as much as the original cost of construction. That makes energy efficiency the business of every builder and inspector.

Energy efficiency in buildings, and thus code compliance, focuses on four areas:

- *Wall openings:* maximum heat transfer and air leakage for windows, doors and skylights

- *Insulation:* minimum levels of insulation for walls, ceilings, floors, foundations and ducts

- *Infiltration:* proper sealing to restrict passage of air through the building envelope

- *Equipment:* selection and sizing of electrical and HVAC equipment

Today, nearly all jurisdictions can be expected to inspect for energy code compliance. That may not have been true a decade or more ago. Most states currently have a mandatory statewide residential energy code in effect. But it's still true that code requirements for energy efficiency vary widely from state to state. For an up-to-date assessment of the standards your state enforces, see the map maintained by OCEAN, the Online Code Enforcement & Advocacy Network at http://bcap-ocean.org/.

Compliance begins with plan review, of course. The primary focus of every inspection for energy efficiency will be verifying compliance with the plans. To make that easier, nearly all materials required by *IRC* Chapter 11 will be labeled with a performance standard. The most common of these ratings will be *R-value*, a measure of any material's ability to resist the flow of heat. You'll also see references in the *IRC* to *U-factor*. That's the ability of a material to conduct heat. *U*-factor is the inverse of the *R*-value. If you know the *R*-value, it's easy to calculate the *U*-factor. The *U*-factor is equal to 1 divided by the *R*-value. For example, if the *R*-value is 16, the *U*-factor is 1 divided by 16, or 0.06.

You'll also see the abbreviation *SHGC* in *IRC* tables. Solar Heat Gain Coefficient is a measure of how well glazing blocks heat from sunlight. The SHGC is the fraction of the heat from the sun that enters through a window or glazed door. SHGC is expressed as a number between 0 and 1. The lower the SHGC, the less solar heat the glazing transmits to a building interior.

One more definition before we begin our inspection. The term *fenestration* refers to the design and arrangement of openings in a building envelope. Of course, the most common openings are windows, doors and skylights.

Insulation requirements in the *IRC* begin with a climate zone — how much heat and cold can be expected in a geographic area. *IRC* Figure N1101.2 is a climate zone map of the U.S. If you have trouble deciphering zone details for your community, *IRC* Table N1101.2 lists the climate zone for every county in the U.S. In the table, the name of every county is preceded by a number and a letter. The number (from 1 to 8) is the climate zone and refers to heating and cooling requirements in that county. The letter (A, B, or C) refers to moisture in the air.

IRC Figure N1101.2 offers two options for meeting energy standards.

"Compliance shall be demonstrated by either meeting the requirements of the International Energy Conservation Code *or meeting the requirements of this chapter."*

That's nothing new. In the last chapter, I described how meeting the requirements of the *National Electrical Code* was an alternative to

Figure 23-1 Attic insulation.

meeting the electrical requirements of the *IRC*. The same policy applies in Chapter 11. As a practical matter, you'll seldom need to fall back to the *International Energy Conservation Code*. Complying with the prescriptive *IRC* is easier.

☐ Is the required *R*-value insulation provided in walls, floors and ceilings, per *IRC* Table N1102.1?

This table brings together in one place most of what both builders and inspectors need to know about insulation values required by *IRC* Chapter 11. Read down the left column until you find your climate zone. Then read across the table to find *R*-values, *U*-factors and SHGC ratings required for residential construction in your climate zone.

Figure 23-1 shows fiberglass insulation installed between rafters in an attic. Attic and wall insulation should be installed according to the approved plans, which will be based on *IRC* Table N1102.1. Verify this by checking the printed *R*-rating on the insulation's paper cover. If the insulation doesn't have a rating label, a written certificate of installation serves as proof of the rating.

☐ Is the required rating (*R*-value) for basement wall insulation provided, per *IRC* Table N1102.1?

Notice in *IRC* Figure N1101.2 that basement wall insulation isn't required in Florida, in coastal areas along the Gulf of Mexico and in

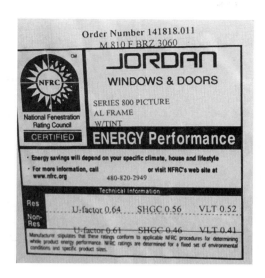

Figure 23-2 Energy performance rating on an exterior door.

southwest Arizona. Read footnote *f* to discover that basement wall insulation isn't required in warm-humid locations as defined by *IRC* Figure N1101.2. That's the southern half of most states below a line extending from North Carolina to Texas. Elsewhere, basement walls require R-5 to R-13 insulation.

Notice also in *IRC* Figure N1101.2 that insulation requirements for crawlspace perimeter walls are the same as insulation requirements for basement walls.

☐ **Is the required rating (*R*-value) for slab perimeter insulation provided, per *IRC* Table N1102.1?**

Zones 4 through 8 require at least R-10 perimeter insulation to a depth of 2 feet (zones 4 and 5) or 4 feet (zones 6 to 8).

☐ **Is the required rating (*R*-value) for steel-frame wall insulation provided according to *IRC* Table N1102.2.5?**

Steel framing requires better insulation because steel is a better conductor of heat and cold than timber. *IRC* Table N1102.2.5 shows equivalences: For example, if R-19 insulation is required in wood-frame walls, insulation in a steel-framed wall could use R-13 insulation in the steel-frame wall cavity and R-9 insulation

in the exterior sheathing. Options in the right column of the table allow for greater design flexibility.

☐ **Do all doors that separate conditioned space from unconditioned space meet the maximum allowable *U*-factor in *IRC* Table N1102.1?**

Figure 23-2 shows the label on an exterior door. This door has a *U*-factor of 0.64 and would meet code requirements in climate zones 1 and 2, but not in climate zones 3 through 8, assuming this isn't an impact-rated door. But keep reading. The SHGC of this door is 0.56 when used in a residence. That's too much solar gain for climate zones 1, 2 and 3 in *IRC* Table N1102.1. But read on. *IRC* Section N1102.3 exempts up to 15 square feet for windows and 24 square feet for doors per dwelling from the *U*-factor limits and allows averaging of other factors to comply with the code.

☐ **Are all joints, seams, penetrations, site-built windows, doors and skylights sealed according to *IRC* Section N1102.4?**

Gaskets, caulking, weatherstripping, wrapping, or other methods are required to seal air leakage (infiltration and exfiltration) in joints. Airflow carries heat through convection. The objective is to reduce air flow to a minimum. There are a number of ways to do this, including gaskets, caulking, weatherstripping and wrapping. The *IRC* requires either a visual inspection of the points listed under *IRC* Table N1102.4.2 or a pressure test conducted in compliance with *IRC* Section N1102.4.2.1. This is a blower door test.

☐ **Does glazing meet the *U*-factor and SHGC standards in *IRC* Table N1102.1?**

Glazing must meet *U*-factor and Solar Heat Gain Coefficient standards for the climate zone where installed. The *U*-factor is normally marked on the windows, as in Figure 23-3. For example, the maximum *U*-factor allowed by the *IRC* is 0.35 when the climate zone is 4 through 8. Solar heat gain through windows and doors isn't a consideration in climate zones 4 through 8.

Regardless of the climate zone, manufactured windows, skylights and sliding glass doors require an air infiltration rate of no more

Figure 23-3   Energy performance rating of a window.

than 0.3 cubic foot per minute per square foot of surface area, per *IRC* Section N1102.4.4. Nearly all manufacturers of windows, sliding glass doors and skylights include labels on their products certifying compliance with *IRC* standards for air infiltration.

☐ **Is duct insulation installed according to *IRC* Section N1103.2.1?**

Properly-installed duct insulation is essential to resist heat flow within an unheated attic or floor space. Supply ducts in attics require R-8 insulation. Ducts in other areas have to be insulated to R-6. Supply ducts can't be run through framing cavities. Note that a duct-tightness test is required either during rough-in or post construction.

Time to Cover the Wall Cavities

When the residence has passed the energy efficiency inspection, it's time to begin installation of finish materials. The inspector will be onsite just once more before final inspection — to check installation of gypsum wallboard. That's what we'll cover in the next chapter.

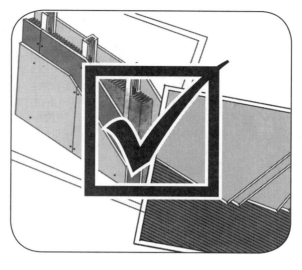

CHAPTER 24

Gypsum Board Inspection

Gypsum board (drywall or wallboard) is the most common interior finish in modern residential construction. *IRC* Section R702 identifies how gypsum board should be installed. Even though installation standards are set by the code, there's seldom a separate inspection for gypsum board. The following areas are inspected only in some jurisdictions, and perhaps as part of the final inspection.

☐ **Is gypsum board secured with approved fasteners in compliance with *IRC* Table R702.3.5?**

Standards for fastening of gypsum board vary with board thickness, where in the building the board is installed, and the spacing of framing members. Nails can still be used to secure gypsum board, but screws are the most common fastener on wood framing. On steel framing, screws are required.

☐ **Are either Type W or Type S screws used in wood framing? Do the screws penetrate the wood at least ⅝ inch, per *IRC* Section R702.3.6?**

Screws must be long enough to penetrate wood framing by at least ⅝ of an inch. Type S is a fine-thread gypsum board screw. Type W is a coarse-thread board screw. Each has different characteristics for strength and resistance to withdrawal. The *IRC* permits use of either Type S or Type W screws for attaching gypsum board to conventional framing.

☐ **Is interior gypsum board installed per *IRC* Table R702.3.5? And is exterior gypsum sheathing installed per *IRC* Table R703.4?**

Exterior gypsum sheathing is regulated by the same chapter as interior gypsum board and will be inspected at the same time. Gypsum sheathing may be used to both form a shear wall and to meet requirements for fire-resistance. Both purposes can be inspected simultaneously.

The standard for nailing gypsum sheathing depends on board thickness. For instance, according to item 36 in the second portion of *IRC* Table R602.3(1), nails for ½-inch gypsum sheathing must be fastened to a structural member with 1½-inch galvanized roofing nails spaced every 7 inches around the edge and every 7 inches at intermediate supports.

☐ **Does the construction of the wall separating a residence from a private garage meet the requirements of *IRC* Table R302.6?**

Because many fires start in the garage, the *IRC* requires a minimum of ½-inch gypsum board applied to the garage side of this wall. Either ½-inch or ⅝-inch board separation will keep fire from spreading to the interior of the dwelling. The board must be fastened according to *IRC* Table R702.3.5.

☐ **Does any adhesive used to fasten gypsum board to the framing conform with ASTM Standard C 557, as required in *IRC* Section R702.3.1?**

Adhesive can be used to fasten gypsum board to the framing. If adhesive is used, *IRC* Section R102.4 requires that adhesive conform to ASTM Standard C 557.

Get Ready for the Final Inspection

When the gypsum board is up, it's time to install finish materials — molding and trim, cabinets, flooring, electrical and plumbing fixtures, paint and all the decorative items that make a house a home. When the home is ready for occupancy, the last step will be a final inspection. That will be our last inspection.

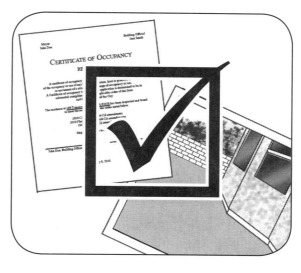

CHAPTER 25

Final Inspection

Among all the building inspections, the most difficult may be final inspection. There are several reasons. First, there's a lot to check, as you'll soon see. Second, pressure to complete the project can get intense. This is perhaps the only time in the construction cycle when interests of an owner and interests of a builder align perfectly. Both want to get it done: For the builder, completion means payment in full. For the owner, completion means occupancy. For both, final inspection will be the last significant obstacle.

Another point to consider — a signature on the certificate of completion relinquishes the authority of the building department. In all probability, the completed project won't come to the attention of the building official again for many years. Under those circumstances, this is the last chance to get it right.

From a builder's perspective, final inspection is either an achievement (if passed), or an embarrassment (if failed). As final inspection approaches, every owner will be making plans.

If it's a residence, those plans usually involve moving family and furnishings on site. Plans like that aren't easy to change. The question on the lips of every owner will be "When can I move in?" It's not easy to explain why occupancy has to be delayed. The more lengthy the delay, the more acute the embarrassment for any contractor.

Fortunately, it's fairly easy to be sure there won't be surprises during final inspection. Check off each item on the list that follows and you'll be well-prepared for final inspection.

Duplicated Effort — for a Good Reason

As we work through the final inspection, you'll notice that some questions seem to duplicate questions asked in prior chapters. In a way, that's true. But there's a very good reason for this apparent duplication. I'll explain by citing an example.

The intermediate electrical inspection included a check of electrical outlets. Were outlet boxes located correctly? It makes sense to find an error like this while wall cavities are still exposed. Making a correction at that point will be quick and easy. It would be a shame to discover a mistake when wallboard is up and everyone is eager to close out the project. So a check of outlet boxes is included in both the intermediate electrical inspection and the final inspection.

There's a good reason for double-checking. A lot can happen to the approved electrical boxes between intermediate and final inspection. They could be covered by wallboard. They could be moved or removed to make way for vents, cabinets, built-ins, etc. They could be damaged by vandals or dislodged by various trades.

From the standpoint of efficient use of building department staff, it probably makes more sense to check the location of outlet boxes just once — at final inspection. But every builder understands the advantage of finding code violations as soon as possible. And that's what I recommend — even though the result is some duplication of effort.

Compliance with the Plans

Many items on the list that follows are obvious and elementary — and too late to change (easily) at the time a builder calls for final inspection. For example, does the roof pitch meet code requirements? It's simply not possible to change roof pitch at any reasonable cost after construction is complete. So why even check for the obvious?

There are several reasons. The first is to evaluate why the system failed. In some cases, it could be a failure by the plans examiner or something missed during an earlier inspection. But in my experience, a major error like roof pitch isn't usually the result of a flaw in the permit-issuing or the inspection process. The approved plans are probably correct — or at least the approved plans are *not* wrong. When an obvious and elementary code violation is discovered during final inspection, it's usually the result of some improvisation or carelessness by the trade involved. Site conditions, lack of experience, and misunderstandings can lead to truly bizarre results on a construction site. Evaluating the cause of a problem is the first step in eliminating similar problems in the future.

Second, I feel it's an inspector's responsibility to vet these issues, even if there's no practical remedy. At the very least, the building department, the contractor, the trades involved and the owner have the right to be fully informed. When everyone understands the problem, it's much easier to form a consensus on the appropriate remedy. In many cases, there will be a practical remedy without bending either the letter or the spirit of the code. In all cases, the building official has authority to interpret the code as required by conditions on site.

Third, vetting the issue at final inspection puts everyone on notice of the problem. There won't be claims of surprise or negligence years later if a problem is discovered. In my opinion, the worst thing any inspector (or contractor) could do would be to ignore or attempt to conceal a major defect. But that's just the opinion of this building official, based on over 30 years in dealing with matters like this. If you know better, please follow your instincts. In any case, I'm going to flag even the most basic compliance issues in this chapter — including many that involve compliance with the plans. What you do with this information is entirely your decision.

Having explained the ground rules, it's time to get started with final inspection.

Check the Paperwork

☐ **Has the project passed all earlier inspections, and is the building permit still valid, per *IRC* Section R109.4?**

Look at the history of the project. Check for any prior inspections that weren't approved the first time. Make sure corrections were made and re-inspection completed. Be alert for any notes on an inspection ticket indicating that work was covered before it could be inspected. Has the inspector seen every part of the job?

Figure 25-1 Final grading slopes away from the building.

☐ **Are the approved plans available for review at the jobsite, per *IRC* Section R106.3?**

Verify that address information on the approved plans, the permit and completed inspection tickets all relate to the same project.

Final Exterior and Garage

☐ **Does the final grade slope away from the building as required, per *IRC* Section R401.3?**

Final grading should be complete at final inspection. *IRC* Section R401.3 requires that the grade fall away from foundation walls a minimum of 6 inches in the first 10 feet, as in Figure 25-1. If the slope is less than 6 inches in 10 feet, a drain or swale may be substituted. Solid surfaces, such as concrete, must slope a minimum 2 percent away from the foundation.

☐ **Is the building generally complete in appearance?**

A tradesman still working at the jobsite could be a sign that work is still in progress. Carpet laying and interior painting aren't a concern. But if mechanical or electrical contractors are making last minute installations or adjustments, it's probably too soon for final inspection.

☐ **Is the lot generally clean and free of debris?**

Most building departments enforce zoning regulations that restrict accumulation of debris in residential neighborhoods. Building inspectors will be alert for violations of zoning regulations. If the address looks more like a construction site than a residence, it's not ready for final inspection.

☐ **Is safety glass installed in hazardous locations, per *IRC* Section R308.4?**

Safety-type glass is permanently marked for identification. All swinging, sliding and bifolding doors with glass panels must be glazed with safety glass. *IRC* Section R308.4 lists hazardous locations, such as swinging, sliding and bifold doors, that require safety glass.

☐ **Do all fireplace chimneys extend high enough above the roof, per *IRC* Section R1003.9?**

To prevent fire damage, fireplace chimneys must be at least 24 inches higher than any point on the roof within 10 feet. The top of the chimney has to be at least 3 feet above the roof at the point where the chimney and the roof intersect.

☐ **Is there a solid core door between the house and the garage, per *IRC* Section R302.5.1?**

Openings between the house and garage require a solid wood, solid or honeycomb core steel or 20-minute fire-rated door at least 1⅜ inches thick. A door like that will help slow the spread of fire from the garage to the residence.

☐ **Is the garage floor of a non-combustible material such as concrete, and does the surface slope toward the main vehicle entry door, per *IRC* Section R309.1?**

Gasoline and oil in the garage present a fire hazard. To reduce the risk of fire, the garage floor has to be made from a non-combustible material, such as concrete, and must slope toward the garage door so liquids drain to the exterior.

Figure 25-2 Roof deck ready for the roof cover.

☐ Does the roof cover comply with *IRC* requirements?

Figure 25-2 shows the deck ready for roof cover. We inspected the roof deck in Chapter 18. But the finish roofing material probably won't be checked until final inspection. The most common code violations are:

- A *cricket or saddle* is required on the high side of any chimney or roof penetration more than 30 inches wide. *IRC* Section R903.2.2

- A *clay or concrete tile roof* requires underlayment. *IRC* Section R905.3.3

- *Metal roof shingles* can't be used on a roof with a slope of less than 3 in 12. *IRC* Section R905.4.2

- *Mineral-surfaced roll roofing* can't be used on a roof with a slope of less than 1 in 12. *IRC* Section R905.5.2

- *Slate shingles* require a minimum headlap of 4 inches on slopes up to 8 in 12. *IRC* Table R905.6.5

- *Wood shingles* supported by spaced sheathing require nominal size sheathing boards at least 1 inch by 4 inches. *IRC* Section R905.7.1

- *Wood shakes* can't be used if the roof slope is less than 3 in 12. *IRC* Section R905.8.2

- A *coal-tar built-up roof* can have a slope of as little as 1/8 in 12. Other types of built-up roofing require at least a 1/4 in 12 slope. *IRC* Section R905.9.1

- A *standing seam metal roof* can have a slope of as little as 1/4 in 12. A lapped (nonsoldered) metal roof with lap sealant has to slope at least 1/2 in 12. The same roof without lap sealant has to slope at least 3 in 12. *IRC* Section R905.10.2

- *Sprayed polyurethane foam roofs* require a slope of at least 1/4 in 12. *IRC* Section R905.14.1

☐ Does the exterior wall covering provide adequate weather protection, per *IRC* Section R703?

No matter what material is used, exterior walls have to resist the entry of water, and must have some means of draining moisture that accumulates in wall cavities. How that's done depends on the type of wall cover. The inspector will check for a water-resistant barrier under the siding and flashing around the windows. Wind resistance is verified by reviewing the manufacturer's specification. There shouldn't be any obvious cracks or openings in the siding.

IRC Table R703.4 identifies the minimum thicknesses and required fasteners for every commonly used exterior wall covering — wood, aluminum, vinyl, masonry, hardboard, etc.

Requirements for EIFS (Exterior Insulation and Finish System) appear in *IRC* Section 703.9. EIFS has to be installed in compliance with the manufacturer's instructions and requires a special inspection by a registered engineer.

☐ Is protection from subterranean termite damage complete and documented, per *IRC* Section R318?

The *IRC* offers several choices on termite protection. For example, either chemical soil treatment or physical barriers (such as metal or plastic termite shields) can be used to meet code requirements. If the soil has been treated, the invoice for work done should include a certificate of compliance with *IRC* Section R318. The inspector will usually ask for proof that treatment has been completed.

Figure 25-3 A column resting on concrete requires lumber approved for the purpose.

☐ **Is exposed wood protected from decay, per *IRC* Section R317?**

The *IRC* has special requirements for wood that's exposed to weather, lumber that comes in contact with the ground, and lumber that rests on concrete. Those applications require either a species and grade that resists decay, or pressure-treated lumber. Figure 25-3 shows a typical situation. Lumber selected for this purpose has to bear the quality mark of an approved inspection agency.

☐ **Is the building address visible from the street, per *IRC* Section R319.1?**

The address must be installed before final inspection. Address numbers must be at least 4 inches high with a brush stroke at least ½ inch wide. Prominent street numbers make it easy for emergency vehicles to find their destination.

☐ **Is flood protection provided, per *IRC* Section R322?**

If the building had to be constructed at a certain elevation above a flood plain, the final inspection has to include a review of the as-built elevation certificate, as referenced in *IRC* Section R322.1.10. This certificate affirms that the floor of the home is at or above the base flood elevation. A registered surveyor has to provide this certificate.

Final Interior Exits and Stairs

☐ **Does the maximum rise and minimum run of stairs comply with *IRC* Sections R311.7.4.1 and R311.7.4.2?**

The maximum rise of stairs is usually 7¾ inches. The minimum run is usually 10 inches. Use a tape measure to check these dimensions. A special rule applies to spiral stairs. *IRC* Section R311.7.9 permits spiral stairs with no more than a 9½-inch rise and a 7½-inch run at a point 12 inches from the narrow edge.

☐ **Is the stair width at least 36 inches, per *IRC* Section R311.7.1?**

Stairs must be at least 36 inches wide. But the handrail can extend into this 36-inch space. The minimum width is 31½ inches if there is one handrail and 27 inches if there are two handrails. Use a tape measure to check the width between handrails. Again, there's a special rule for spiral stairways. Spiral stairs can be as little as 26 inches wide below the handrail.

☐ **Is the handrail height between 34 and 38 inches above the nosing on each tread, per *IRC* Section R311.7.7.1?**

Most adults feel comfortable with a handrail between 34 and 38 inches above the stairway. There are a couple of exceptions to this general rule: First, the rule doesn't apply to any volute, turnout or easing on the lowest tread. Second, where handrail fittings or bendings provide continuous transitions between flights, the transition to a guardrail may be higher than 38 inches.

☐ **Does the stairway have at least 6 feet 8 inches of headroom, per *IRC* Section R311.7.2?**

Headroom in a stairwell generally must be at least 6 feet 8 inches. This dimension is measured

Figure 25-4 This railing prevents falls from the raised floor area.

vertically from a sloped line connecting the tread nosings. Adequate headroom is important for safe evacuation, of course. But it's also important when moving furniture between floors.

☐ **Are guards installed on stairwells, raised floor areas, balconies and porches, per *IRC* Section R312?**

This guardrail must be at least 36 inches high, as in Figure 25-4. When finished, the railing requires vertical balusters spaced so a sphere 4 inches or more in diameter can't pass through the assembly. That keeps small kids from falling through the railing.

☐ **Is there at least one exit door with a clear width of 32 inches and a clear height of 78 inches, per *IRC* Section R311.2?**

Look for at least one egress door from the habitable area to the exterior. This door must be side hinged.

☐ **Do exit doors have any latches or keyed locks that could prevent easy exit, as prohibited by *IRC* Section R311.2?**

Egress doors require locks or latches that allow easy passage to the exterior. The door must open without a key and with no special effort. A thumb-latch deadbolt is acceptable, but a keyed lock on the interior isn't, because the key may not be readily available.

☐ **Are hallways at least 36 inches wide, per *IRC* Section R311.6?**

There are no exceptions to this general rule. The inspector has to verify hallway width at final inspection. But this should be just a formality. Hallway width should have been verified at the framing stage before drywall went up.

☐ **Does every sleeping room have an emergency exit (egress) window that meets the minimum size requirements in *IRC* Section R310?**

One window in a bedroom must meet four general criteria: First, the window opening must be at least 20 inches wide and 24 inches high. The aggregate opening area must be at least 5.7 square feet on other than the ground floor and 5 square feet on a ground floor. The sill of the window must be no more than 44 inches above the floor. This is worth checking again. Window openings may have been changed since the framing inspection.

☐ **Do habitable basement and attic areas have at least one emergency exit that meets the minimum size requirements in *IRC* Section R310?**

Like bedrooms, all basement and attic rooms must have at least one exit window or door suitable for emergency escape and rescue. This escape route has to open without use of a key or special tools. Any bars, grilles, covers or screens installed over the emergency escape exit must have an interior release latch.

☐ **Do landings on stairways and at exits comply with *IRC* Sections R311.7.5 (stairways) and R311.3 (exit doors)?**

With one exception, a landing is required at the top and bottom of each stairway. The exception: Interior stairs don't require a landing at the top of the flight unless a door swings over the stairs. If the vertical rise is more than 12 feet, a landing is required each 12 feet. The landing has to be at least as wide as the stairway and has to extend for at least 36 inches in the direction of travel.

A landing or floor is required on each side of exterior doors. The width of the landing has to be at least as wide as the doorway. Note that

Figure 25-5   A landing is required outside these sliding glass doors.

this requirement applies to all doors, including sliding glass doors, as in Figure 25-5. The depth of the landing can't be less than 36 inches measured in the direction of travel. The depth of small balconies (less than 60 square feet) may be less than 36 inches in the direction of travel.

☐ **Is the slope of any ramp no more than 1:12, per *IRC* Section R311.8?**

Ramps are limited to a maximum slope of 1:12 (8.3 percent) to prevent accidental falls. In construction situations where compliance with this standard is impossible, the code permits an exception, allowing a ramp to have a maximum slope of 1:8 (12.5 percent).

Final Interior Architectural

☐ **Does the supplier's insulation comply with *IRC* Table N1102.1?**

IRC Section N1101.9 requires that insulation values be posted on a permanent certificate affixed to the electrical panel. If your jurisdiction

doesn't inspect insulation, review the installer's certificate of installation. If your jurisdiction inspects insulation, check that the insulation installed has *R*-value and *U*-factor ratings that comply with *IRC* Table N1102.1. The certificate can be completed either by the builder or a registered design professional.

☐ **Is foam plastic protected from exposure, per *IRC* Section R316?**

Foam plastic ignites easily and can produce toxic smoke when burning. Covering foam plastic with a thermal barrier reduces the risk of fire. That barrier could be drywall or other approved finish material. The barrier must be rated to remain in place for at least 15 minutes during exposure to fire.

☐ **Do interior wall coverings comply with *IRC* Section R702?**

Chapter 24 covered interior gypsum board inspections. I mentioned that some jurisdictions don't perform a separate inspection of gypsum board. Where that's the case, board will be inspected during the final inspection.

Where and how the gypsum board is installed determines the minimum board thickness and the type of fasteners required. Details are in *IRC* Section R702.3 and Table R702.3.5.

Mixing proportions for cement plaster vary with the sequence of coatings and the plaster type. Details are in *IRC* Section R702.1.

☐ **Do windows meet design requirements for energy conservation, per *IRC* Table N1102.1?**

We covered standards for window glazing in Chapter 23. If there was no separate inspection for compliance with energy efficiency standards, this is an issue for final inspection.

Windows must have thermal performance characteristics appropriate for the climate zone. Windows that comply with code standards will be labeled with all the required information. To summarize:

In warmer climates (Zones 1, 2 and 3) the windows must have a *U*-factor of 1.2, 0.65 and 0.5 respectively. In colder climates (Zones 4 to 8) windows must have a *U*-factor of 0.35. The *U*-factor (sometimes expressed as "μ") is a measure of the flow of heat through a material. Thus, the lower the *U*-factor, the greater its resistance to heat transfer, and the higher its *R*-value. In warmer climates (Zones 1, 2 and 3) windows must have a Solar Heat Gain Coefficient (SHGC) of 0.35. Solar Heat Gain Coefficient is a measure of the ability of glass to retard solar heat gain.

☐ Do rooms have a 7-foot ceiling height, per *IRC* Section R305?

The minimum ceiling height required for habitable rooms, hallways, corridors, bathrooms, toilet rooms, laundry rooms and basements is 7 feet. Exceptions are permitted for sloped ceilings and bathrooms, as well as non-habitable basement areas where beams, girders and ducts intrude into the living area.

☐ Do all habitable rooms have approved openings equal to at least 8 percent of the floor area, per *IRC* Section R303?

At least 8 percent of the floor area must be provided with glazing; therefore, a 200-square-foot room must have at least 16 square feet of glazing.

☐ Do all habitable rooms meet the minimum dimension and area requirements in *IRC* Section R304?

There must be at least one habitable room in a dwelling unit with an area of at least 120 square feet. Other habitable rooms, except kitchens, must have an area of at least 70 square feet. All habitable rooms except kitchens must have a minimum width and length of at least 7 feet.

☐ Are fireplaces and wood stoves installed per the manufacturer's instructions and *IRC* Sections R1005 and M1414?

Manufactured fireplaces and wood stoves are approved for a particular use and installation following specific procedures. So installation has to comply with the manufacturer's instructions.

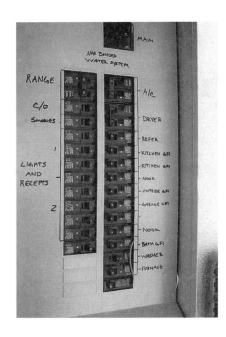

Figure 25-6 Labels on this service panel will pass inspection.

Installation instructions will show required setbacks from wall and ceiling materials for both the equipment and the chimney.

Final Interior Electrical

☐ Is the electrical service disconnect clearly identified? Does the disconnect have good access and clearance, per *IRC* Sections E3404.11, E3404.12 and E3405?

Each disconnect must be marked to identify the purpose. Markings written by hand should be made with indelible ink. In my opinion, labeling in Figure 25-6 meets code requirements. Easy access to the service disconnect is required.

☐ Is all electrical equipment approved, listed, and labeled for the intended use, per *IRC* Section E3403.3?

Every piece of installed electrical equipment should include a data plate, as in Figure 25-7. The data plate identifies the approving agency, indicates the intended use and describes the

Figure 25-7 Typical data plate on installed electrical equipment.

required installation. Figure 25-7 shows the approval, listing and labeling required by the code.

☐ Is all electrical equipment in working condition and free of damage, foreign debris or contamination, per *IRC* Section E3404.7?

Look for damage caused by improper installation or careless construction — such as spilled paint or plaster, broken, bent or cut parts — or vandalism. You wouldn't buy a new car with paint splatters or damaged parts, or that had been vandalized. The owner of a new or newly remodeled home deserves the same advantage.

☐ Is any electrical equipment exposed to physical damage protected by guards, per *IRC* Section E3404.10?

Back in Chapter 20, I explained that a pole or barrier should be installed to protect exposed plumbing equipment in a garage or shop. The same is true of electrical equipment in a garage or shop. Any equipment exposed to damage from a vehicle should be protected by a guard or

enclosure. The need for protection may not be apparent until you see the equipment actually installed. At final inspection, the issue should be obvious.

☐ Is artificial lighting provided for indoor service equipment and panelboards, per *IRC* Section E3405.6?

If service equipment or panelboards are installed indoors, some type of lighting is required. Nearly any type of switched light fixture will meet the requirement.

☐ Does conductor and terminal identification meet the requirements of *IRC* Section E3407?

All equipment grounding conductors have to be green or bare. All grounded conductors must be either white or natural gray or have three continuous white stripes. This color has to extend the length of the wire — the exception being unless the gauge is larger than 6 AWG. In that case, only the terminations have to be marked.

☐ Is electrical service equipment grounded properly, per *IRC* Sections E3607 and E3608?

All grounded conductors should be connected to the grounding bus bar at the service panel. These two *IRC* sections present several alternatives, including concrete-encased electrodes, metal underground water pipes, ground rings, plate electrodes and other listed grounding electrodes.

☐ Are metal parts of the service equipment bonded, per *IRC* Section E3609?

Bonding is part of grounding. Bonding implies that conductors are joined well enough to provide a durable electrical connection to the grounding system. There are many different types of bonding, including a bonding jumper, main bonding jumper, system bonding jumper, and equipment bonding conductor. A main bonding jumper connects the equipment grounding conductor and the service disconnection enclosure (panel box) with the system ground.

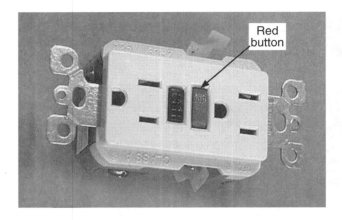

Figure 25-8 An approved GFCI outlet provides protection in bathrooms, kitchens, and outdoor areas.

Figure 25-9 Electrical receptacles above a kitchen counter.

☐ **Are branch circuits for general lighting and outlets protected, per *IRC* Section E3705.5?**

Overcurrent protection refers to breakers in a panel box. Be sure that the rating of each breaker is consistent with the wire size and type. *IRC* Table E3705.5.3 lists overcurrent protection for small circuits (15, 20 and 30 amp). For example, for a circuit using 14 AWG wire, the maximum breaker size allowed is 15 amps.

☐ **Are branch circuits for bathrooms, kitchens, and outdoor areas protected with GFCIs, per *IRC* Section E3902?**

Ground fault circuit interrupters are required in these and a few other locations. Figure 25-8 shows an approved GFCI outlet. The red button in the center of the receptacle pops out when a ground fault is detected. These receptacles weren't installed at the time of the intermediate electrical inspection, so they have to be checked at final inspection.

☐ **Are all outlets installed in habitable rooms as required by *IRC* Section E3901 and Figures E3901.2, E3901.4 and E3901.4.1? Is arc-fault circuit protection provided in all areas not served by GFCI protection, per *IRC* Section E3902.11?**

The spacing of outlets should have been checked during intermediate inspection if they were installed at that time. But it doesn't hurt to double-check — a drywall installer may have covered up an outlet or switch box following the last electrical inspection. Check the type of outlet (either GFCI or AFCI) at this time. GFCI protection and arc fault protection are required at specific locations. Each of these outlets or breakers will be identified. Verify the installation.

☐ **Does spacing of outlets above the kitchen counter comply with *IRC* Section E3901.4 and Figures E3901.4 and E3901.4.1?**

Outlet spacing in the kitchen was checked as part of the intermediate electrical inspection. But outlets sometimes get moved or covered during cabinet installation. Check to be sure all the outlets are still available for use, as in Figure 25-9.

☐ **Is an electrical outlet available for use by anyone servicing HVAC equipment located in an attic or crawlspace, per *IRC* Section E3901.11? Is a switch-controlled light installed, as required by *IRC* Section E3903.4?**

Receptacle | Switch

Figure 25-10 Electric switch and receptacle for use while servicing HVAC equipment.

A 125-volt, single-phase, 15- or 20-amp-rated convenience receptacle must be located on the same level and within 25 feet of HVAC equipment. In addition, a switch-controlled light must be installed to illuminate the equipment. Figure 25-10 shows a receptacle outlet and a wall-switched light within 25 feet of the equipment. Once again, we checked for rough-in of both the receptacle and the switch during intermediate inspection; but at final inspection, both the receptacle and the switch should be installed and operational.

□ **Is there at least one wall-switch-controlled lighting outlet in every habitable room and bathroom, per *IRC* Section E3903.2?**

Though this was checked at the intermediate inspection, check again to be sure switched lights work. A switched outlet (for a lamp) is permitted in lieu of a lighting outlet in rooms other than kitchens and bathrooms.

□ **Is there at least one wall-switch-controlled lighting outlet installed in hallways, stairways, garages and at outdoor exits, per *IRC* Section E3903.3?**

Stairs must be lit at the top and bottom and have a switch installed at each level. Make sure these are installed and operate normally. Every exte-rior door must have a switched light that illuminates the exit. This includes doors from garages. Hallways need at least one switch for a light.

□ **Are all outlets installed in outdoor locations equipped with a weatherproof enclosure, per *IRC* Section E4002.8?**

Outlets exposed to the weather must be protected with an approved weatherproof enclosure. The required cover reduces the risk of a ground fault during wet weather. Be sure the outlet cover is listed for exterior use.

□ **Are outlet and switch boxes covered and protected, per *IRC* Section E4004.1?**

Unless an outlet box will be covered with a luminaire canopy, lampholder or device faceplate, every outlet box needs a cover.

□ **Are all metal faceplates grounded, per *IRC* Sections E3906.10 and E4002.4?**

Any metal part of an electrical system can become energized. Metal faceplates have to be grounded so they can't cause an electric shock.

Final Interior Plumbing

□ **Are bathroom and kitchen fixtures operable, per *IRC* Section R306?**

Every dwelling unit needs a kitchen with a sink. Turn on the water supply in the kitchen sink to test for adequate pressure. Look for any leaks. In bathrooms, flush the toilet, turn on faucets over the sink and bathtub. All plumbing fixtures must be connected to an approved water supply. They must also be connected to a sanitary sewer or to an approved private sewage disposal system.

□ **Do plumbing fixtures comply with *IRC* Section P2701.1?**

Plumbing fixtures must be made from approved materials, have a smooth impervious surface, be without defects and conform to standards in the code. All fixtures must have an adequate supply of potable water.

Figure 25-11   Combination pressure- and temperature-relief valve.

□ **If ceramic tile is installed in shower surrounds, does the height of that tile comply with *IRC* Sections R307 and P2708?**

The tile should extend to at least 6 feet above the floor and at least 70 inches above the drain inlet. Keep in mind that the drain inlet will probably be lower than the edge of the tile wall you're measuring but probably above the floor.

□ **If the water heater is in a location where leakage will cause damage, is a galvanized steel pan (or other approved pan) installed, per *IRC* Section P2801.5? And does it have a drain that terminates as specified in *IRC* Section P2801.5.2?**

Every water heater is going to fail eventually. The first sign of failure will usually be a leak — sometimes a very substantial leak — and sometimes when the occupants aren't home. A drain pan will prevent most damage to the building interior when there is a leak. The pan must be at least 1½ inches deep and adequately sized. The pan must drain to an indirect waste pipe, at least ¾ inch in diameter, terminating over an indirect waste receptor or outside the building, and between 6 and 24 inches above the adjacent ground.

□ **Is the water heater installed according to the manufacturer's instructions and *IRC* Section M2005?**

Whether gas-fired, electric, or oiled-fired, water heater installation must meet installation specs for location, access, and clearance. Water heaters shouldn't be isolated in a small closet where they can't be properly serviced. *IRC* Section M2005 lists several other prohibited locations.

□ **Does the water heater have a temperature- and pressure-relief valve, per *IRC* Section P2803?**

If the water temperature exceeds 210° F, a combination temperature- and pressure-relief valve, such as in Figure 25-11, will open. There are both temperature valves and pressure valves and combination temperature- and pressure-relief valves. In any case, the relief valve must connect to a pipe that extends to the floor, to the outside of the building, or to an indirect waste receptor.

□ **Does the discharge end of the temperature- and pressure-relief pipe comply with *IRC* Section P2803.6.1?**

When the T & P valve trips, very hot water is going to get sprayed for a considerable distance. That water shouldn't get sprayed across a room or closet. *IRC* Section P2803.6.1 sets 13 conditions for the T & P discharge pipe. Among other requirements, the outlet end has to be 6 inches or less above finished floor or waste receptor. That guarantees no one is going to be sprayed in the face with scalding water.

Figure 25-12   Checking the water pressure.

Figure 25-13 Showerhead marked with the maximum flow rate.

☐ **Is the water supply pressure between 40 psi and 80 psi, per *IRC* Section P2903.3?**

To check the water pressure, use a water pressure gauge, as shown in Figure 25-12. It can be attached somewhere inside for the check, or to an outside hose bib. The reading should be between 40 and 80 psi. If it's higher, a pressure-reducing valve may be required. If it's lower, something is wrong with the water supply system.

☐ **Do fixtures meet requirements for maximum flow rate and water consumption, per *IRC* Tables P2903.1 and P2903.2?**

The showerhead in Figure 25-13 is marked with a maximum flow rate of 2.5 gpm. If you don't see the flow rate marked, check the manufacturer's product specifications. Look for other maximum flow rates in *IRC* Table P2903.2. For example, a flushometer tank toilet should be marked as 1.6 gallons per flush (gpf).

☐ **Do plumbing fixtures, except bathtubs and showers, have shut-off valves, per *IRC* Section P2903.9.3?**

Nearly every plumbing fixture will need to be serviced occasionally. Most servicing will require a disconnect from the water supply. That's easy if a wall stop is provided under the fixture. These valves must be accessible, as in Figure 25-14. Bathtubs and showers also need

shut-off valves. But because these fixtures are within a compartment, the valves don't have to be accessible.

☐ **Does any installation of any water treatment unit comply with the manufacturer's instructions and *IRC* Section P2908?**

Water softening and water treatment equipment (such as the reverse osmosis system shown in Figure 25-15) can create a cross-connection between the potable water system and the waste disposal system. Correct installation is important. The manufacturer's installation instructions should be available for inspection. Verify compliance with those instructions.

☐ **Are all hose connections equipped with a backflow preventer, per *IRC* Section P2902.3?**

Landscape irrigation hoses can siphon contaminants back into the public water supply if the water pressure fails. A backflow preventer, as in

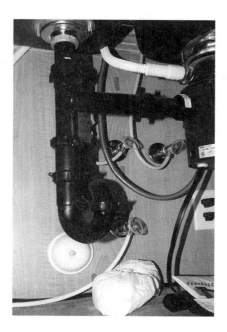

Figure 25-14 Access is required for shut-off valves for fixtures under a kitchen sink.

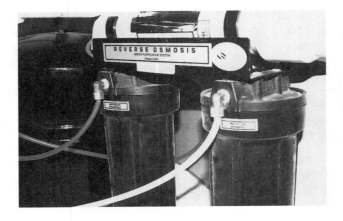

Figure 25-15 A reverse osmosis system must be correctly installed to avoid a cross-connection.

Figure 25-16 A backflow preventer at a hose bib stops siphoning.

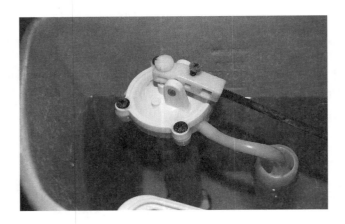

Figure 25-17 Most new toilets now come packaged with anti-siphon fill valves.

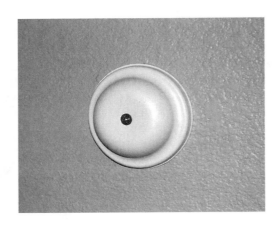

Figure 25-18 A correctly-installed cleanout with cap, located on a wall.

Figure 25-16, is required at each hose bib. An atmospheric vacuum breaker like this prevents siphoning.

☐ **Do all flush tanks have an anti-siphon fill valve, per *IRC* Section P2902.4.1?**

An anti-siphon fill valve, as in Figure 25-17, must be installed in every flush tank. The fill valve must be at least 1 inch above the full opening of the overflow pipe. A valve like this will be packaged with nearly all new toilets.

☐ **Do DWV cleanouts comply with *IRC* Section P3005.2?**

Check placement of cleanout fittings. We inspected cleanout pipe in Chapter 20. All you'll see of most cleanouts will be a cap, as in Figure 25-18. But be sure the cleanout wasn't covered by finish wall materials, and that it's been capped properly.

☐ **Is DWV piping protected by insulation, heat, or both in areas subject to freezing temperatures, per *IRC* Section P3001.2?**

Water in DWV pipe can freeze in very cold weather, making connected fixtures — and maybe the entire house — unusable. In cold climates, be sure DWV piping is protected with insulation, auxiliary heat, or both.

□ **Has any piping intended for future fixtures been terminated with an accessible plug or cap fitting, per *IRC* Section P3005.1.6?**

If there's a provision for future installation of plumbing fixtures, the supply and drain pipes have to be secured with an approved permanent plug or fitting. Figure 25-19 shows an example.

□ **Has a sump pump or sewage ejector been installed, per *IRC* Section P3007 and Table P3113.4.1?**

Installation details are in Chapter 20. But now is the time to be sure the ejector works properly.

□ **Has waterproof flashing been installed around all vent pipes that penetrate the roof? Does each pipe extend far enough above the roof, per *IRC* Section P3103?**

The last time you checked vents through the roof, no finished roofing material had been installed. Now, the finish roofing is in place. It's worth checking vent height once again.

The height of vent pipe above the roof is based on the anticipated accumulation of snow and is specified by each jurisdiction. These vent pipes must extend at least 6 inches above either the roof or anticipated snow accumulation, whichever is greater.

□ **Is every trap sized correctly for the plumbing fixture, per *IRC* Table P3201.7, and the maximum distance from the vent, per *IRC* Table P3105.1?**

Check that all traps are the proper size for the plumbing fixture and that trap length doesn't exceed the maximum distance from the vent. *IRC* Table P3105.1 shows proper sizes and the maximum distances. Using a trap the wrong size will cause drainage problems. If the trap arm is too long, the vent won't work properly.

Figure 25-19   A supply pipe secured with an accessible fitting for future use.

□ **Are all air admittance valves installed according to the manufacturer's installation instructions and the requirements of *IRC* Section P3114?**

An air admittance valve is an alternative to a traditional vent. The valve must be accessible and at least 4 inches above the horizontal branch drain or fixture drain being vented. If installed in an attic, the valve must be installed at least 6 inches above insulation materials. An air admittance valve must be the proper size for the fixture it serves. Factory-built air admittance valves make it possible to install plumbing fixtures where venting would be complicated, such as for a kitchen sink mounted in island cabinets.

□ **Do all fixture tailpieces meet the minimum size requirements in *IRC* Section P2703?**

A tailpiece extends from the fixture to a drainage pipe, as in Figure 25-20. The tailpiece must be 1½ inches in diameter for sinks, dishwashers, laundry tubs, bathtubs, and similar fixtures. The tailpiece must be at least 1¼ inches for bidets, lavatories, and similar fixtures.

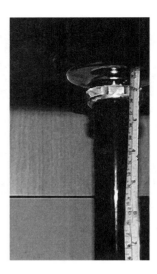

Figure 25-20 Fixture tailpiece under a sink.

☐ **Does the water supply for the dishwasher have an air gap or integral backflow protector, per *IRC* Section P2717?**

An air gap or integral backflow preventer protects the water supply to the dishwasher. The air gap also keeps contamination from the dishwasher out of the water supply system.

☐ **Is there an access panel or door on any whirlpool bathtub, per *IRC* Section P2720?**

Service, repair or replacement of equipment in a whirlpool bath requires an access panel or door. *IRC* Section P2720 requires that the access opening measure at least 12 inches square unless the manufacturer specifies a larger size. If pumps are more than 2 feet away from the access opening, the door must be at least 18 inches square.

☐ **Do bathtubs have waste and overflow drains at least 1½ inches in diameter, per *IRC* Section P2713?**

The code requires that the size of waste and overflow pipe be consistent with the trap size required for the fixture. In the case of a bathtub, you need a 1½-inch-diameter waste and overflow connected to a 1½-inch trap.

☐ **Is the hot water valve on the left of every two-valve fixture, per *IRC* Section P2722.2?**

This is simply convention. But it makes sense. The hot water valve has to be on the left. The cold water valve has to be on the right. This helps users predict whether they're adjusting cold water or hot water.

☐ **Has a final plumbing test been done on traps and fixture connections to test for leaks, per *IRC* Section P2503.5.2?**

Traps and fixture connections must be watertight. Do a visual inspection by filling each sink with water (making sure the traps are filled). Then watch for a leak under the basin.

Final General Mechanical

☐ **Are all appliances labeled, per *IRC* Section M1303?**

Every HVAC appliance must be labeled with a nameplate permanently fixed by the factory. This label must include the manufacturer's name or trademark, serial and model numbers, and the testing agency's seal or marking. Figure 25-21 shows a typical label on a furnace.

☐ **Are appliances installed according to their listing and *IRC* Sections M1302 and M1307?**

Check for ease of access, clearances from combustibles, and compliance with the manufacturer's installation standards. Check the cord length for compliance with *IRC* Table E4101.3. Does cord connection, overcurrent protection and the means of disconnect comply with *IRC* Table E4101.5?

☐ **Are appliances installed according to the manufacturer's installation instructions and *IRC* Section M1307?**

Appliances should be anchored or fixed in position to accommodate seismic forces. When gas appliances are in a garage, the source of

Figure 25-21 Label affixed to a furnace.

Figure 25-22 Foundation for a heat pump.

ignition must be elevated at least 18 inches above the floor unless the appliance is rated for installation at ground level.

☐ **Are all appliances accessible for inspection, service, repair or replacement, per *IRC* Section M1305?**

Access requirements vary with the location. For example, appliances in rooms must be accessible by a door and passageway at least 24 inches wide. In attics, the opening and passageway must be large enough to remove the largest piece of equipment, but not less than 30 inches. Under floors, the access opening must be large enough to remove the largest piece of equipment but not less than 30 inches high by 22 inches wide. No matter the location, working space is required in front of the controls.

☐ **Do all appliances meet requirements for clearances from unprotected combustible materials, per *IRC* Section M1306 and Table M1306.2?**

Check the appliance label and the manufacturer's installation instructions for clearances from unprotected combustible materials. Meas-

ure the distance from appliances to the nearest combustible material. *IRC* Table M1306.2 permits a reduction in clearance space if specific types of protection are available.

☐ **Is the foundation for any outdoor heat pump at least 3 inches above grade, per *IRC* Section M1403.2?**

A heat pump has to be at least 3 inches above ground level so defrost water can drain away from the unit. In addition, the support or foundation for an outdoor unit must comply with the manufacturer's installation instructions; see Figure 25-22.

Final HVAC

☐ **Is the heating system capable of maintaining a room temperature of at least 68 degrees, per *IRC* Section R303.8?**

The heating system is required to maintain a temperature of at least 68 degrees at a point 3 feet above the floor and 2 feet from exterior walls. This issue was considered during plan review. If the unit installed is the same as the unit specified in the plans and specs, you can be reasonably sure of compliance with *IRC* Section R303.8.

☐ **Is condensation from cooling equipment properly disposed of, per *IRC* Section M1411.3?**

Condensation drains were checked at the intermediate inspection. At final inspection, make sure the disposal pipe ends in a code-approved location, not on a street, alley or in other areas where dripping water could be a nuisance. Be sure the condensation drain slopes to allow gravity drainage of condensate.

☐ **Is any evaporative cooling equipment installed per the manufacturer's installation instructions and *IRC* Section M1413?**

Evaporative coolers must be on a level platform or base not less than 3 inches above the adjoining surface and must be secured to prevent displacement.

☐ **Does the clothes dryer exhaust system comply with *IRC* Section M1502?**

Check that the duct is installed properly. Is the dryer exhaust system independent of all other ducts? Is the duct vent installed so that moisture will be directed outdoors and not into some enclosed space, such as an attic? The maximum length of dryer duct depends on the number and type of duct fittings. In general, the maximum length is 25 feet. Each bend reduces that maximum. Details are in *IRC* Table M1502.4.4.1.

☐ **Is the range hood installed per *IRC* Section M1503?**

Range hoods are required to exhaust cooking fumes to the outdoors. Every hood I've seen has been manufactured to meet requirements for the appropriate listing. Read the manufacturer's directions. Check height of the hood above the range and clearance to combustible materials.

☐ **Is the return air system installed properly and does it operate in compliance with *IRC* Section M1602?**

A properly-sized return air system is essential for proper operation of HVAC equipment. Return air duct can't be installed in some locations. *IRC* Section M1602.2 lists several locations that may not be used for return air. These include closets, bathrooms, toilet rooms, a kitchen, garage or mechanical room. Compliance with the plans should yield a return air system that works perfectly. We checked the return air system during intermediate inspection. But it's worth a second check now.

Done at Last!

When final inspection is complete, the inspector should call to have permanent utilities turned on. An inspector's signature on a certificate of occupancy ends construction and begins what should be years of trouble-free occupancy.

I've seen hundreds of code changes in my 30+ years in code compliance and enforcement. When I started building, the code was a slim little pamphlet — and even it wasn't enforced in some communities. True, many of the changes I've seen tend to complicate the work of contractors and subcontractors. But I hope you agree that modern building codes — and enforcement of modern building codes — contributes significantly to the value of the nation's building stock. Homes built today are leagues ahead of the homes our parents occupied. And they're much safer, thanks largely to work by the code-writing organizations and homebuilders who support them.

I get real satisfaction every time I drive by a home I've inspected. And there are thousands. I take pride in knowing that the occupants are safer and better housed as a result of work I've done. The people living there don't know me and will probably never meet me. But they can appreciate every day the product of my effort. I feel good about that. And I hope you feel the same about every home you build or inspect.

Glossary

A

ABS is an abbreviation for Acrylonitrile-Butadiene-Styrene, a plastic material used to fabricate pipe; commonly used in drain, waste and vent systems.

Accessible (plumbing) means that access to a device or fixture must be possible with minor effort.

Air Admittance Valve is a local, one-way air valve used on drain, waste and vent systems that avoids the use of a vent.

Air Gap is a space between the faucet and the flood rim of a fixture such as a sink, which prevents siphonage.

Allowable Soil Bearing Capacity is a measure of the strength of the soil to resist an imposed load.

Alluvial Soil is sedimentary material deposited in a delta or a riverbed.

Amperage is the unit that measures the amount of electrical current flowing in a circuit.

Anti-Siphon Valve is a valve that prevents siphoning of waste into a fresh water system. Commonly used on hose bibs.

Approved Agency means an organization charged with the testing and certification of materials used in construction. *Approved* means approved by the Building Official.

ASHRAE is an abbreviation for American Society of Heating, Refrigeration and Air Conditioning Engineers.

B

Backfill is soil used to fill a cavity created by excavation.

Base Course is a layer of graded earthen material placed on subgrade or subbase under a footing or slab.

Beam is a horizontal structural member which supports rafters or joists and is supported by posts or walls.

Bearing Wall is a wall that supports a load such as a roof or a higher floor.

Bending Moment is a measure of the load imposed on a structural member.

Board Foot is a unit of measure of lumber volume. A board 1 inch thick, 12 inches wide and 12 inches long is equal to one board foot. Similarly, a board 2 inches thick, 6 inches wide and 12 inches long is one board foot.

Bonding (electrical) is the connection between any metal part and the building ground.

Branch Drain is a part of the drain system other than the main drain.

Branch Vent is a vent serving more than one fixture. It connects to a vent through the roof.

Building Drain is the name for a main drain within the perimeter of a building. It doesn't include various branch lines, trap arms or venting associated with the DWV pipe.

Building Sewer is the name for the drain outside the perimeter of a building that conveys sewage from the building drain to a septic tank or a sewer.

C

Caisson is a concrete foundation cast in a circular excavation.

Camber is a slight upward curve toward the center in a beam that helps resist vertical load.

Canales is a channel or duct used to divert rain off a low slope roof bordered by a parapet.

Caulk is a joint-sealing compound, commonly used around window and door frames.

Certificate of Occupancy is legal permission from a jurisdiction to occupy a building. Issued after all required inspections have been completed successfully.

Cleanout is an access point to the DWV piping system that allows removal of obstructions in the pipe interior.

Closed Circuit is an electrical circuit that carries current.

Closet Bend is the 90-degree plumbing fitting specially designed to convey soil waste from a water closet (toilet) to the building drain.

Closet Flange is a transition fitting between the closet bend and the water closet (toilet).

Column is a vertical supporting member.

Common (wire) is a term for a neutral conductor within an electrical system.

Compressible Soil is earth which is likely to subside under load, often leading to a general failure of the supported structure.

Concrete Masonry Unit (CMU) is a manufactured block designed for construction.

Concrete Slab-on-Grade is a concrete surface layer cast directly on subgrade.

Conduit is a pipe or tube through which electrical wiring is installed.

Cripple Studs are smaller studs above and below openings in a wall frame, such as a window or door.

Crown refers to the slight natural bend in the long dimension of a wood framing member.

D

Dead Load is the weight of the structure itself and includes the wall, floor and roof framing, roof decking, insulation, siding, windows, doors, drywall, stucco, roofing, etc. It doesn't include the weight of furnishings put into the structure after it's occupied, or people, or nature, such as snow, See *Live Load*.

Deflection is the distance a structural member contorts from its original shape when under load.

Developed Length is the total running length of a plumbing pipe, including the fittings.

Dimension is the distance between points. Commonly reduced by a specific scale on a building plan, such as ¼ inch to the foot.

Distribution Box is a device or fitting that connects two or more leaching trench fields to the outlet side of the septic tank.

Drainage Fitting connects sections of drain pipe to permit a change in direction or pipe size.

Dried-In refers to the condition of the interior of a building when enough roofing has been installed to offer protection from adverse weather.

Drywall refers to sheets of interior wall covering commonly made of gypsum. Sometimes called wallboard, sheetrock, or gypsum board.

DWV is an abbreviation for Drain, Waste and Vent pipe.

E

Easement is the right to use land owned by someone else. Commonly granted by an owner to a utility company to bring water, power or sewer lines to a parcel.

Eaves are the lower part of a roof that projects beyond an exterior wall.

Elevation View is a plan of a building exterior seen from the sides, front and rear.

Engineered Fill is a soil fill material specified by an engineer for density, bearing pressure, and other conditions.

Existing Grade is the ground surface prior to any excavation.

Expansive Soil is soil that has the potential of increasing in volume when absorbing moisture.

F

Façade is the principal face of the building.

Feeder is a conductor supplying electricity from one panelboard to another, as in a subpanel.

Fiber Stress is a measure of the pressure imposed on a structural member, such as a wood beam or floor joist.

Fixture (plumbing) refers to a device such as a bathtub, sink, shower or lavatory designed to collect water for use and dispose of waste.

Fixture Unit (plumbing) is a measure of water usage that can be anticipated from a specific plumbing fixture.

Footing is the lowest structural support of any bearing wall, usually concrete poured into trenches.

Foundation is the structural support of exterior or interior bearing walls. A foundation is supported by a footing.

Framing is the assembly of structural floor, wall and roof components and usually includes wood studs, joists, rafters, trusses, beams and posts.

Free Conductor Length identifies the distance a cable assembly must extend from an electrical outlet or switch box to allow equipment installation.

G

General Contractors manage building projects for property owners and often subcontract work to be done by trades such as framing, plumbing, mechanical and electrical.

Girder is a large or principal bearing support, such as a beam or a truss, which holds other framing members.

Glazing is another word for glass or glass products used in windows and doors.

Grade (building) refers to the ground level.

Grade (plumbing) refers to the slope of pipe in relation to the horizontal.

Grader (lumber) is anyone who classifies wood products for use in construction.

Gray Water is wastewater from sinks, showers, tubs and washing machines that may be used for irrigation or flush water in a toilet.

Gypsum Board is the broad name for a variety of gypsum sheet products with a paper covering.

H

Headers are solid or built-up beams within a wall frame that support loads over a door or window opening. Headers are supported by trimmer or jack studs.

Heating Degree Days are the sum of the differences between outdoor temperatures and indoor design temperature throughout the heating season.

Hertz is a term for cycles per second and is the measure of frequency of alternating current.

Homerun is the name for wire that runs between an electrical service panel and the first outlet or device in a circuit.

Horizontal Shear is the measure of tensile or compressive forces resolving themselves in the center of a horizontal structural member.

HVAC is an abbreviation for Heating, Ventilation and Air Conditioning.

I

Individual Vent is a pipe that conducts air from the drain, waste and vent system to a single fixture trap.

Insolation is solar radiation exposed to a certain area.

Insulation is any material that resists heat transfer. Insulation is required in wall cavities, crawl spaces and in the attic.

J

Jack Stud, also known as a trimmer stud, is the supporting member under the end of a header in a wall frame.

Joinery is a term for any method of connecting wood members, usually in finish work.

Joint is a connection between two similar building materials, such as a pipe joint or a masonry joint.

Joist is a horizontal structural member used as part of a series of parallel framing members to support a floor or ceiling.

K

Kicker is a temporary brace for a wall frame.

King Stud is the full-height stud adjacent to a trimmer or jack stud in a wall frame.

L

Lateral Bracing is the portion of a wall frame that resists horizontal loads, such as from wind or earthquakes. Lateral bracing helps to create a shear wall.

Lath is attached to building walls and serves as a base for plaster or stucco. Lath can be made from any material approved by the IRC, but is most commonly made from woven steel wire.

Leach Lines are pipes that distribute liquid waste from a septic tank to an absorption field in the ground.

Ledger is a horizontal structural element on the side of a wall that supports a joist or truss.

Let-in Bracing provides lateral support in a stud wall. Studs are cut to allow a 1-inch board to be let-in to the stud.

Lien is a right to receive money secured by a claim against property.

Lift is a layer of material such as sand or fine aggregate used to backfill an excavation. Each layer is installed and compacted in sequence to ensure uniform consolidation.

Light Construction identifies residences and smaller commercial buildings framed with lumber or light gauge metal studs, joists and rafters.

Light-Frame Construction refers to wood or light gauge steel framing. Includes studs, floor and ceiling joists and roof rafters or trusses.

Lintel is another term for a header. Usually, it defines a horizontal element over an opening in a masonry wall.

Listed (in the *IRC*) means any material that has been approved for a particular application by a recognized testing agency.

Live Load is the pressure imposed on a structure by anything other than the structure itself (the *dead load*). Live loads in a residence include rain, snow, wind, earthquakes, furniture and human traffic.

Load (electrical) is the demand in watts by a particular motor, outlet or other device.

Load (structural) is the weight that must be supported by structural elements of a building: *Dead Load* is the weight of all of the building materials. *Live Load* is the weight anticipated from nature and the occupants.

Load-Bearing Capacity is the ability of the soil to resist loads applied by a structure before collapsing.

M

Member is any portion of a building's structural system. For example, a post is a structural member supporting a beam.

Modulus of Elasticity is a number unique to a structural bending member that describes its elastic behavior prior to rupture.

Monolithic Slab describes concrete that is poured all at one time and may include a footing, foundation and slab.

N

Neutral Wire is an electrical conductor that carries unbalanced current back to the transformer in a circuit.

Nominal Size refers to the named size of a sawn wood framing member. For example; a nominal 2 x 4 actually measures 1½ inches x 3½ inches.

Non-Bearing Partition is a wall that does not support any load except itself.

O

On Center (oc) refers to the distance between centers of framing members, such as a 2 x 4 @ 16 inches o.c.

Open Circuits do not carry electrical current because there is a break or open switch somewhere in the wiring.

P

Panel Board is an electrical panel that distributes electrical current through circuits.

Partition is a wall that separates one room or space from another, and can be either load-bearing or non-load-bearing.

Passive Solar is a method of obtaining and using solar energy without mechanical or electrical devices.

PB refers to Polybutylene, a plastic material used to fabricate pipe.

PE refers to Polyethylene, a plastic material used to fabricate pipe.

Permit is the legal permission from a jurisdiction to begin construction on a proposed project.

Pier is a small structural support, usually made from masonry or concrete.

Pitch is the slope of a surface and is usually identified by units of rise (vertical distance) per 12 units of run (horizontal distance). For example, a 3:12 pitch means the surface rises 3 inches vertically in each 12 inches measured horizontally.

Plan (in the *IRC*) is a scale drawing of a proposed construction project.

Plates are horizontal framing members in a wall used to secure studs, trimmers and headers. Most frame walls in residential construction have one bottom plate and two top plates.

Potable Water is water fit for human consumption.

Power (electrical) can be measured in watts, which is the product of volts multiplied by amps.

Prism (masonry) is a model of a masonry wall built with mortar and grout similar to the actual wall but intended to be used for structural testing.

R

Rafter is one of a series of repetitive structural members that support the roof surface.

Rake Walls have studs that vary in length, defining the slope of the roof.

Readily Accessible means anyone can walk to the object without obstruction or an access panel.

Retaining Walls hold soil at a higher grade above a lower grade, such as a basement wall.

Rim is the lip or edge of a fixture such as a lavatory bowl.

Riser (plumbing) is a pipe that extends in a vertical direction.

Riser (in stairs) is one of a series of vertical elements. Treads and risers form a stairway.

Rough Opening is the length and width of the opening in a frame wall intended to receive a window or a door frame.

Rough-In (plumbing and electrical) is the portion of the plumbing or electrical system that will be hidden in wall and ceiling cavities when the building is finished.

S

Scaffold Nails are double-headed nails that allow for easy removal. Used as connectors for temporary construction.

Scarify is action that mechanically loosens or breaks down existing soil structure.

Section Modulus is a number unique to a structural bending member that describes its strength as a function of its cross-sectional shape. For rectangular members, the section modulus in inches equals the width times the depth squared and divided by 6.

Septic Tanks are watertight vessels made from durable materials such as concrete, grouted block, metal, plastic or fiberglass and intended to hold liquid waste.

Service (electrical) is the equipment that receives electricity from the power company and distributes it inside the building for various uses. The service is the location where power can be disconnected.

Setback is the area inside a property line where no building or part of a building may be erected or extend into. A common error is to build a wall of a building so close to the setback that the eaves extend beyond the setback.

Sewage Ejector is a pump that lifts waste water to a point where it can flow by gravity in the drainage system.

Sewage is liquid waste from a drainage system.

Shear Panel is a section of a wall frame designed to resist wind and seismic forces by transferring loads from the roof through the wall to the foundation.

Sheathing can refer to exterior siding or roof decking material.

Shoring is any means of bracing a structural element to resist collapse.

Siding is the exterior covering of a wall. Commonly plywood, aluminum, stucco or vinyl.

Soil Pipe is drainage pipe that carries human waste.

Soil Series or ***Profile*** is a description of the physical properties of soil in a particular area. Usually produced by a county soil survey.

Span is the total horizontal distance between supporting framing members.

Stringers support the treads and risers of a stairway.

Studs are the full length, vertical members in a frame wall.

Sub Panel is a secondary electrical distribution panel located remote from the primary distribution panel.

Sump Pumps are used to eject waste water from plumbing fixtures in a basement or lower floor to the point where gravity permits flow into a sewage discharge line.

Survey (as used in the *IRC*) is an exact map of a particular property drawn to scale and with dimensions, angles and distances established by a registered land surveyor.

T

T & P Valve is a temperature and pressure relief valve, such as for a domestic water heater.

Tailpiece is a plumbing pipe that connects the outlet of a plumbing fixture to the fixture's trap.

Toe Nailing is a way of connecting two framing members by driving a nail into the side of one member at a 45-degree angle.

Topographic Maps portray elevation differences within a defined area.

Trap (plumbing) is a pipe fitting that keeps sewer gas out of the building interior. A water seal in the trap prevents passage of air backward through the drainage system. When working correctly, a trap doesn't affect the flow of wastes.

Trap Arm is a section of pipe between the vent and the fixture trap.

Trap Seal is the section inside a trap that, when filled with water, seals sewage gas out of the room or space.

Tributary Area is that portion of a building that's being supported by a particular structural member.

Tributary Width is that portion of a span that's being supported by a particular structural member.

Trimmer Studs are lengths of framing lumber within a wall frame shorter than adjacent studs that support headers. The top of a trimmer defines the opening height of a window or door frame.

True and Plumb describes the perfect positioning between horizontal and vertical members in wall framing.

Truss is a structural floor or roof support designed by a registered professional engineer.

V

Vent is a pipe that allows air to enter the DWV system.

Volt is an electrical unit that measures the potential difference in electrical force.

W

Wallboard is any of several sheet materials fastened to the building frame to form a finished surface.

Water Closet is a toilet.

Watt is a measure of electrical power which identifies the rate at which a device converts electrical current to another form of energy. Also known as volt-amps.

Wet Vent is a vent or portion of a vent that acts as both a vent for a downstream fixture as well as a drain for an upstream fixture.

Y

Yard Line refers to a water supply pipe that taps into a water meter or well and carries water to the building.

Index

Practical References for Builders

National Construction Estimator

Current building costs for residential, commercial, and industrial construction. Estimated prices for every common building material. Provides manhours, recommended crew, and gives the labor cost for installation. Includes a CD-ROM with an electronic version of the book with *National Estimator*, a stand-alone *Windows*™ estimating program, plus an interactive multimedia video that shows how to use the disk to compile construction cost estimates. **672 pages, 8½ x 11, $62.50. Revised annually**

2009 *International Residential Code*

Replacing the *CABO One- and Two-Family Dwelling Code*, this book has the latest technological advances in building design and construction. Among the changes are provisions for steel framing and energy savings. Also contains mechanical, fuel gas and plumbing provisions that coordinate with the *International Mechanical Code* and *International Plumbing Code*. **868 pages, 8½ x 11, $88.00**
Also available:
2006 *International Residential Code* $81.50
2003 *International Residential Code*, $72.50
2000 *International Residential Code*, $59.00
2000 *International Residential Code* on CD-ROM, $48.00

Construction Forms for Contractors

This practical guide contains 78 practical forms, letters and checklists, guaranteed to help you streamline your office, organize your jobsites, gather and organize records and documents, keep a handle on your subs, reduce estimating errors, administer change orders and lien issues, monitor crew productivity, track your equipment use, and more. Includes accounting forms, change order forms, forms for customers, estimating forms, field work forms, HR forms, lien forms, office forms, bids and proposals, subcontracts, and more. All are also on the CD-ROM included, in Excel spreadsheets, as formatted Rich Text that you can fill out on your computer, and as PDFs. **360 pages, 8½ x 11, $48.50**

Home Builders' Jobsite Codes

A spiral-bound, quick reference to the 2009 *International Residential Code* that's filled with easy-to-read and understand code requirements for every aspect of residential construction. This user-friendly guide through the morass of the code is packed with illustrations, tables, and figures, to illuminate your path to inspection and approval. **281 pages, 5½ x 8½, $28.95**

Residential Property Inspection Reports on CD-ROM

This CD-ROM contains 50 pages of property inspection forms in both Rich Text and PDF formats. You can easily customize each form with your logo and address, and use them for your home inspections. Use the CD-ROM to write your inspections with your word processor, print them, and save copies for your records. Includes inspection forms for grounds and exterior, foundations, garages and carports, roofs and attics, pools and spas, electrical, plumbing, and HVAC, living rooms, family rooms, dens, studies, kitchens, breakfast rooms, dining rooms, hallways, stairways, entries, laundry rooms. **$79.95**

CD Estimator

If your computer has *Windows*™ and a CD-ROM drive, CD Estimator puts at your fingertips over 150,000 construction costs for new construction, remodeling, renovation & insurance repair, home improvement, framing & finish carpentry, electrical, concrete & masonry, painting, earthwork and heavy equipment, and plumbing & HVAC. Monthly cost updates are available at no charge on the Internet. You'll also have the *National Estimator* program — a stand-alone estimating program for *Windows*™ that *Remodeling* magazine called a "computer wiz," and *Job Cost Wizard*, a program that lets you export your estimates to QuickBooks Pro for actual job costing. A 60-minute interactive video teaches you how to use this CD-ROM to estimate construction costs. And to top it off, to help you create professional-looking estimates, the disk includes over 40 construction estimating and bidding forms in a format that's perfect for nearly any *Windows*™ word processing or spreadsheet program. **CD Estimator is $98.50**

National Home Improvement Estimator

Current labor and material prices for home improvement projects. Provides manhours for each job, recommended crew size, and the labor cost for removal and installation work. Material prices are current, with location adjustment factors and free monthly updates on the Web. Gives step-by-step instructions for the work, with helpful diagrams, and home improvement shortcuts and tips from experts. Includes a CD-ROM with an electronic version of the book, and *National Estimator*, a stand-alone *Windows*™ estimating program, plus an interactive multimedia tutorial that shows how to use the disk to compile home improvement cost estimates. **520 pages, 8½ x 11, $63.75. Revised annually**

DeWalt Building Code Reference

Based on the 2006 *International Building Code*, this spiral-bound Code reference illustrates hundreds of the most common Code requirements, violations and installation concerns. Large, color illustrations and photos show exactly what the Code requires, so there's never any doubt in your mind. Illustrated on thick glossy industrial-strength pages made to survive — even in the harsh environment of your tool kit. With this reference you'll get the job done right — the first time — even if you have questions on materials, notching and cutting, stairs, foundations and footings, concrete, egress requirements, wall and floor framing, roof framing and coverings, trenching and excavation, and more. **88 pages, 5 x 8, $24.95**

Contractor's Guide to the Building Code

Explains in plain, simple English just what the 2006 *International Building Code* and *International Residential Code* require. Building codes are elaborate laws, designed for enforcement; they're not written to be helpful how-to instructions for builders. Here you'll find down-to-earth, easy-to-understand descriptions, helpful illustrations, and code tables that you can use to design and

build residential and light commercial buildings that pass inspection the first time. Written by a former building inspector, it tells what works with the inspector to allow cost-saving methods, and warns what common building shortcuts are likely to get cited. Filled with the tables and illustrations from the *IBC* and *IRC* you're most likely to need, fully explained, with examples to guide you. Includes a CD-ROM with the entire book in PDF format, with an easy search feature. **408 pages, 8½ x 11, $66.75**

Builder's Guide to Accounting Revised

Step-by-step, easy-to-follow guidelines for setting up and maintaining records for your building business. This practical guide to all accounting methods shows how to meet state and federal accounting requirements, explains the new depreciation rules, and describes how the Tax Reform Act can affect the way you keep records. Full of charts, diagrams, simple directions and examples to help you keep track of where your money is going. Recommended reading for many state contractor's exams. Each chapter ends with a set of test questions, and a CD-ROM included FREE has all the questions in interactive self-test software. Use the Study Mode to make studying for the exam much easier, and Exam Mode to practice your skills. **360 pages, 8½ x 11, $35.50**

Basic Engineering for Builders

This book is for you if you've ever been stumped by an engineering problem on the job, yet wanted to avoid the expense of hiring a qualified engineer. Here you'll find engineering principles explained in non-technical language and practical methods for applying them on the job. With the help of this book you'll be able to understand engineering functions in the plans and how to meet the requirements, how to get permits issued without the help of an engineer, and anticipate requirements for concrete, steel, wood and masonry. See why you sometimes have to hire an engineer and what you can undertake yourself: surveying, concrete, lumber loads and stresses, steel, masonry, plumbing, and HVAC systems. This book is designed to help you, the builder, save money by understanding engineering principles that you can incorporate into the jobs you bid. **400 pages, 8½ x 11, $39.50**

Basic Lumber Engineering for Builders

Beam and lumber requirements for many jobs aren't always clear, especially with changing building codes and lumber products. Most of the time you rely on your own "rules of thumb" when figuring spans or lumber engineering. This book can help you fill the gap between what you can find in the building code span tables and what you need to pay a certified engineer to do. With its large, clear illustrations and examples, this book shows you how to figure stresses for pre-engineered wood or wood structural members, how to calculate loads, and how to design your own girders, joists and beams. Included FREE with the book — an easy-to-use limited version of NorthBridge Software's *Wood Beam Sizing* program. **272 pages, 8½ x 11, $38.00**

Planning Drain, Waste & Vent Systems

How to design plumbing systems in residential, commercial, and industrial buildings. Covers designing systems that meet code requirements for homes, commercial buildings, private sewage disposal systems, and even mobile home parks. Includes relevant code sections and many illustrations to guide you through what the code requires in designing drainage, waste, and vent systems. **202 pages, 8½ x 11, $29.95**

Steel-Frame House Construction

Framing with steel has obvious advantages over wood, yet building with steel requires new skills that can present challenges to the wood builder. This book explains the secrets of steel framing techniques for building homes, whether pre-engineered or built stick by stick. It shows you the techniques, the tools, the materials, and how you can make it happen. Includes hundreds of photos and illustrations, plus a FREE download with steel framing details and a database of steel materials and manhours, with an estimating program. **320 pages, 8½ x 11, $39.75**

DeWalt Electrical Code Reference

Based on the 2005 and 2008 *National Electrical Codes*, this spiral-bound reference illustrates hundreds of the most common electrical Code requirements and installations. Color illustrations and photos show exactly what the Code requires, so there's no guesswork. Find what you need, illustrated on thick glossy industrial-strength pages made to survive — even in your tool kit. Covers branch circuits, receptacle placement, 3- and 4-way switch wiring, panelboard wiring, GFCI and AFCI requirements, conductor ampacity tables, and workspace requirements. You'll find information on terminals, common wiring methods, overcurrent protection, wiring services calculations, smoke detector wiring; and wiring layout for bedrooms, bathrooms, kitchens, dining and living rooms, laundry rooms and garages. Gives requirements for HVAC, conductor sizing, subpanels, underground raceways, service grounding, and ground rods. **88 pages, 5 x 8, $19.95 By: American Contractors Exam Service.**

Code Check Complete

Every essential building, electrical and mechanical code requirement you're likely to encounter when building or remodeling residential and light commercial structures. Comes spiral-bound, with over 400 drawings that answer your code questions with up-to-date answers. Includes quick-glance summaries to alert you to important code changes. Compiled by code-certified building/home inspectors, this new book is like having four guides in one, big, easy-to-understand guide. **240 pages, 6½ x 8½, $40.00**

Concrete Construction

Just when you think you know all there is about concrete, many new innovations create faster, more efficient ways to do the work. This comprehensive concrete manual has both the tried-and-tested methods and materials, and more recent innovations. It covers everything you need to know about concrete, along with Styrofoam forming systems, fiber reinforcing adjuncts, and some architectural innovations, like architectural foam elements, that can help you offer more in the jobs you bid on. Every chapter provides detailed, step-by-step instructions for each task, with hundreds of photographs and drawings that show exactly how the work is done. To keep your jobs organized, there are checklists for each stage of the concrete work, from planning, to finishing and protecting your pours. Whether you're doing residential or commercial work, this manual has the instructions, illustrations, charts, estimating data, rules of thumb and examples every contractor can apply on their concrete jobs. **288 pages, 8½ x 11, $28.75**

Estimating Home Building Costs Revised

Accurate estimates are the foundation of a successful construction business. Leave an item out of your original estimate and it can take the profit out of your entire job. This practical guide to estimating home construction costs has been updated with Excel estimating forms and worksheets with active cells that ensure accurate and complete estimates for your residential projects. Load the enclosed CD-ROM into your computer and create your own estimate as you follow along with the step-by-step techniques in this book. Clear, simple instructions show how to estimate labor and material costs for each stage of construction, from site clearing to figuring your markup and profit. Every chapter includes a sample cost estimate worksheet that lists all the materials to be estimated. Even shows how to figure your markup and profit to arrive at a price. **336 pages, 8½ x 11, $38.00**

Constructionary

A unique pocket-sized dictionary of up-to-date construction words and phrases in English-Spanish and Spanish-English. Here you'll find over 1000 construction terms and 70 commonly used on-the-job phrases. This dictionary includes phonetic pronunciation, tool section, commonly used sentences, and conversion tables. **318 pages, 4 x 7, $19.95. Published by I.C.C.**

Plumber's Handbook Revised

Explains how to install plumbing systems that will pass inspection — the first time. Clearly illustrated, with diagrams, charts and tables that make it easy to select the right material and install it correctly. Covers vents, waste piping, drainage, septic tanks, hot and cold water supply systems, wells, fire protection piping, fixtures, solar energy systems, gas piping and more. Completely updated to comply with the current editions of the *International Plumbing Code (IPC)* and the *Uniform Plumbing Code (UPC)* that are standards for most cities and code jurisdictions. New tables, illustrations and chapters bring this book current with recent amendments to the plumbing codes. **304 pages, 8½ x 11, $41.50**

Contractor's Guide to the Plumbing Code

This publication by *ICC* explains the 2003 *International Plumbing Code* in plain English. It's filled with illustrations and figures to help contractors meet code on all plumbing work. Covers the history of the code, conventional DWV systems, cost factors that may affect plumbing design and much more. **112 pages, 8½ x 11, $26.25**

Contractor's Guide to *QuickBooks Pro* 2010

This user-friendly manual walks you through *QuickBooks Pro's* detailed setup procedure and explains step-by-step how to create a first-rate accounting system. You'll learn in days, rather than weeks, how to use *QuickBooks Pro* to get your contracting business organized, with simple, fast accounting procedures. On the CD included with the book you'll find a *QuickBooks Pro* file for a construction company. Open it, enter your own company's data, and add info on your suppliers and subs. You also get a complete estimating program, including a database, and a job costing program that lets you export your estimates to *QuickBooks Pro*. It even includes many useful construction forms to use in your business. **344 pages, 8½ x 11, $57.00**
See checklist for other available editions.

The Benchmark Report

If you do home inspections you have to file a report. The Benchmark's one-time reports are as comprehensive as you're likely to find. They come as checklists with complete illustrations of the area being inspected, on 4-part NCR paper, in a three-ring binder. Every area is covered: grounds, exterior, foundation, roof, plumbing, heating, cooling, electrical, interior, garage, kitchen, bathroom, well, septic, and more. Each aspect of an inspection is here to save you time and prevent mistakes.
60 pages, 8½ x 11, $21.00

Basic Plumbing with Illustrations, Revised

This completely-revised edition brings this comprehensive manual fully up-to-date with all the latest plumbing codes. It is the journeyman's and apprentice's guide to installing plumbing, piping, and fixtures in residential and light commercial buildings: how to select the right materials, lay out the job and do professional-quality plumbing work, use essential tools and materials, make repairs, maintain plumbing systems, install fixtures, and add to existing systems. Includes extensive study questions at the end of each chapter, and a section with all the correct answers.
384 pages, 8½ x 11, $33.00

Residential Construction Performance Guidelines

Created and reviewed by more than 300 builders and remodelers, this guide gives cut-and-dried construction standards that should apply to new construction and remodeling. It defines corrective action necessary to bring all construction up to standards. Standards are listed for sitework, foundations, interior concrete slabs, basement and crawl spaces for block walls and poured walls, wood-floor framing, beams, columns and posts, plywood and joists, walls, wall insulation, windows, doors, exterior finishes and trim, roofs, roof sheathing, roof installation and leaks, plumbing, sanitary and sewer systems, electrical, interior climate control, HVAC systems, cabinets and countertops, floor finishes and more. **120 pages, 6½ x 8½, $44.95. Published by NAHB Remodelers Council.**

Visual Handbook of Building and Remodeling

If you've ever had a question about different types of material, or the dimensions required by Code in most installations – you'll find the answers quickly and easily in this 632 page illustrated encyclopedia. This expanded third edition of the classic reference includes the latest Code information, new full-color drawings, and a new section on making homes green. 1,600 full-color drawings provide a clear look at every aspect of home construction and systems, to visualize exactly how to tackle any building project or problem. There are charts, dimensions, and illustrations on design, site and climate, masonry, foundations, wood, framing, sheathing, siding, roofing, windows and doors, plumbing, wiring, the thermal envelope, floors, walls and ceilings, storage, heating, cooling, passive solar, lighting, sound, and more. **632 pages, 8½ x 11, $29.95**

Markup & Profit: A Contractor's Guide

In order to succeed in a construction business, you have to be able to price your jobs to cover all labor, material and overhead expenses, *and* make a decent profit. The problem is knowing what markup to use. You don't want to lose jobs because you charged too much, and you don't want to work for free because you charged too little. If you know how to calculate markup, you can apply it to your job costs to find the right sales price for your work. This book gives you tried and tested formulas, with step-by-step instructions and easy-to-follow examples, so you can easily figure the markup that's right for *your* business. Includes a CD-ROM with forms and checklists for your use. **320 pages, 8½ x 11, $32.50**

Illustrated Guide to the *International Plumbing & Fuel Gas Codes*

A comprehensive guide to the *International Plumbing* and *Fuel Gas Codes* that explains the intricacies of the code in easy-to-understand language. Packed with plumbing isometrics and helpful illustrations, it makes the code requirements clear for installation methods and materials for plumbing and fuel gas systems. Includes code tables for pipe sizing and fixture units, and code requirements for just about all areas of plumbing, from water supply and vents to sanitary drainage systems. Covers the principles and terminology of the codes, how the various systems work and are regulated, and code-compliance issues you'll likely encounter on the job. Each chapter has a set of self-test questions for anyone studying for the plumber's exam, and tells where to look in the code for the details. Written by a former plumbing inspector, this guide has the help you need to install systems in compliance with the *IPC* and the *IFGC*.
312 pages, 8½ x 11, $37.00

2008 *National Electrical Code*

This new electrical code incorporates sweeping improvements to make the code more functional and user-friendly. Here you'll find the essential foundation for electrical code requirements for the 21st century. With hundreds of significant and widespread changes, this 2008 *NEC* contains all the latest electrical technologies, recently-developed techniques, and enhanced safety standards for electrical work. This is the standard all electricians are required to know, even if it hasn't yet been adopted by their local or state jurisdictions.
784 pages, 8½ x 11, $75.00

National Renovation & Insurance Repair Estimator

Current prices in dollars and cents for hard-to-find items needed on most insurance, repair, remodeling, and renovation jobs. All price items include labor, material, and equipment breakouts, plus special charts that tell you exactly how these costs are calculated. Includes a CD-ROM with an electronic version of the book with *National Estimator*, a stand-alone *Windows*™ estimating program, plus an interactive multimedia video that shows how to use the disk to compile construction cost estimates.
488 pages, 8½ x 11, $64.50. Revised annually

The Contractor's Legal Kit

Stop "eating" the costs of bad designs, hidden conditions, and job surprises. Set ground rules that assign those costs to the rightful party ahead of time. And it's all in plain English, not "legalese." For less than the cost of an hour with a lawyer, you'll learn the exclusions to put in your agreements, why your insurance company may pay for your legal defense, and how to avoid liability for injuries to your sub and his employees. It also includes a FREE CD-ROM with contracts and forms you can customize for your own use.
352 pages, 8½ x 11, $69.95

DeWalt Contractor's Daily Logbook and Jobsite Reference

The secrets of today's successful contractors include two things: having a way to logically and efficiently document jobsite activity, as well as the resources and references to complete the documentation. This new book gives you a two-in-one resource that provides all of the necessary elements needed to run and complete a construction project. Part One offers daily log pages, carefully designed to assist in documenting everything necessary on the jobsite, from daily activities to weather conditions to schedules, deliveries, subcontractors, OSHA requirements, and more. Part Two includes a variety of resources related to the daily log, including a math/calculations section, an extensive jobsite safety/OSHA requirements section, Spanish/English translations and a comprehensive reference section. **335 pages, 8½ x 11, $24.95**

Craftsman Book Company
6058 Corte del Cedro
P.O. Box 6500
Carlsbad, CA 92018

☎ **24 hour order line**
1-800-829-8123
Fax (760) 438-0398

In A Hurry?
We accept phone orders charged to your
○ Visa, ○ MasterCard, ○ Discover or ○ American Express

Card#_____

Exp. date_____Initials_____

Tax Deductible: Treasury regulations make these references tax deductible when used in your work. Save the canceled check or charge card statement as your receipt.

Name_____

e-mail address (for order tracking and special offers)
_____

Company_____

Address_____

City/State/Zip _____ ○ This is a residence
Total enclosed _____ (In California add 8.25% tax)
We pay shipping when your check covers your order in full.

Order online http://www.craftsman-book.com
Free on the Internet! Download any of Craftsman's estimating database for a 30-day free trial!
www.craftsman-book.com/downloads

Download all of Craftsman's most popular costbooks for one low price with the Craftsman Site License. http://www.craftsmansitelicense.com

10-Day Money Back Guarantee | **Prices subject to change without notice**

○ 39.50 Basic Engineering for Builders
○ 38.00 Basic Lumber Engineering for Builders
○ 33.00 Basic Plumbing with Illustrations, Revised
○ 21.00 The Benchmark Report
○ 35.50 Builder's Guide to Accounting Revised
○ 98.50 CD Estimator
○ 40.00 Code Check Complete
○ 28.75 Concrete Construction
○ 19.95 Constructionary
○ 48.50 Construction Forms for Contractors
○ 57.00 Contractor's Guide to *QuickBooks Pro* 2010
○ 56.50 Contractor's Guide to *QuickBooks Pro* 2009
○ 54.75 Contractor's Guide to *QuickBooks Pro* 2008
○ 53.00 Contractor's Guide to *QuickBooks Pro* 2007
○ 49.75 Contractor's Guide to *QuickBooks Pro* 2005
○ 48.50 Contractor's Guide to *QuickBooks Pro* 2004
○ 47.75 Contractor's Guide to *QuickBooks Pro* 2003
○ 45.25 Contractor's Guide to *QuickBooks Pro* 2001
○ 66.75 Contractor's Guide to the Building Code
○ 26.25 Contractor's Guide to the Plumbing Code
○ 69.95 Contractor's Legal Kit
○ 24.95 DeWalt Building Code Reference
○ 24.95 DeWalt Contractor's Daily Logbook and Jobsite Reference
○ 19.95 DeWalt Electrical Code Reference
○ 38.00 Estimating Home Building Costs Revised

○ 28.95 Home Builders' Jobsite Codes
○ 37.00 Illustrated Guide to the *International Plumbing & Fuel Gas Codes*
○ 88.00 2009 *International Residential Code*
○ 81.50 2006 *International Residential Code*
○ 72.50 2003 *International Residential Code*
○ 59.00 2000 *International Residential Code*
○ 48.00 2000 *International Residential Code* on CD-ROM
○ 32.50 Markup & Profit: A Contractor's Guide
○ 62.50 National Construction Estimator with FREE *National Estimator* on a CD-ROM
○ 75.00 2008 *National Electrical Code*
○ 63.75 National Home Improvement Estimator with FREE *National Estimator* on a CD-ROM
○ 64.50 National Renovation & Insurance Repair Estimator with FREE *National Estimator* on a CD-ROM
○ 29.95 Planning Drain, Waste & Vent Systems
○ 41.50 Plumber's Handbook Revised
○ 44.95 Residential Construction Performance Guidelines
○ 79.95 Residential Property Inspection Reports on CD-ROM
○ 39.75 Steel-Frame House Construction
○ 29.95 Visual Handbook of Building and Remodeling
○ 32.50 Building Code Compliance for Contractors & Inspectors
○ FREE Full Color Catalog

Download free construction contracts legal for your state. www.construction-contract.net